MW00845310

Autism Spectrum Disorders - Recent Advances and New Perspectives

Edited by Marco Carotenuto

Published in London, United Kingdom

Autism Spectrum Disorders - Recent Advances and New Perspectives
http://dx.doi.org/10.5772/intechopen.100837
Edited by Marco Carotenuto

Contributors
Sarah Radja Bendiouis, Yamina Hammas, April Hargreaves, David Mothersill, Gerard Loughnane, Rosemarie Sacco, Nigel Camilleri, Judith Eberhardt, Katja Umla-Runge, Dorothy Newbury-Birch, Marion Rutherford, Lorna Johnston, Terje Solsvik Kristensen, Emanuela Balestrieri, Paola Sinibaldi-Vallebona, Chiara Cipriani, Claudia Matteucci, Enrico Garaci, Paola Venuti, Arianna Bentenuto, Silvia Perzolli, Lu Wang, Zhiqiang Tan, Weijian Ye, Hao Xu, Krupa Venkatraman, Prathibha Karanth, Manabu Saito, Yui Sakamoto, Ai Terui, Susan Diane D. Rich, Mian Wang, Rachel Schuck, Kaitlynn M. P. Baiden, Alan Lincoln, Felicia Pryor, Angela Woolard, Shamiron Bales, Tânia Plens Shecaira, Nathalia Bernardes, Leonardo Ribeiro Miedes, Fabrício Porto Matrone, Nayara Barbosa Lopes, Thais Miriã da Silva Santos, Giulia Purpura, Annarita Contaldo, Francesco Cerroni, Raffaella Salatiello, Paola Alessandra Albano, Ludovica Cira Nocerino

First published in London, United Kingdom, 2023 by IntechOpen
IntechOpen is the global imprint of INTECHOPEN LIMITED, registered in England and Wales, registration number: 11086078, 5 Princes Gate Court, London, SW7 2QJ, United Kingdom

British Library Cataloguing-in-Publication Data
A catalogue record for this book is available from the British Library

Additional hard and PDF copies can be obtained from orders@intechopen.com

Autism Spectrum Disorders - Recent Advances and New Perspectives
Edited by Marco Carotenuto
p. cm.
Print ISBN 978-1-83768-342-0
Online ISBN 978-1-83768-343-7
eBook (PDF) ISBN 978-1-83768-344-4

Meet the editor

Professor Marco Carotenuto was born in Italy in 1974 and his great dream was to be a doctor since childhood. in July 2000 he obtained the master's degree of Doctor of Medicine and Surgery at the University of Campania "Luigi Vanvitelli and began specialist *cum laude* in Child Neuropsychiatry in October 2005. In February 2008 he obtained a Ph.D. in Behavioral Sciences and Learning Disorders and since November 2018 he works as an Associate Professor of Child Neuropsychiatry at the University of Campania "Luigi Vanvitelli". Since November 2018 he has been President of the Degree Course in Neuro and Psychomotor Therapy of Developmental Age (TNPEE) of the University of Campania "Luigi Vanvitelli". Moreover, since December 2018 he has been the Director of the Child Neuropsychiatry Unit at the same University Clinic. Since June 2022 he has been President of the National Commission of Neuro and Psychomotricity Therapy in developmental age (TNPEE). Since November 2022 he has been Director of the School of Specialization in Child Neuropsychiatry of the University of Campania "Luigi Vanvitelli". He is the author of about 200 scientific papers in indexed journals with an impact factor. The main fields of investigation concern the diagnostic evaluation and therapeutic management of neurodevelopment disorders with particular attention to infantile autism, sleep disorders, pediatric headaches and epilepsies, and neurocognitive and behavioral rehabilitation in children.

Contents

Preface

The Greek philosopher Aristotle wrote in his work Politics that "man is by nature a social animal; an individual who is unsocial naturally and not accidentally is either beneath our notice or more than human." Thus, typical social development represents a milestone in the life of every individual, regardless of their age.

Social skills and interactions form the foundation of human consciousness and dictate many human thoughts and activities. Social skills emerge gradually during developmental age through a dynamic interaction between an individual and the environment. These skills are critical to an individual's ability to develop and maintain lasting relationships and participate and function within communities.

Multiple decades of study have identified the so-called social brain, which includes the facial fusiform area (FFA), posterior superior temporal sulcus (PST), amygdala, temporoparietal junction (TPJ), anterior medial rostral prefrontal cortex (MPFC), the anterior cingulate cortex (ACC), the anterior temporal cortex (ATC), and the inferior frontal gyrus. Studies based on functional magnetic resonance imaging (fMRI) show differences in the development of activity patterns in some of these regions, and more recently in synaptic functioning. Furthermore, MRI allows us to detect the continuous structural development of some brain regions during the developmental age.

Autism spectrum disorder (ASD) is a complex neurodevelopmental disorder characterized by impairments in social interaction and communication along with repetitive stereotypic behaviors. Currently, there are no specific biomarkers for diagnostic screening or treatments available for autistic patients. ASD represents an increasingly important health emergency throughout the life span, but its onset in early childhood seriously alters the developmental trajectory. In the last two decades, the level of knowledge and social acceptance of this neurodevelopmental disorder has certainly changed positively. Unfortunately, there is still much to be elucidated about ASD, particularly its diagnosis and treatment. As such, a book like this is needed to fill in the gaps in our knowledge of this complex and challenging disorder.

This book presents different and innovative conceptual perspectives of diagnostic and therapeutic approaches for ASD, ranging from mathematical models to therapeutic strategies.

The emergence of social neuroscience is providing a framework for exploring the neural foundation of social skills. Although this area has attracted increased interest in recent years, to date little attention has been paid to: (1) substantiating these findings in children and adolescents, whose nervous systems are still rapidly developing, (2) using development-based principles, which could provide insight into typical and atypical maturation patterns, and the environmental factors that could influence them, and (3) determining the potential clinical and therapeutic management. We believe that the emergence of multidimensional theoretical paradigms is essential to acquire a more complete understanding of the function of social factors in the context of child development, especially in order to contribute to clinical diagnosis and therapeutic assistance.

This book addresses current gaps in this field by providing the reader with diverse perspectives and different but complementary models, encouraging communication between relevant disciplines, and focusing on development. Our rationale is that in order to gain a full understanding of ASD resulting from developmental or acquired neurological disorders, it is imperative to draw on (1) a coherent theoretical framework, supported by a knowledge base, (2) knowledge of normal CNS development and social development in infancy and adolescence, and (3) appropriate therapeutic tools, by integrating child-directed assessments. In this way, it will be possible to implement models of diagnosis and intervention based on the level of functional development of the CNS.

Marco Carotenuto
Department of Mental and Physical Health and Preventive Medicine,
University of Campania "Luigi Vanvitelli",
Caserta, Italy

Section 1

Worldwide Epidemiology

Chapter 1

The Prevalence of Autism Spectrum Disorder in Europe

Rosemarie Sacco, Nigel Camilleri, Judith Eberhardt, Katja Umla-Runge and Dorothy Newbury-Birch

Abstract

This chapter set out to present a comprehensive review on the prevalence of autism spectrum disorder (ASD) among 5–18-year-olds living in Europe. The review was based on studies published between 2015 and 2020. Separate meta-analyses were conducted for population studies and register-based studies to determine the random effects pooled prevalence rate (REPPR) for ASD. The European REPPR for ASD among young people was estimated at 0.8% based on register-based studies and 1.4% based on population. Comparative analysis was carried out to identify trends of prevalence rates across countries, gender, and level of education. The prevalence among primary school children was four times that of secondary school children. A male: female ratio of 3.5:1 was obtained. A range of challenges toward young people with ASD are portrayed, including diagnostic limitations, poor awareness on ASD, and socioeconomic inequality. Nationwide screening, early intervention services, and further research on gender and culture-specific presentations are recommended.

Keywords: autism, prevalence, Europe, children, adolescents

1. Introduction

Autism is a neurodevelopmental disorder characterized by persistent and pervasive deficits in social interaction and communication, as well as restricted repetitive behaviors [1]. This definition of autism encapsulates a greater range of presentations when compared with the definition provided by the Diagnostic and Statistical Manual (DSM)-III [2], which listed criteria such as "perversive lack of responsiveness to other people" and "gross deficits in language development." This shift has undoubtedly led to an increase in prevalence rates, ranging from 21 in 10,000 in 1979 [3] to a global figure of 1 in 100 [4] more recently (are there quotes for 1 in 66 too?).

The prevalence is the proportion of individuals in a population with a disease at a specific point in time. This rate is obtained from epidemiological studies such as register-based and population studies. The latter refers to studies that assess all the individuals sampled from a target population to determine the prevalence in that population. On the other hand, register-based studies use registers to determine the number of individuals who are registered with a diagnosis in the target population. Prevalence studies on autism give an indication of the condition's impact in terms of the number of cases, as well as socioeconomical costs. They also indicate the level of awareness, identification, and supportive services offered to the population in question. These data should serve as a foundation from which policymakers plan service development to ensure that the present needs of the population are met [5].

This chapter presents a systematic review on the prevalence of autism among 5–18-year-old young people in Europe. The focus on Europe was intended to obtain a more in-depth understanding among European countries with similar sociodemographic characteristics. Including data from multiple continents may have been interesting to evaluate the entire body of evidence, increase statistical power, and highlight differences in the distribution of autism across different continents. However, adequate clinical and research competence for autism is still developing in low- and middle-income countries [4]. With considerable variation in sociodemographic factors, awareness, and diagnostic expertise [6], there is a risk of prevalence rates being greatly underestimated in certain parts of the world, in fact considerable variation in prevalence rates has been reported across different regions [7, 8]. Cross-national comparisons across countries with very different levels of awareness and expertise on autism may therefore be inappropriate. Furthermore, an overall global prevalence rate may not accurately reflect the situation in Europe.

The review gives a comprehensive appraisal of the eligible prevalence studies, which were published between 2015 and 2020. The short and recent time frame was intended to draw a clearer picture on the current prevalence situation. Previously published meta-analyses have estimated the prevalence of autism by including studies dating back to 1966 [8]. While including studies from the distant past may improve the statistical power, the pooled prevalence rates may not be generalized to the current situation and not reflect the reported rise in prevalence over time [4]. Moreover, the chapter presents cross-national comparisons of prevalence rates to ascertain trends across countries, gender, and level of education. These were used to draw inferences on present barriers to identification of autism, such as stigma, poor diagnostic systems, and unequal diagnostic sensitivity across gender and age. Methodological and diagnostic factors that may under- or overestimate the true prevalence of autism are also discussed.

2. Methodology

2.1 Literature search and search strategy

PubMed and Google Scholar were used to review the existing literature and identify a gap in the literature on the prevalence of all mental disorders among children and adolescents in Europe. A search on Prospero [9] confirmed that there were no reviews registered in this area, so a protocol for this study was then registered there (Registration number: CRD42020210451). A search strategy was developed using the SPIDER model and conducted on MEDLINE, Embase, and PsychInfo on the 30th April 2020. The search was limited to studies with a title and abstract in English.

2.2 Eligibility criteria

Studies were considered eligible if they were original epidemiological studies that determined the prevalence of a mental disorder as defined by ICD-10, DSM-IV, or DSM-V criteria, among 5–18-year-olds in European countries. Studies were excluded if they did not include the general population, for instance, by focusing on minority groups, or if they were published before 2015.

2.3 Study identification and selection procedure

Studies found by the search were screened independently by title and abstract by RS. The studies that met inclusion criteria were screened independently by full text by RS. DNB screened 20% of all the studies at title/abstract and at full text review stage. Reference lists and gray literature were searched manually by RS.

2.4 Quality analysis

The reliability, validity, and bias of each eligible study were assessed using the Appraisal Tool for Cross-Sectional Studies (AXIS) [10] and the Risk of Bias in Prevalence Studies Tool (RBPS) [11].

2.5 Data analysis

Only the eligible studies that estimated the prevalence of autism were included in the analysis for this chapter. Median and average estimates and ranges of autism prevalence rates for young people in Europe were determined. Comprehensive meta-analysis software [12] was used to analyze prevalence data from the eligible studies. A random effects model was used to determine the random effects pooled prevalence rate of autism in Europe. Prevalence rates obtained from population and register-based studies were analyzed separately since the two study types have non-homogeneous populations, and there may be significant discrepancy of factors at many levels of the variable of interest. Data from the two study designs were therefore analyzed separately to avoid Simpson's paradox [13]. The standardized residual values (SRV) were evaluated from the forest plots and a cutoff of +/−3 at 95% confidence interval was used to identify outliers [14].

Cross-national prevalence comparisons were made across countries, gender, and level of education. The latter was done to compare prevalence rates between young children who attend primary school, to older children who attend secondary school. Prevalence rates were not compared according to specific age groups since the eligible studies presented results for a mixed range of age groups, which were incomparable. The contribution of specific cofactors to heterogeneity could not be evaluated through a meta-regression analysis because results would be insignificant due to the low number of eligible studies [15].

3. Results

Nine eligible studies were identified that provided prevalence estimates for 11 European countries as illustrated in **Table 1**. The AXIS and RBPS tools indicated low-level bias among all the eligible studies.

3.1 The Prevalence of Autism among 5–18-year-olds in Europe

Based on the eligible studies, the prevalence ranged from 0.3% in the West Pomeranian and Pomeranian regions of Poland to 14.3% in Romania (**Figure 1**). The median prevalence was 1%, and the average prevalence was 1.97%.

Author Year	Region [Nationwide]	Study Design (Register based study (RBS)/ population study (PS))	Sample Number (% Male, % Females)	Age Range (Years)	Level of Education			Diagnostic Classification	Risk of Bias (ROB) Scores ** (AXIS, RBPS)
					Primary	Secondary	Both		
Boilson, A.M. et al. 2016.	Ireland (Galway, Waterford, Cork) [No]	PS	7951 (54%, 46%)	6–11	Yes	No	No	DSM-IV TR	2, 1
Budisteanu, M. et al. 2017.	Romania [Yes]	PS	NA	7–9	Yes	No	No	DSM-IV TR	7, 3
Delobel-Ayoub, M. et al. 2020.	Denmark, Finland, Iceland, South West France, South East France [Yes]	RBS	NA	7–9	Yes	No	No	ICD-10	3, 3
Elberling, H. et al. 2016.	Denmark (Copenhagen) [No]	PS	1585 (52%, 48%)	5–7	Yes	No	No	ICD-10	0, 1
Lesinskiene, S. et al. 2018.	Lithuania (Nationwide) [Yes]	PS	526 (54%, 41%)	7–17	Yes	Yes	Yes	ICD-10	1, 0
Morales-Hidalgo, P. et al. 2018.	Spain (Tarragona) [No]	PS	1449 (50%, 50%)	10–12	Yes	No	No	DSM-V	3, 1
Narzisi, A. et al. 2018.	Italy (Pisa) [No]	PS, RBS	10,138 (52%, 48%)	7–9	Yes	No	No	DSM-V	1, 2
NHS 2018.	England [Yes]	PS	6219 (50%, 50%)	5–16	Yes	Yes	Yes	ICD-10	2, 1
Skonieczna-Żydecka, K. et al. 2017.	Poland [No]	RBS	2514 (81%, 19%)	8–16	Yes	Yes	Yes	ICD-10	2, 2

**Ages were estimated from additional sources showing the age groups of children in the mentioned school grades [16, 17].*
***Scores for ROB reflect the number of elements in each tool that indicate potential for bias. AXIS has a total of 20 items whereas RBPS has 10 items.*

Table 1.
Eligible studies and their characteristics.

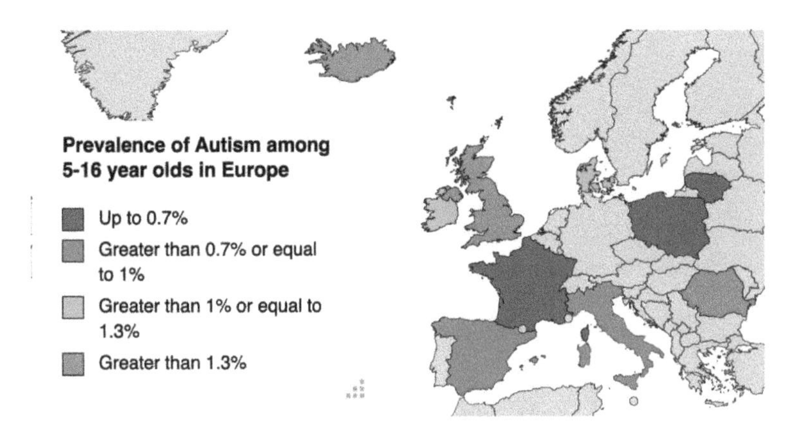

Figure 1.
The prevalence of autism among 5–18-year-old young people in Europe.

3.2 Prevalence rates from different study designs

One study [18] used both register-based and population study methods, thereby providing two prevalence rates for autism in Italy (Pisa). Two other studies were register-based studies, and six were population studies.

3.3 Prevalence rates from register-based studies

Three studies used registers to determine the prevalence. These studies estimated the prevalence of Pisa, West Pomeranian and Pomeranian region of Poland, South East and South West of France as well as the nationwide prevalence of Denmark, Finland, and Iceland. The prevalence of autism from these studies ranged from 0.3% in the West Pomeranian and Pomeranian regions of Poland to 2.7% in Iceland. There was a discrepancy of 2.4% between the highest and lowest prevalence rate. The median of these rates was 0.8%, and the average was 1%. **Figure 2** shows a forest plot with the REPPR of young people with a diagnosis of autism being 0.8% (95%CI: 0.5%–1.4%, $I^2 = 99.5\%$). Although the prevalence reported in Iceland was much higher than that reported in other regions, its SRV was 1.80 and was therefore not considered to be an outlier.

3.4 Prevalence rates from population studies

Seven population studies with a pooled sample size of 33,579 individuals estimated the prevalence of autism in European countries. Three studies determined the

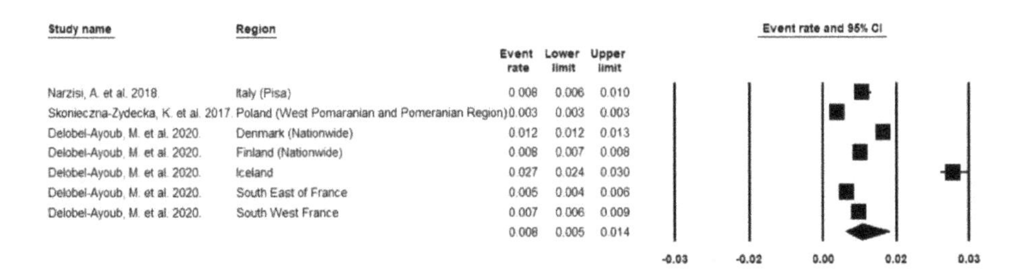

Figure 2.
Forest plot of the prevalence rates of autism among young people in Europe from register-based studies.

nationwide prevalence in Romania, Lithuania, and England. Another four studies determined the prevalence in Pisa (Italy), Galway, Waterford, and Cork in Ireland, Tarragona in Spain, and Copenhagen in Denmark. The prevalence rates ranged from 0.4% Lithuania to 14.3% in Romania. The prevalence rate estimated in Romania is much higher when compared with other prevalence rates; however, the SRV is 1.44. The median prevalence was 1.2%, and the mean was 2.9%. The REPPR of autism among young people in Europe based on population studies was estimated at 1.4% (CI: 5.4%–0.4%, I2 = 99.7%) as shown in **Figure 3**.

3.5 Prevalence of autism across level of education

Seven of the eligible studies estimated the prevalence of primary school children, whereas two estimated the prevalence of secondary school children. These are depicted in **Figure 4**. The prevalence among primary school children ranged from 0.8% (95% CI: 0.6%–1.0%) in Pisa to 14.3% (95% CI: 13.6–15.1%) in Romania. The median prevalence rate for primary school children was 1.2%, and the mean was 3%. A REPPR for primary school children of 1.6% (95%CI: 0.4%–6.1%, I^2 = 95.5%) was obtained. The prevalence of autism among secondary school students ranged from 0.1% (95%CI: 0.00%–0.4%) in Lithuania to 1.2% (95% CI: 0.9%–1.7%) in England. A REPPR for secondary school children of 0.4% (95% CI: 0.00%–4.5%, I^2 = 92.2%) was obtained. The REPPR among primary school children was four times greater than that estimated for secondary school children. I2.

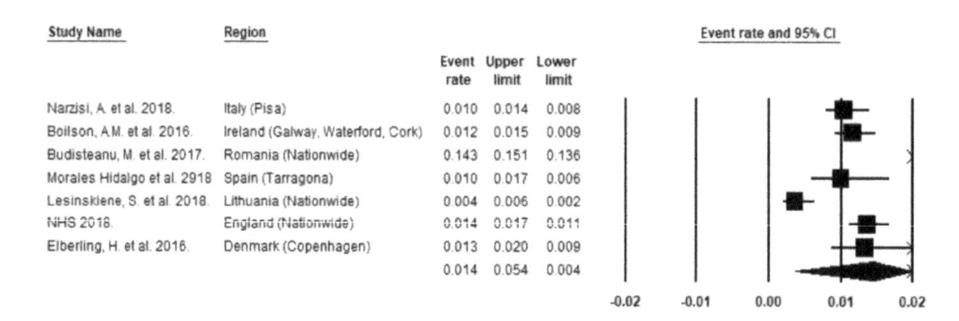

Figure 3.
Forest plot of the prevalence rates of autism among young people in Europe from population studies.

Study	Level of Education	Event rate	Lower limit	Upper limit
Boilson, A.M. et al. 2016.	Primary	0.012	0.009	0.015
Budisteanu, M. et al. 2017.	Primary	0.143	0.136	0.151
Morales-Hidalgo, P. et al. 2018.	Primary	0.010	0.006	0.017
Lesinskiene, S. et al. 2018.	Primary	0.009	0.005	0.017
NHS 2018.	Primary	0.015	0.011	0.019
Elberling, H. et al. 2016.	Primary	0.013	0.009	0.020
Narzisi, A. et al. 2018.	Primary	0.008	0.006	0.010
		0.016	0.004	0.061
Lesinskiene, S. et al. 2018.	Secondary	0.001	0.000	0.004
NHS 2018.	Secondary	0.012	0.009	0.017
		0.004	0.000	0.045
		0.011	0.003	0.038

Event rate and 95% CI: -0.06, -0.03, 0.00, 0.03, 0.06

Figure 4.
Forest plot showing the prevalence rates of autism among young people in Europe with the level of education as the unit of analysis. The lines in magenta represent the REPPR for primary and secondary school children.

Region	Gender	Event rate	Lower limit	Upper limit
NHS 2018	Female	0.005	0.003	0.009
Elberling et al. 2016	Female	0.008	0.004	0.017
		0.006	0.004	0.009
NHS 2018	Male	0.021	0.017	0.027
Elberling et al. 2016	Male	0.017	0.010	0.029
		0.021	0.017	0.025
		0.016	0.013	0.019

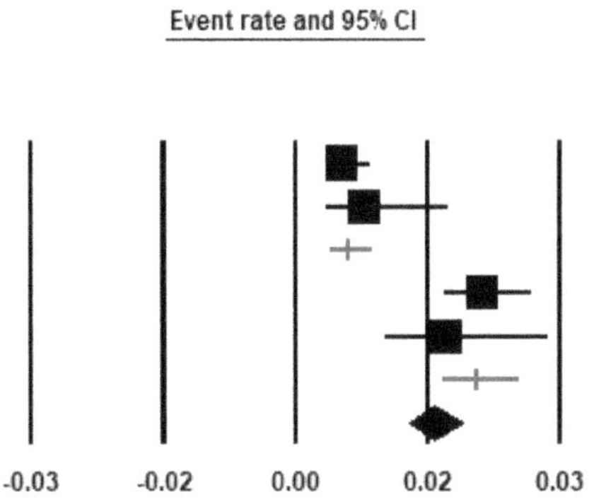

Event rate and 95% CI

-0.03 -0.02 0.00 0.02 0.03

Figure 5.
Forest plot showing the prevalence rates of autism among young people in Europe with gender as the unit of analysis. The lines in magenta represent the REPPR for females and males.

3.6 Prevalence of autism across gender

Only two studies provided separate prevalence rates for males and females (**Figure 5**). Based on these, the REPPR of autism is 0.6% (95%CI: 0.4%–1.7%, $I^2 = 0\%$) and 2.1% (95%CI: 1.7%–2.5%, $I^2 = 0\%$) for young females and males respectively. Based on these figures, the REPPR of males is 3.5 times greater than that in females.

4. Discussion

This chapter provides a comprehensive review of the original prevalence studies on autism in European countries published between 2015 and 2020. Factors that may have influenced the estimation of prevalence rates are discussed below.

4.1 Study designs

Register-based studies use administrative databases in educational or health systems to determine the number of individuals who have obtained a diagnosis in the target population. These studies are limited because they only include individuals who actively sought help from professionals and gave consent for their diagnosis to be reported . Since autism includes a range of phenotype variants, milder forms may be missed, so prevalence rates may be underestimated by register-based studies. These factors may contribute to the lower prevalence rates estimated among register-based studies when compared with population studies.

When considering the register-based studies, the prevalence ranged from 0.3% in Poland to 2.7% in Iceland. Reasons for the low prevalence documented in Poland may include both under-diagnosis and under-reporting. At the time of the study, in Poland, there were non-standardized diagnostic systems [19], poor levels of awareness, and high levels of stigma, which could prevent parents and young people from seeking help [20]. Moreover, there were no enforcements for reporting diagnosed cases of autism [20]. These factors may have contributed to an underestimation of the prevalence rates. Interestingly, these factors were reversed when the study in Iceland was conducted. In fact, the study occurred after improved awareness and access to autism diagnostic services [21], which were upgraded to formally diagnose high functioning autism [22]. These factors may have improved the accuracy of autism identification, bringing about a higher estimation.

Population studies assess a sample of individuals from the target population. Some of these studies use gold-standard diagnostic tool on all the participants as seen in the study conducted in England [23]. Since diagnostic assessments are very time-consuming and costly, most studies use a multistage approach whereby the sample is first screened and a diagnostic assessment is carried out on individuals who scored up and a proportion of individuals who did not score up, to confirm whether criteria for a diagnosis estimated the prevalence rate.

Screening tools used in the eligible studies include EDUTEA [24], CAST [25], SCQ [26], and the SDQ [27]. Diagnostic tools used by the eligible studies include the ADI-R [28], ADOS [29], and DAWBA [30]. Although these are standardized tools, their accuracy depends on the proficiency of the data collectors administering them [6]. Moreover, when these tools are used within clinical or educational services, clinicians may be more inclined to give a diagnostic label to enable access to services [6].

Another difficulty is that screening tools do not have a 100% sensitivity rate, and there are no clear guidelines for how to combine conflicting results from multiple informants. As a result, true cases may be missed, and prevalence rates may be underestimated. A further limitation is that population studies have a variable participation rate. The participation rate of the eligible studies ranged from 49.5 to 100% in the screening phase and from 14 to 100% in the diagnostic phase. Although statistical weights were applied to account for participation rates across each study phase, there remains the possibility for participation to be associated with having a diagnosis [6] or with good mental health [31], which would bias the prevalence rates upward or downward.

4.2 Diagnostic criteria

The two main gold standard classification systems used in Europe are the Diagnostic and Statistical Manual (DSM) and the International Classification of Diseases (ICD). The editions currently being used are the DSM-5 [32] and the ICD-11 [33], which started to be put in use in 2013 and 2022 respectively. The eligible studies in this review made use of DSM-IV TR [34], DSM-5 [32], and ICD-10 [35]. The diverse diagnostic criteria may partly contribute to the varied prevalence rates obtained. Studies have shown that DSM-5 criteria result in fewer individuals diagnosed with autism when compared with DSM-IV TR [36–38]. Moreover, another study has shown that among individuals diagnosed with autism on ICD-10, only 58% met DSM-5 criteria [39]. Furthermore, ICD-10 and DSM-IV distinguish between different autism subtypes, whereas DSM-5 considers a single spectrum. The study carried out in Lithuania [40] was the only eligible study in this review to use a restricted case definition of "Autistic Disorder" based on ICD-10. This definition excludes young people with Asperger's syndrome that would meet criteria for autism spectrum disorder in other studies. This limited definition may underestimate the prevalence of autism in Lithuania and further contribute to prevalence discrepancies.

4.3 Culture

Culture may influence behavioral presentations, as well as parents' and clinicians' appraisal of what is considered acceptable and undesirable behavior [41].

The ADI [28] and ADOS [29], which are gold standard diagnostic criteria for autism, were developed in the United States. These include items such as shared eye contact, social smiling, and social interactions that may be characteristic in countries such as Italy, Spain, and England but less so in other countries such as Romania where eye contact may be avoided and interaction may be of a more formal nature [42]. While these examples are undependable, they call for cultural sensitivity in working across cultures. A systemic investigation to determine the extent of variation in autism phenotype across cultures may inform adaptations in scoring autism diagnostic tools [6].

4.4 Age

Most prevalence studies on autism include age groups at which school attendance is compulsory, to support widespread sampling. Moreover, a diagnosis of autism may be validated with robust diagnostic tools by 8 years of age [6]. Although some epidemiological studies have started to include preschoolers, there are limited sensitivity and specificity in the screening tools available for this age group [6]. On the other hand, in older-age groups, there may be improved detection with increased social demands [43], as well as a risk of milder phenotypes getting more easily missed [6]. Autism was first described as a childhood disorder by Kanner in 1943 [44] and continued to be recognized as one until the relatively recent appreciation of its persistence in adulthood [45]. This historical detail may influence the identification of autism at different age groups. In fact, there is still a gap in research and awareness on adults with autism [46], and many adults remain undiagnosed [47]. This may suggest underestimation of prevalence among the older-age groups, producing a higher pooled prevalence for primary school children when compared with secondary school children.

4.5 Gender

In this review, the estimated prevalence of autism was 3.5 times greater for males when compared with females. This is in keeping with findings from other studies [48]. Many theories such as the "extreme male brain" [49] and the "female protective effect" [50] have sought to justify this gender difference. The "extreme male brain" considers autism as an "extreme" of the normal male profile in which systemizing is better than empathizing. The "female protective effect" refers to the notion that females require a greater genetic load to obtain an autism phenotype. However, females have often been excluded from research on autism, which may have resulted in limited sensitivity of diagnostic criteria toward the female autistic presentation [51]. Moreover, there is growing evidence that females are diagnosed later and need a worse presentation when compared with males, to obtain a diagnosis [52]. These data may suggest that gender prevalence discrepancy may be caused by poor detection among females, rather than actual prevalence differences.

4.6 Trends over time

A rising trend in the prevalence of autism has been reported over time. In fact, the estimated pooled prevalence of 1.4% for autism, from population studies published between 2015 and 2020, is considerably higher when compared with the prevalence of 0.2% estimated in the 1990s [53]. This rise may be partly attributed to broader diagnostic criteria, improved study methodologies, and improved knowledge and detection of autism [54]. Other dynamic risk factors that may increase the actual prevalence of autism may also play a role. These may include advancing parental age [55], improved neonatal care [56], and increased maternal substance misuse [57]. However these environmental factors may not explain the considerable and sudden prevalence rise of autism.

Strengths and limitations.

To our knowledge, this was the first study to provide a comprehensive review of the prevalence of autism among young people in Europe based on recent studies published from 2015. Moreover cross-national comparisons have brought to light several factors that may influence the estimation of autism prevalence rates. While this study makes a positive contribution to the present knowledge on autism prevalence, a number of limitations also need to be acknowledged. Firstly, there is a risk of selection bias since all the studies were identified by one researcher and only 20% of these were checked by another researcher; therefore, some studies may have been overlooked. Another limitation is that prevalence rates could not be compared across various age groups since different original studies group ages differently. An important limitation is that the review only includes nine original studies. This limited further analysis such as a meta-regression analysis that would investigate the effect of various covariates on the prevalence rate estimated. Nevertheless, the data were synthesized comprehensively to elicit aspects relevant to policymakers as well as the research and clinical communities.

5. Conclusion

This was an up-to-date review on autism epidemiology in Europe, estimating a pooled prevalence of 0.8% and 1.4% from register-based studies and population studies respectively. Importantly, this review calls policymakers to develop strategies that aim improve awareness and reduce stigma on autism as these may serve as barriers for individuals with autism to get identified. Furthermore, it calls for further research to determine the extent of phenotype variation across different cultures and gender since present diagnostic tools and criteria may have unequal sensitivity for certain groups. Finally, improving diagnostic sensitivity and developing routine nationwide screening and early intervention strategies may greatly improve the trajectory of individuals with autism.

Conflict of interest

The authors declare no conflict of interest.

Notes/thanks/other declarations

This chapter presents findings from an original systematic review that evaluated the prevalence of mental disorders among young people in Europe. Only aspects of this study that were relevant to autism were presented in this chapter.

Author details

Rosemarie Sacco[1*], Nigel Camilleri[2], Judith Eberhardt[3], Katja Umla-Runge[4] and Dorothy Newbury-Birch[3]

1 Teesside University, Cardiff University, University of Malta, Malta

2 University of Malta, Teesside University, Malta

3 Teesside University, United Kingdom

4 Cardiff University, Wales

*Address all correspondence to: r.sacco@tees.ac.uk

References

[1] Regier DA, Kuhl EA, Kupfer DJ. The DSM-5: Classification and criteria changes. World Psychiatry. 2013;**12**(2):92-98. Available from: https://onlinelibrary.wiley.com/doi/full/10.1002/wps.20050. [Accessed: July 13, 2020]

[2] American Psychiatric Association. Diagnostic and statistical manual of mental disorders (3rd Edition) (DSM-III). Washington DC: American Psychiatric Association; 1980

[3] Wing L, Gould J. Severe impairments of social interaction and associated abnormalities in children: Epidemiology and classification. Journal of Autism and Developmental Disorders. 1979;**9**(1):11-29

[4] Zeidan J, Fombonne E, Scorah J, Ibrahim A, Durkin MS, Saxena S, et al. Global prevalence of autism: A systematic review update. Autism research: Official journal of the International Society for Autism Research. 2022;**15**(5):778-790. DOI: 10.1002/aur.2696

[5] Merikangas KR, Nakamura EF, Kessler RC. Epidemiology of mental disorders in children and adolescents. In: Dialogues in Clinical Neuroscience. Vol. 11. Les Laboratoires Servier; 2009. pp. 7-20

[6] Fombonne É. Current issues in epidemiogical studies of autism. Psicologia Teoria e Prática. 2019;**21**(3):405-417. Available from: http://pepsic.bvsalud.org/scielo.php?script=sci_arttext&pid=S1516-36872019000300011&lng=pt&nrm=iso&tlng=en. [Accessed: September 5, 2022]

[7] Sheldrick RC, Carter AS. State-level trends in the prevalence of autism spectrum disorder (ASD) from 2000 to 2012: A reanalysis of findings from the autism and developmental disabilities network. Journal of Autism and Developmental Disorders. 2018;**48**(9):3086-3092

[8] Elsabbagh M, Divan G, Koh YJ, Kim YS, Kauchali S, Marcín C, et al. Global prevalence of autism and other pervasive developmental disorders. Autism Research. 2012;**5**(3):160-179. Available from: https://onlinelibrary.wiley.com/doi/full/10.1002/aur.239. [Accessed: August 22, 2022]

[9] PROSPERO. Available from: https://www.crd.york.ac.uk/prospero/. [Accessed: July 9, 2022]

[10] Downes MJ, Brennan ML, Williams HC, Dean RS. Development of a critical appraisal tool to assess the quality of cross-sectional studies (AXIS). BMJ Open. 2016;**6**(12):e011458. Available from: http://bmjopen.bmj.com/. [Accessed: August 25, 2020]

[11] Hoy D, Brooks P, Woolf A, Blyth F, March L, Bain C, et al. Assessing risk of bias in prevalence studies: Modification of an existing tool and evidence of interrater agreement. Journal of Clinical Epidemiology. 2012;**65**(9):934-939. Available from: https://pubmed.ncbi.nlm.nih.gov/22742910/. [Accessed: August 25, 2020]

[12] Comprehensive Meta-Analysis Software (CMA). Available from: https://www.meta-analysis.com/. [Accessed: January 12, 2022]

[13] Wang B, Wu P, Kwan B, Tu XM, Feng C. Simpson's Paradox: Examples. Shanghai Archives of Psychiatry. 2018;**30**(2):139-143. Available from: pmc/articles/PMC5936043/?report=abstract [Accessed: August 25, 2020]

[14] Viechtbauer W, Cheung MW-L. Outlier and influence diagnostics for meta-analysis. Research Synthesis Methods. 2010;**1**(2):112-125. Available from: https://onlinelibrary.wiley.com/doi/full/10.1002/jrsm.11. [Accessed: August 25, 2020]

[15] Borenstein M, Hedges L V, Higgins JPT, Rothstein HR. Meta-Regression. 2009

[16] Italy - Educational System—overview - School, European, Community, and Schools - StateUniversity.com. Available from: https://education.stateuniversity.com/pages/716/Italy-EDUCATIONAL-SYSTEM-OVERVIEW.html. [Accessed: June 2, 2020]

[17] EURYDICE. Spain: Organisation of the Education System and of its Structure. 2019. Available from: https://eacea.ec.europa.eu/national-policies/eurydice/content/organisation-education-system-and-its-structure-79_en. [Accessed: June 3, 2020]

[18] Narzisi A, Posada M, Barbieri F, Chericoni N, Ciuffolini D, Pinzino M, et al. Prevalence of autism spectrum disorder in a large italian catchment area: a school-based population study within the ASDEU project. Epidemiology and Psychiatric Sciences. 2018;**29**:1-10

[19] Piskorz-Ogórek K, Ogórek S, Cieślińska A. Autism in Poland in comparison to other countries. Polish Ann Med [Internet]. 2015;**22**(1):35-40 Available from: http://www.elsevier.com/journals/polish-annals-of-medicine/1230-8013

[20] K. S-Z, I. G, J. P-S. The Prevalence of Autism Spectrum Disorders in West Pomeranian and Pomeranian Regions of Poland. J Appl Res Intellect Disabil [Internet]. 2017;**30**(2):283-289. Available from: http://ovidsp.ovid.com/ovidweb.cgi?T=JS&PAGE=reference&D=emexa&NEWS=N&AN=627147009

[21] Autism Research News. Icelandic inquiry. 2020. Available from: https://www.spectrumnews.org/opinion/icelandic-inquiry/. [Accessed: June 21, 2020]

[22] Delobel-Ayoub M, Saemundsen E, Gissler M, Ego A, Moilanen I, Ebeling H, et al. Prevalence of autism spectrum disorder in 7-9-year-old children in Denmark, Finland, France and Iceland: A population-based registries approach within the ASDEU project. Journal of Autism and Developmental Disorders. 2020;**50**(3):949-959. Available from: http://www.wkap.nl/journalhome.htm/0162-3257. [Accessed: May 30, 2020]

[23] NHS. Mental health of children and young people in England, 2017 [PAS]. NHS Digital. 2018. Available from: https://digital.nhs.uk/data-and-information/publications/statistical/mental-health-of-children-and-young-people-in-england/2017/2017. [Accessed: May 30, 2020]

[24] Morales-Hidalgo P, Hernández-Martínez C, Voltas N, Canals J. EDUTEA: A DSM-5 teacher screening questionnaire for autism spectrum disorder and social pragmatic communication disorder. International Journal of Clinical and Health Psychology. 2017;**17**(3):269-281. Available from: https://www.elsevier.es/en-revista-international-journal-clinical-health-psychology-355-articulo-edutea-a-dsm-5-teacher-screening-S1697260017300340. [Accessed: September 11, 2022]

[25] Williams J, Scott F, Stott C, Allison C, Bolton PA, Baron-cohen S, et al. The CAST (Childhood Asperger Syndrome Test). 2005; Available from: www.sagepublications.com. [Accessed: September 11, 2022]

[26] Michael Rutter M, Anthony Bailey M, Catherine Lord P. (SCQ) Social Communication Questionnaire. Available from: https://www.wpspublish.com/scq-social-communication-questionnaire. [Accessed: September 11, 2022]

[27] SDQ, Youthinmind. Available from: https://youthinmind.com/products-and-services/sdq/. [Accessed: April 27, 2022]

[28] Kim SH, Lord C. Autism Diagnostic Interview, Revised. Encycl Clin Neuropsychol. 2011:313-315 Available from: https://link.springer.com/referencework entry/10.1007/978-0-387-79948-3_1519. [Accessed: September 11, 2022]

[29] Gotham K, Risi S, Pickles A, Lord C. The Autism Diagnostic Observation Schedule: Revised algorithms for improved diagnostic validity. Journal of Autism and Developmental Disorders. 2006;**37**(4):613-627. DOI: 10.1007/s10803-006-0280-1

[30] Goodman R, Ford T, Richards H, Gatward R, Meltzer H. The development and well-being assessment: Description and initial validation of an integrated assessment of child and adolescent psychopathology. Journal of Child Psychology and Psychiatry. 2000;**41**(5):645-655

[31] Cheung KL, Ten Klooster PM, Smit C, De Vries H, Pieterse ME. The impact of non-response bias due to sampling in public health studies: A comparison of voluntary versus mandatory recruitment in a Dutch national survey on adolescent health. BMC Public Health. 2017;**17**(1):1-10. Available from: https://bmcpublichealth.biomedcentral.com/articles/10.1186/s12889-017-4189-8 [Accessed: September 11, 2022]

[32] American Psychiatric Association. Diagnostic and Statistical Manual of Mental Disorders DSM-5. Fifth ed2013. Available from: https://www.appi.org/Diagnostic_and_Statistical_Manual_of_Mental_Disorders_DSM-5_Fifth_Edition [Accessed: March 28, 2021]

[33] World Health Organization. International Classification of Diseases, Eleventh Revision (ICD-11). World Health Organization. 2022. Available from: https://icd.who.int/en [Accessed: July 24, 2022]

[34] American Psychiatric Association. Diagnostic and Statistical Manual of Mental Disorders. 4th ed1994 Available from: https://www.amazon.com/Diagnostic-tatistical-Disorders-Revision-DSM-IV-TR/dp/0890420254/ref=pd_sbs_1?pd_rd_w=ClHQu&pf_rd_p=9b2fa3e3-61fa-4ec8-8379-561f99c805d8&pf_rd_r=7SQ44DQ0WW3HD7NBVT50&pd_rd_r=c6d0e53d-2887-42bf-8d01-dcef73079204&pd_rd_wg=nQ0Dh&pd_rd [Accessed: March 28, 2021]

[35] World Health Organization. International Classification of Diseases, Tenth Revision. Clinical Modification (ICD-10-CM). WHO. World Health Organization. 1992. Available from: http://www.who.int/classifications/icd/icdonlineversions/en/. [Accessed: August 25, 2020]

[36] Taheri A, Perry A. Exploring the proposed DSM-5 criteria in a clinical sample. Journal of Autism and Developmental Disorders. 2012;**42**(9):1810-1817

[37] Frazier TW, Youngstrom EA, Speer L, Embacher R, Law, P, Constantino J, et al. Validation of proposed DSM-5 criteria for autism spectrum disorder. Journal of the American Academy of Child and Adolescent Psychiatry. 2012;**51**(1):28-40.e3. DOI: 10.1016/j.jaac.2011.09.021

[38] Mcpartland JC, Reichow B, Volkmar FR. Sensitivity and specificity of proposed DSM-5 diagnostic criteria for autism spectrum disorder Running Head: DSM-5 ASD. Journal of the American Academy of Child and Adolescent Psychiatry. 2012;**51**(4):368-383

[39] Wilson CE, Gillan N, Spain D, Robertson D, Roberts G, Murphy CM, et al. Comparison of ICD-10R, DSM-IV-TR and DSM-5 in an adult autism spectrum disorder diagnostic clinic. Journal of Autism and Developmental Disorders. 2013;**43**(11):2515-2525

[40] Lesinskiene S, Girdzijauskiene S, Gintiliene G, Butkiene D, Puras D, Goodman R, et al. Epidemiological study of child and adolescent psychiatric disorders in Lithuania. BMC Public Health. 2018;**18**(1):1-8. Available from: https://bmcpublichealth.biomedcentral.com/articles/10.1186/s12889-018-5436-3 [Accessed: April 25, 2022]

[41] Dwivedi OP. The challenge of cultural diversity for good governance. Indian J Public Adm. 2002;**48**(1):14-28. DOI: 10.1177/0019556120020102 [Accessed: August 25, 2020]

[42] Iniculescu. Why Romanians do not smile? – Ioana's catastrophe. 2014. Available from: https://iniculescu.wordpress.com/2014/09/16/why-romanians-do-not-smile/ [Accessed: September 12, 2020]

[43] Rydzewska E, Hughes-McCormack LA, Gillberg C, Henderson A, MacIntyre C, Rintoul J, et al. Age at identification, prevalence and general health of children with autism: Observational study of a whole country population. BMJ Open. 2019;**9**(7). Available from: /pmc/articles/PMC6629388/?report=abstract [Accessed: June 29, 2020]

[44] Leo Kanner HJ, Autism. 75-year perspective. In: International Review of Psychiatry. Vol. 30. Taylor and Francis Ltd; 2018. pp. 3-17 Available from: https://pubmed.ncbi.nlm.nih.gov/29667863/ [Accessed: September 9, 2020]

[45] Tantam D. Asperger's syndrome. Journal of Child Psychology and Psychiatry. 1988;**29**(3):245-255. Available from: https://www.academia.edu/917964/Aspergers_syndrome [Accessed: September 9, 2022]

[46] Roestorf A, Bowler DM, Deserno MK, Howlin P, Klinger L, McConachie H, et al. "Older Adults with ASD: The Consequences of Aging." Insights from a series of special interest group meetings held at the International Society for Autism Research 2016-2017. Research in Autism Spectrum Disorder. 2019;**63**:3. Available from: /pmc/articles/PMC6559228/ [Accessed: September 9, 2022]

[47] Brugha TS, McManus S, Bankart J, Scott F, Purdon S, Smith J, Bebbington P, Jenkins R, Meltzer H. Epidemiology of autism spectrum disorders in adults in the community in England. Archives of general psychiatry. 2011;**68**(5):459-465. DOI: 10.1001/archgenpsychiatry.2011.38

[48] Loomes R, Hull L, Mandy WPL. What is the male-to-female ratio in autism spectrum disorder?. A systematic review and meta-analysis. Journal of the American Academy of Child and Adolescent Psychiatry. Elsevier Inc. 2017;**56**:466-474. Available from: https://pubmed.ncbi.nlm.nih.gov/28545751/ [Accessed: June 29, 2020]

[49] Baron-Cohen S, Tsompanidis A, Auyeung B, Nørgaard-Pedersen B, Hougaard DM, Abdallah M, et al. Foetal oestrogens and autism. Molecular Psychiatry. 2019:1-9. DOI: 10.1038/s41380-019-0454-9 [Accessed: August 25, 2020]

[50] Robinson EB, Lichtenstein P, Anckarsäter H, Happé F, Ronald A. Examining and interpreting the female protective effect against autistic behavior. Proceedings of the National Academy of Sciences of the United States of America. 2013;**110**(13):5258-5262. DOI: 10.1073/pnas.1211070110 [Accessed: August 25, 2020]

[51] Happé F, Frith U. Annual research review: Looking back to look forward – Changes in the concept of autism and implications for future research. Journal of Child Psychology and Psychiatry. 2020;**61**(3):218-232. DOI: 10.1111/jcpp.13176 [Accessed: September 8, 2020]

[52] Carpenter, Barry, Happé Francesca, Egerton Jo, Hollins BS. Girls and autism: Educational, family and personal perspectives. 2019. Available from: https://www.amazon.co.uk/Girls-Autism-Educational-Personal-Perspectives/dp/0815377266 [Accessed: August 25, 2020]

[53] Charman T. The prevalence of autism spectrum disorders: Recent evidence and future challenges. In: European Child and Adolescent Psychiatry. Vol. 11. Springer; 2002. pp. 249-256. DOI: 10.1007/s00787-002-0297-8 [Accessed: June 28, 2020]

[54] Wing L, Potter D. The epidemiology of autistic spectrum disorders: Is the prevalence rising? Mental Retardation and Developmental Disabilities Research Reviews. Ment Retard Dev Disabil Res Rev. 2002;**8**:151-161. Available from: https://pubmed.ncbi.nlm.nih.gov/12216059/ [Accessed: June 28, 2020]

[55] Lee BK, McGrath JJ. Advancing parental age and autism: multifactorial pathways. Trends in molecular medicine. 2015;**21**(2):118-125. DOI: 10.1016/j.molmed.2014.11.005

[56] Agrawal S, Rao SC, Bulsara MK, Patole SK. Prevalence of autism spectrum disorder in preterm infants: A meta-Analysis. In: Pediatrics. Vol. 142. American Academy of Pediatrics; 2018

[57] McCaul ME, Roach D, Hasin DS, Weisner C, Chang G, Sinha R. Alcohol and women: A brief overview. Alcoholism, Clinical and Experimental Research. 2019;**43**(5):774-779. DOI: 10.1111/acer.13985 [Accessed: August 12, 2020]

Chapter 2

Epidemiology of ASD in Preschool-age Children in Japan

Manabu Saito, Yui Sakamoto and Ai Terui

Abstract

In recent years, it has been reported that the prevalence of autism spectrum disorder (ASD) is increasing, but there are few research reports in Asia equivalent to those in Europe and the United States. Since large-scale epidemiological studies of neurodevelopmental disorders (NDDs) have not been conducted in Japan, the delay in early detection is conspicuous compared to other countries. Therefore, we started epidemiological studies in a medium-sized city (Hirosaki City) in northern Japan from 2013 to elucidate the prevalence of ASD and have been conducting a 9-year community cohort survey. In 2020, we published an adjusted prevalence of ASD of 3.2% at the age of 5 years, no change in 4-year incidence, and comorbidity of ASD. Since then, we have focused on sleep problems at the age of 5 years and have been studying the estimation of the prevalence of sleep disorders and the relationship with neurological development disorders. In this chapter, in addition to our research results since 2013, we will introduce the screening and support system in the community in Japan.

Keywords: autism spectrum disorder, prevalence, preschooler, sleep problems, screening system

1. Introduction

In epidemiological studies, the prevalence of autism spectrum disorder (ASD) has changed significantly over the last 20 years. A 2018 study by the Centers for Disease Control and Prevention (CDC) reported a prevalence of 2.30% (1 in 44 children) among children aged 8 years [1]. In 2008, the prevalence was 1 in 88 children [2], so the ADDM network reported that the prevalence of ASD has doubled in 10 years. Diagnostic criteria are American Psychiatric Association's the Diagnostic and Statistical Manual of Mental Disorders (DSM), Fourth Edition, Text Revision (DSM-IV-TR), 5th ed. (DSM-5), the World Health Organization's International Statistical Classification of Diseases and Related Health Problems (ICD), Ninth Revision (ICD-9) or Tenth Revision (ICD-10), indicating the importance of following the same criteria [3–6].

In Asia, a large-scale study by YS Kim et al. in 2011 reported the prevalence of ASD with similar diagnostic criteria, reporting 2.64% in children aged 7–11 years [7]. In Japan, there has been no large-scale epidemiological study by DSM criteria, and in 2020 we reported for the first time that the prevalence of 5-year-old ASD in the community was 3.22% [8].

IntechOpen

In recent years, as the heterogeneous nature of brain and sensory functions in neurodevelopmental disorders (NDDs) has been clarified, it has been suggested that ASD symptoms can be improved by early intervention, and ASD has undergone a paradigm shift as a disorder in which neuroplasticity can be expected [9]. In addition, it has been reported that people with neurodevelopmental disorders often have complications such as depression, anxiety disorders, and conduct disorders [10, 11]. Many of these complications occur as secondary disorders of neurodevelopmental disorders (NDDs), and early detection of developmental characteristics and early intervention are considered important to prevent secondary disorders [12]. In this chapter, in addition to our research results since 2013, we will introduce the screening and support system in the community in Japan.

2. Epidemiology of ASD in preschool-age children in Japan

2.1 Infant health checkup system in Japan

In Japan, the Maternal and Child Health Law requires municipalities to conduct health and development checkups for children aged 18 and 36 months [13]. At these checkups, public health nurses and pediatricians assess physical, motor, social, emotional, behavioral, verbal development, and general health (medical and dental). If these assessments are found to be abnormal, the public health nurse and/or pediatrician should refer the patient to a specialist for further evaluation, if necessary, and have the child's caregiver available for early intervention, such as speech therapy. Providing local resources where possible is encouraged (but not compulsory). According to a Ministry of Health, Labor, and Welfare report published in 2020, the 18-month health checkup rate in Japan was 95.2%, and the 36-month health checkup rate was 94.5% [14].

While the participation rate in infant health checkups is high and infant deaths are sufficiently prevented, the rate of finding prominent neurodevelopmental disorders in health checkups is extremely low at 0.2–1.3%. Therefore, in 2017, the government made recommendations for early detection of neurodevelopmental disorders in infant health checkups [15]. The number of children receiving special support after entering elementary school has tripled from 10 years ago [16]. There is a gap between the high need for support due to the awareness of neurodevelopmental disorders by guardians and caregivers and the low detection rate in the health checkup system.

2.2 The Hirosaki five-year-old children developmental health check-up (HFC) study

The Hirosaki Five-year-old Children Developmental Health Check-up (HFC) study was established in 2013 using a total population sample of 5-year-olds living in Hirosaki City, Japan. The rationale for this study is that, despite the high participation rate in these assessments, the data of children who screened positive for NDD at 18-month or 36-month health checkup or follow-up arose from concerns about the limited. There were also concerns about whether children who screened positive before the age of 5 years were subsequently evaluated and received appropriate services. This study, in collaboration with the University of California, San Francisco (UCSF), used HFC data from 2013 to 2016 to estimate the prevalence and 5-year cumulative incidence of ASD at the age of 5 years. We investigated patterns of comorbidity of NDDs in children with ASD, including hyperactivity disorder (ADHD), developmental coordination disorder (DCD), and intellectual disability (ID) [8].

Five-year-old Children Developmental Health Check-up was conducted annually between January 2013 and December 2016, and four cohorts were created. HFC was conducted in two stages and aimed to detect all children with NDD in the community. The primary screening was a series of questionnaires mailed by Hirosaki City to the parents and kindergarten or nursery school teachers of all 5-year-olds living in the city. The questionnaire used epidemiological information (children's gender, family composition, parental education, and employment history, etc.) and the following scales: Autism Spectrum Screening Questionnaire (ASSQ), Strengths and Difficulties Questionnaire (SDQ), ADHD Rating Scale-IV (ADHD-RS-IV), Developmental Coordination Disorder Questionnaire (DCDQ), and Parenting Stress Index (PSI) [17]. The parent has completed all of the above questionnaires, and the teacher has completed SDQ. All of the above tools have been translated into Japanese, and their reliability and validity had previously been established [18–22].

In the second stage of evaluation, a comprehensive evaluation of NDDs in screen-positive children was performed at Hirosaki University Hospital. Caregivers of screen-positive children were invited to participate in a comprehensive evaluation. **Figure 1** is a flow chart of the screening and evaluation stages of HFC research.

At the comprehensive assessment, developmental history and concerns were collected using items derived from the Diagnostic Interview for Social and Communication Disorders (DISCO) [23]. The DISCO is a semi-structured interview schedule designed to collect information on development and behavior. It can be used to assist in identifying possible diagnostic categories, including ASDs and other developmental disorders affecting social interaction and communication.

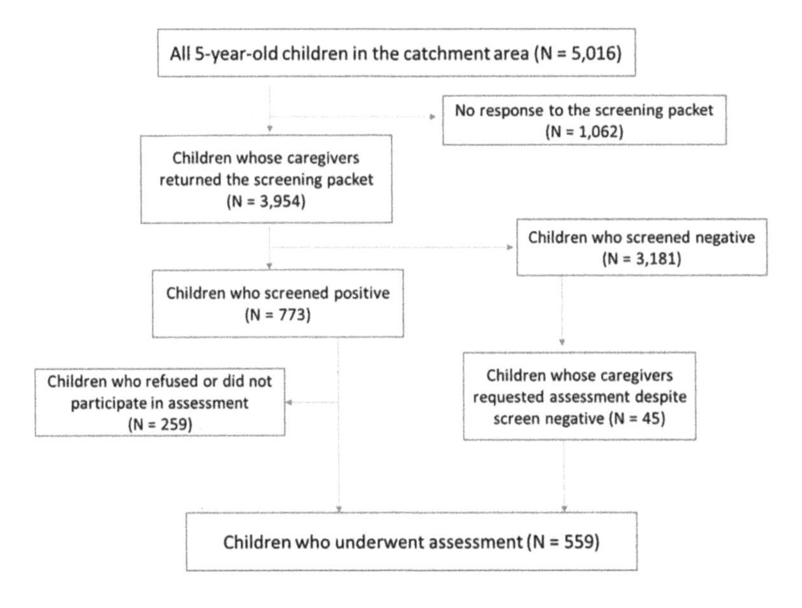

Figure 1.
Flow chart of the Hirosaki five-year-old developmental Checkup and assessment.

Cognitive assessments were conducted by psychologists using the Japanese version of the Wechsler Intelligence Scale for Children, 4th edition (WISC-IV) [24] only for children who did not have an ID diagnosis before participating in the present study. Assessment of children's coordination skills was performed by trained occupational therapists and psychologists using the Movement Assessment Battery for Children, 2nd edition (MABC-2) [25]. MABC-2 is a test of coordination disorders for children aged 3–16 years. It consists of three fine motor measures, two ball skill measures, and three balance skill measures. Screening test scores, parent interviews and child examinations, and other test results were reviewed by multiple professionals, including child psychiatrists. If ASD is diagnosed or suspected, the child is added to the Autism Diagnostic Observation Schedule (ADOS)-2 [26], and they were assured of research reliability. The definitive diagnosis was determined on the basis of findings consistent with screening evaluation and diagnosis. We used the DSM-5 criteria for the diagnosis of ASD, ADHD, and both the DSM-5 and the European Academy of Childhood Disability guidelines [27] for the diagnosis of DCD. Criteria for ID were defined as an IQ <70.

2.3 Prevalence and cumulative incidence of ASDs and the patterns of co-occurring neurodevelopmental disorders in a total population sample of 5-year-old children

Of the 559 children who underwent secondary assessment, 87 children (60 boys and 27 girls) were diagnosed with ASD. The 4-year mean ASD crude prevalence was 1.73% (95% CI 1.37–2.10%), with a 95% CI of 1.37 to 2.10%. Gender crude prevalence estimates for ASD were 2.35% (95% CI 1.76–2.94%) for boys and 1.09% (95% CI 0.68–1.51%) for girls, with the gender ratio of 2.2:1. After statistically adjusting for nonparticipants in comprehensive developmental assessment, the adjusted prevalence of ASD was estimated to be 3.22% (95% CI 2.66–3.76%). Gender-adjusted prevalence of ASD was 4.06% (95% CI 3.20–4.92%) in boys and 2.22% (95% CI 1.57–2.88%) in girls, with the gender ratio of 1.8:1.

The cumulative incidence of ASD by the age of 5 years within this research period (2013–2016) was 1.31% (95% CI 1.00–1.62%), with no significant increase in the 5-year cumulative incidence. The prevalence and 5-year cumulative incidence for each study year are summarized in **Table 1**.

Of the children with ASD (N = 87), 88.5% (n = 77) had at least one comorbid NDD (ADHD, DCD, ID, and/or borderline intellectual function (BIF)) and 20 children with ASD (23%) had 3 comorbid NDDs. Gender ratio of comorbidities was ADHD 50.6% (boys: girls = 2.4:1), DCD 63.2% (2.1:1), ID 36.8% (1.7:1), and BIF 20.6% (2.6,1) (**Figure 2** and **Table 2**).

Only 21 of 87 ASD children had received a diagnosis of ASD prior to this study. Of the 59 children who were assisted by the age of 5 years, 38 had other diagnoses (developmental or language delay). Twenty-eight (32%) had no developmental problems and no remedial intervention by the age of 5 years. **Figure 3** shows the problem of undiagnosed and unintervention of ASD.

Our study revealed that 5-year-old children with ASD have a high incidence of concurrent NDD, suggesting that ASD has a wide range of difficulties in daily life, such as attention and motor control, in addition to social problems. In infant screening, it is necessary to broadly evaluate various characteristics and provide early developmental support to children.

		year 2013	2014	2015	2016	Total
Crude Prevalence (95% Confidence Interval: CI)	male	2.04 (0.98 - 3.10)	2.03 (0.94 - 3.13)	3.00 (1.64 - 4.36)	2.82 (1.42 - 4.23)	2.35 (1.76 - 2.94)
	female	1.28 (0.40 - 2.16)	1.13 (0.30 - 1.95)	1.13 (0.30 - 1.96)	0.83 (0.11 - 1.56)	1.09 (0.68 - 1.51)
	total	1.68 (0.98 - 2.38)	1.59 (0.90 - 2.28)	2.05 (1.25 - 2.84)	1.63 (0.92 - 2.34)	1.73 (1.37 - 2.10)
Adjusted prevalence (95% CI)	male	Prevalence of ASD was 3.2%				4.06 (3.20 - 4.92)
	female					2.22 (1.57 - 2.88)
	total					3.22 (2.66 - 3.76)
Cumulative incidence up to 5 years of age (95% CI)	male	1.14 (0.35 - 1.92)	1.39 (0.49 - 2.29)	2.19 (1.06 - 3.33)	2.16 (1.00 - 3.32)	1.70 (1.20 - 2.19)
	female	0.76 (0.10 - 1.43)	1.15 (0.30 - 1.99)	0.90 (0.18 - 1.62)	0.85 (0.11 - 1.59)	0.91 (0.54 - 1.28)
	total	0.96 (0.44 - 1.47)	1.27 (0.65 - 1.89)	1.53 (0.87 - 2.20)	1.51 (0.82 - 2.20)	1.31 (1.00 - 1.62)

ASD = Autism Spectrum Disorder, Prevalence (%) = N of ASD cases / the total N of target population in the catchment area * 100, A total N of 5-year-old children in the catchment area=5016

Five-year cumulative incidence (%) = N of ASD cases who were born in the catchment area / N of birth cohort in the catchment area * 100, N of birth cohort in the catchment area=5112

Table 1.
Crude prevalence, adjusted prevalence, and cumulative incidence up to the age of 5 years of autism spectrum disorders in each survey year.

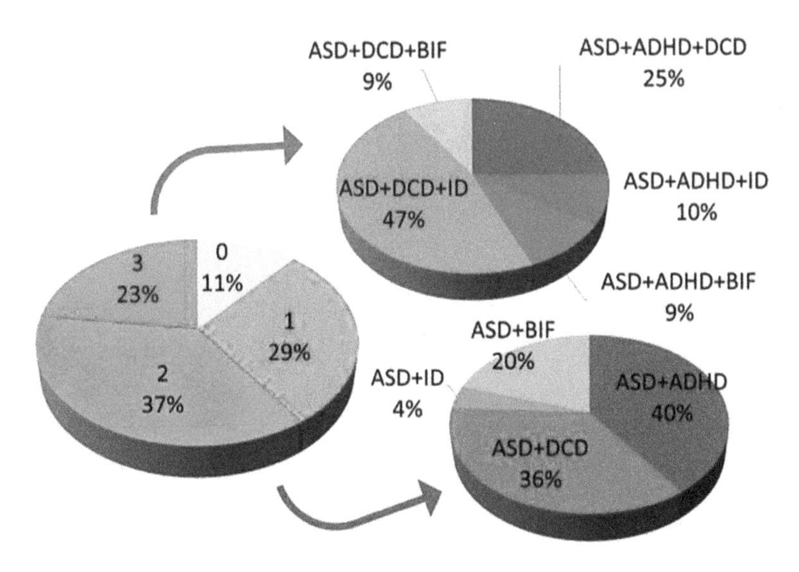

Figure 2.
Number of comorbidities of autism spectrum disorder.

For this reason, children who were diagnosed with some form of NDD at a health checkup were promptly given support and prepared for entering elementary school. Children who have been diagnosed with the disease should visit the Hirosaki University Hospital regularly at least once every 1 to 2 years for examinations and consultations and follow up until the age of 15 years to reconsider the diagnosis and determine the need for treatment. Some children require medication. The effects of these interventions need to be analyzed separately.

Co-occurring NDDs	n	%
None (i.e. ASD alone)	10	11.49
ADHD alone or ADHD and other NDDs	44	50.57
DCD alone or DCD and other NDDs	55	63.22
ID alone or ID and other NDDs	32	36.78
BIF alone or BIF and other NDDs	18	20.69

Table 2.
Comorbid patterns of neurodevelopmental disorders in 87 individuals with ASD.

2.4 Prevalence of sleep problems in Japanese Preschoolers and children with developmental disabilities

Sleep problems are not only associated with emotions and behaviors but also affect mental and physical health over time. Our previous study reported 80% of 482 children had sleep problems in Japan [28]. Among Chinese urban kindergarten children, also, almost 80% (78.8%) of the children scored above the original Children's Sleep Habits Questionnaire (CSHQ) cutoff point for global sleep disturbance [29]. However, there has been no report of a larger-scale study and the comorbid rate of neurodevelopmental disorders. The aim of this study was to estimate the prevalence of sleep problems in preschoolers and children with developmental disabilities using the Children's Sleep Habits Questionnaire (CSHQ), which is widely used in large community-based surveys.

Subjects were 1800 children who participated in 5-year-olds developmental checkup in a city, Japan. Six hundred and nine participants in the secondary checkup were diagnosed whether NDD or not according to DSM-5 criteria. The data include 1421 TDs (boys: girls = 726:695), 118 ASDs (83:35) and 125 ADHDs (79:46), and 136 other DDs (91,45). Caregivers of 5-year-old children completed CSHQ. We compared with CSHQ total and subscale scores in four groups using Kruskal–Wallis's test and analyzed the relation between z-score of CSHQ total and subscale and diagnosis using a logistic multiple regression analysis ($p < 0.05$).

Children's Sleep Habits Questionnaire (CSHQ) consists of nine subscales: Bedtime Resistance, Sleep Onset Delay, Sleep Duration, Sleep Anxiety, Night Waking, Parasomnias, Sleep Disordered Breathing, Daytime Sleepiness, and Sleep/wake patterns [30].

Percentage of children suspected of having sleep problems (CSHQ co > 41) was 80% in TD, 89.0% in ASD, 90.4% in ADHD, and 83.8% in Other DD, respectively (see **Figure 4**). ASD and ADHD children have significantly higher scores of Total score, Sleep Duration, Sleep Anxiety, Parasomnias, Sleep-Disordered Breathing, and Daytime Sleepiness than TD (see **Figure 5**). When the CSHQ total score z-score increases by 1 (1SD), the probability of being diagnosed with ASD increases by 1.45 odds.

This study showed Japanese preschoolers have high percentage of sleep problems. In addition to comorbid rate of those in ASD were so high that we can predict ASD diagnosis from CSHQ. We must pay attention more that many children have sleep problems, and it would occur some health problems in the future.

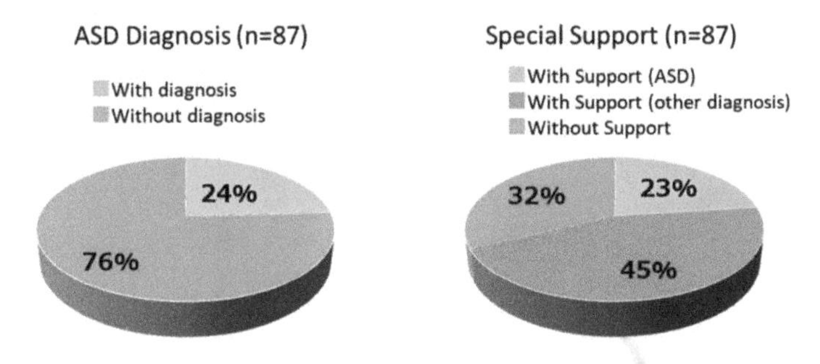

Figure 3.
The problem of undiagnosed and unintervention of ASD.

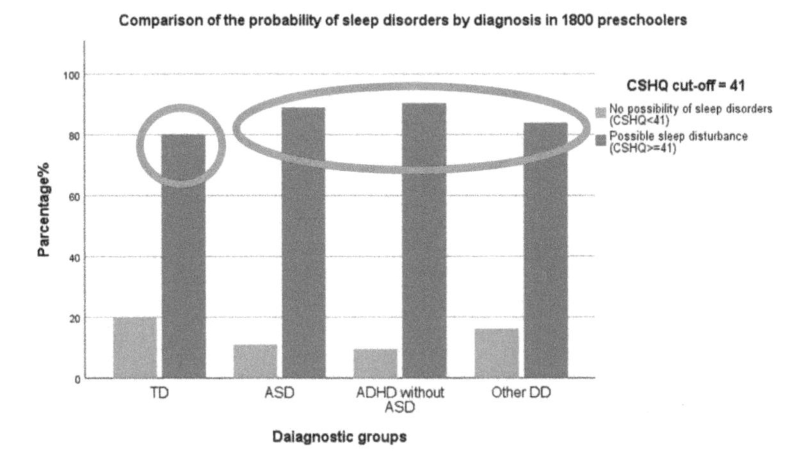

Figure 4.
Comparison of the probability of sleep disorders by diagnosis in 1800 preschoolers.

2.5 Verification of new screening tools for neurodevelopmental disorders in 5-year-old children

We analyzed multiple questionnaires completed by the parents and teachers of 954 5-year-old primary screening participants in 2013 and the DSM-5 diagnoses of 156 individuals who participated in the secondary examination, then we invented an algorithm to extract the NDD risk group. Children were considered "screen positive" if one of the following criteria (a)–(d) was met:

a. Parent assessment ASSQ score of 19 or higher.

b. PSI scores >75 percentile.

c. Parent-rated ASSQ scores between 9 and 19 and parent-assessed ADHD-RS total scores or at least one of subscale scores were above-defined cutoff.

d. One or more among parent-assessed ASSQ, ADHD-RS, and DCDQ scores were above the cutoff and the teacher-assessed SDQ total or one SDQ subscale scores were above the cutoff.

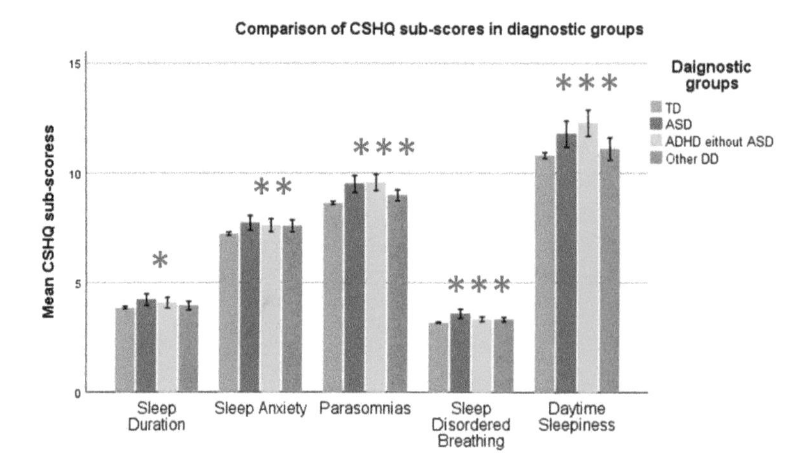

Figure 5.
Comparison of CSHQ subscales.

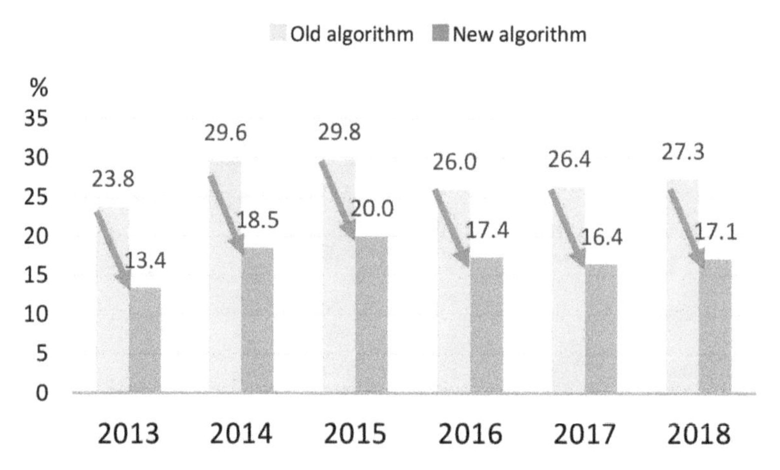

Figure 6.
Comparison the proportion of NDDs high-risk children with old and new algorithm.

Old algorithm	Children who scored at least one of the PSDQ, PASSQ, PADHD-RS, PDCDQ, and K6 cutoffs were considered risk children.
New algorithm	Children who met one or more of the following four criteria were considered risk children.

Table 3.
Old algorithm and new algorithm.

We validated the algorithm on 965 people in 2014, 1004 people in 2015, 1031 people in 2016, 967 people in 2017, and 1040 people in 2018. The confirmation method is as follows.

First, we compared the rate of high-risk group extraction for her NDD by year under the old and new algorithms (see **Figure 6**). **Table 3** shows old algorithm and new algorithm.

Next, we compared between the proportion of children with special needs who diagnosed with NDD, those who were below the diagnostic criteria but required observation and had no problems by year (see **Figure 7**). Finally, we calculated the

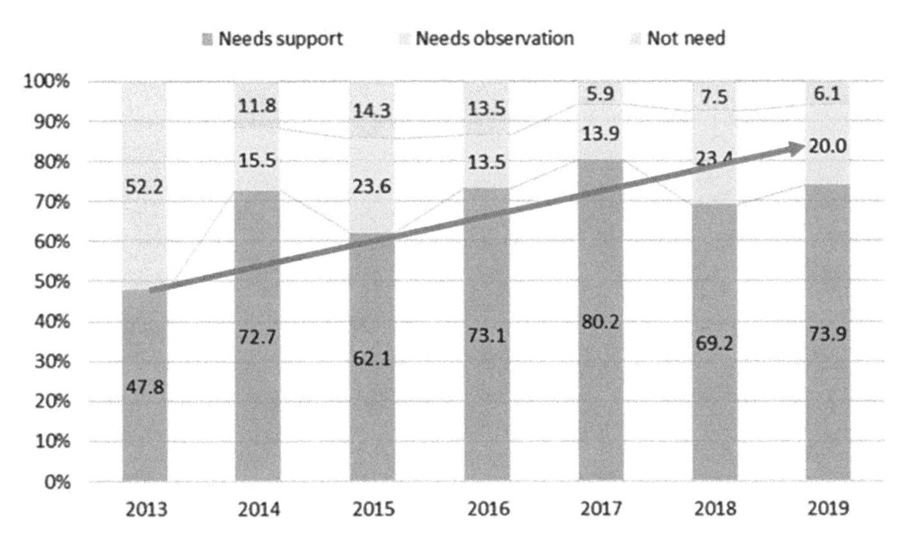

Figure 7.
Changes in the rate of children who need supports and observation, or no needs.

sensitivity and specificity of the new algorithm for extracting children with special needs and observation needs, which were 0.89 and 0.99, respectively.

The new algorithm, created by combining multiple tests, has made it possible to extract risk children more efficiently than the old algorithm. This algorithm was put into a web system in 2019, and from 2020 it was used in developmental health checkups in Hirosaki City [31]. Due to the spread of COVID-19, it was difficult to hold face-to-face health checkups, but with the introduction of the web system, the participation rate of 5-year-old developmental health checkups increased from 85–94%, and the secondary health checkup rate also increased. As a result, more children with NDD are receiving support for adjusting to primary school than before.

3. Conclusions

Epidemiological research in medium-sized cities in northern Japan will soon reach its 10th anniversary. Epidemiological studies are carried out as observational studies over time, repeating the same methods as much as possible. In Japan, where early detection is delayed, intervention support is provided after investigation and diagnosis. It had to be used for individual profit. Although this study reported an analysis of a 4-year survey, a 10-year trajectory and prognostic study of NDD diagnosis in 5-year-olds will begin in the future. We hope that our research will continue and help build a comfortable society for NDD.

Acknowledgements

We would like to express our heartfelt gratitude to all children, their families, teachers, and Hirosaki City staff who participated in HFC study and the Hirosaki University faculty members and researchers (Hirota T, Sakamoto Y, Mikami T,

Terui A, Osato A, Koeda S, Mikami M, Kuribayashi M, and Nakamura K) who were involved in the examination, diagnosis, and statistical analysis of health checkups.

This study was supported by the following grants: Grants-in-Aid for Scientific Research (KAKENHI: grant numbers JP16K10239 and JP19K08062), Hirosaki City Commissioned Research Fund, Hirosaki University Institutional Research Grant for Future Innovation, Industry-Academia Joint Development Research Fund, and Hirosaki Institute of Neuroscience in Japan.

Conflict of interest

The authors declare no conflict of interest.

Author details

Manabu Saito[1,2]*, Yui Sakamoto[3] and Ai Terui[3]

1 Department of Comprehensive Rehabilitation Science, Graduate School of Health Sciences, Department of Clinical Psychological Science, School of Medicine, Hirosaki University, Hirosaki, Japan

2 Research Center for Child Mental Development, Graduate School of Medicine, Hirosaki University, Hirosaki, Japan

3 Departments of Neuropsychiatry, Graduate School of Medicine, Hirosaki University, Hirosaki, Japan

*Address all correspondence to: smanabu@hirosaki-u.ac.jp

References

[1] Matthew JM, Kelly AS, Amanda VB, et al. Prevalence and characteristics of autism spectrum disorder among children aged 8 years — Autism and developmental disabilities monitoring network, 11 Sites, United States, 2018. MMWR Surveillance Summaries. 2021;**70**(11):1-16

[2] Autism and Developmental Disabilities Monitoring Network Surveillance Year 2008 Principal Investigators; CDC. Prevalence of autism spectrum disorders—Autism and Developmental Disabilities Monitoring Network, 14 sites, United States, 2008. MMWR Surveillance Summaries. 2012;**2012**:61

[3] American Psychiatric Association. Diagnostic and Statistical Manual of Mental Disorders. 4th ed. Washington, DC: American Psychiatric Association; 2000

[4] American Psychiatric Association. Diagnostic and Statistical Manual of Mental Disorders. 5th ed. Arlington, VA: American Psychiatric Association; 2013

[5] World Health Organization (WHO). 2022. Available from: https://www.who.int/standards/classifications/classification-of-diseases. [Accessed: September 3, 2022]

[6] The Centers for Disease Control and Prevention (CDC). 2022. Available from: https://www.cdc.gov/ncbddd/autism/addm.html. [Accessed: September 3, 2022]

[7] Kim YS, Leventhal BL, Koh Y-J, et al. Prevalence of autism spectrum disorders in a total population sample. The American Journal of Psychiatry. 2011;**168**(9):904-912

[8] Saito M, Hirota T, Sakamoto Y, et al. Prevalence and cumulative incidence of autism spectrum disorders and the patterns of co-occurring neurodevelopmental disorders in a total population sample of 5-year-old children. Molecule Autism. 2020;**11**:35

[9] Dawson G, Bernier R. A quarter century of progress on the early detection and treatment of autism spectrum disorder. Development and Psychopathology. 2013;**25**:1455-1472

[10] Corsello CM. Early intervention in autism. Infants & Young Children. 2005;**18**(2):74-85

[11] Doshi-Velez F, Ge Y, Kohane I. Comorbidity clusters in autism spectrum disorders: An electronic health record time-series analysis. Pediatrics. 2014;**133**(1):e54-e63

[12] Larson K, Russ SA, Kahn RS, Halfon N. Patterns of comorbidity, functioning, and service use for US children with ADHD, 2007. Pediatrics. 2011;**127**(3):462-470

[13] Ministry of Health, Labor and Welfare (MHLW). Available from: https://elaws.e-gov.go.jp/document?lawid=340AC0000000141. [Accessed: September 3, 2022]

[14] Ministry of Health, Labor and Welfare reports. Available from: https://www.mhlw.go.jp/toukei/saikin/hw/c-hoken/20/dl/R02gaikyo.pdf. [Accessed: September 3, 2022]

[15] Ministry of Internal Affairs and Communications. Available from: https://www.soumu.go.jp/main_content/000458776.pdf. [Accessed: September 3, 2022]

[16] Ministry of Education, Culture, Sports, Science and Technology reports. Available from: https://www.mext.go.jp/kaigisiryo/2019/09/__icsFiles/afieldfile/2019/09/24/1421554_3_1.pdf. [Accessed: September 3, 2022]

[17] Ehlers S, Gillberg C. The epidemiology of Asperger syndrome. Journal of Child Psychology and Psychiatry. 1993;**34**(8):1327-1350

[18] Adachi M, Takahashi M, Takayanagi N, et al. Adaptation of the Autism Spectrum Screening Questionnaire (ASSQ) to preschool children. PLOS One. 2018;**13**(7):e0199590

[19] Matsuishi T, Nagano M, Araki Y, et al. Scale properties of the Japanese version of the Strengths and Difficulties Questionnaire (SDQ): A study of infant and school children in community samples. Brain Development. 2008;**30**(6):410-415

[20] Takayanagi N, Yoshida S, Yasuda S, et al. Psychometric properties of the Japanese ADHD-RS in preschool children. Research in Developmental Disabilities. 2016;**55**:268-278

[21] Nakai A, Miyachi T, Okada R, et al. Evaluation of the Japanese version of the Developmental Coordination Disorder Questionnaire as a screening tool for clumsiness of Japanese children. Research in Developmental Disabilities. 2011;**32**(5):1615-1622

[22] Narama M, Kanemasu Y, Araki A, et al. Validity and reliability of Japanse version of the Parenting Stress Index [in Japanese]. Journal of Child Health. 1999;**58**(5):610-616

[23] Wing L, Leekam SR, Libby SJ, Gould J, Larcombe M. The diagnostic interview for social and communication disorders: Background, inter-rater reliability and clinical use. Journal of Child Psychology and Psychiatry. 2002;**43**(3):307-325

[24] Wechsler D, Japanese WISC-IV Publication Committee. Japanese Version of the Wechsler Intelligence Scale for Children-fourth Edition. Tokyo, Japan: Nihon Bunka Kagakusha; 2010

[25] Henderson SE, Sugden DA, Barnett A. The Movement Assessment Battery for Children. 2nd ed. London: The Psychological Corporation; 2007

[26] Lord C, Rutter M, Dilavore PC, Risi S, Gotham K, Bishop LS. The Autism Diagnostic Observation Schedule 2nd Edition (ADOS-2). Los Angeles, CA: Western Psychological Services; 2012

[27] Blank R, Smits-Engelsman B, Polatajko H, Wilson P. European Academy for Childhood Disability. European Academy for Childhood Disability (EACD): Recommendations on the definition, diagnosis and intervention of developmental coordination disorder (long version). Developmental Medicine and Child Neurology. 2012;**54**(1):54-93

[28] Takahashi M, Adachi M, Yasuda S, Osato-Kaneda A, Saito M, et al. Prevalence of sleep problems in Japanese preschoolers in a medium-sized city: Community-based survey using the Children's Sleep Habits Questionnaire. Pediatrics International: Official Journal of the Japan Pediatric Society. 2012;**59**(6):747-750

[29] Liu Z, Wang G, Geng L, Luo J, Li N, Owens J. Sleep patterns, sleep disturbances, and associated factors among Chinese Urban Kindergarten Children. Behavioral Sleep Medicine. 2016;**14**(1):100-117

[30] Owens JA, Spirito A, McGuinn M. The Children's Sleep Habits

Questionnaire (CSHQ): Psychometric properties of a survey instrument for school-aged children. Sleep. 2000;**23**:1043-1051

[31] Saito M, et al. Patent application examination pending in Japan: Tokugan, 2019-59991

Chapter 3

Identification of Autism Spectrum Disorder: The First Signs Identified by Algerian Parents

Yamina Hammas and Sarah Bendiouis

Abstract

Early detection and identification of the first signs of autism play an important role in the implementation of support projects and appropriate interventions. Our study aims, on the one hand, to study the variations of the age of detection of the first signs of autism by the parents and, on the other hand, to explore the nature of these signs. It also seeks to verify whether the age of detection of early signs depends on certain characteristics such as the socioeconomic level of the parents. To do this, an analysis of the data collected as part of a prospective study of a population of 120 children was carried out. The results obtained indicate that the average age of identification of the first signs is around 19 months; and that the most reported signs relate to the area of verbal communication. However, no significant relationship was found between the age of the detection of the first sign and the economic level of the parents.

Keywords: autism, tracking, signs, parents, worries

1. Introduction

Autism is a neurodevelopmental disorder that disrupts the early development of the child in different areas, namely social, emotional, cognitive, communicative, verbal, etc. The most up-to-date classification used to define autism is that of the DSM-V (Diagnostic and Statistical Manual of Mental Disorders, fifth edition). Called ASD (Autism Spectrum Disorder), autism is currently classified in the category of Neurodevelopmental Disorders. It is a set of conditions that begin during the developmental period leading to an impairment of personal, social, school, or professional functioning. This alteration is mainly characterized by two symptomatic dimensions: A. "Persistent deficit in communication and social interactions observed in various contexts" and B. "Restricted and repetitive nature of behaviors, interests or activities" [1].

In Algeria, the Ministry of Health has identified a number that varies between 400,000 and 500,000 in 2018. The prevalence was estimated 10 years ago at 1 per 10,000 inhabitants, while it has currently reached 1 child per 100 inhabitants. It is therefore a growing phenomenon.

The journey of the child and his family begins as soon as the warning signs are identified. This is the first stage during which parents, family members, or any actor in the early childhood sector notices unusual signs in favor of one or more developmental particularities. The High Authority of Health [2] specifies that any parental concern regarding verbal development and social communication (absence of babbling and communicative gestures at 12 months, absence of words at 18 months, and absence of word association at 18 months) should be considered a major warning sign and should be the subject of a specialist consultation focused on identifying an ASD.

All research agrees that the signs of ASD appear during the first 2 years of life. There is currently no pathognomonic marker for progression to ASD. Indeed, the majority of parents begin to notice the first signs from the age of 6 months. However, this disorder can only be diagnosed from the age of 30 months [3]. Before the age of 1, the signs noted relate mainly to sensory reactivity (hyporeactivity, hyperreactivity, or search for sensory stimulation), the flexibility of attention, and the quality of the production of spontaneous movements (hypo or hypertonicity) [4]. This period can also be characterized by certain specificities relating to the level of alertness of the child (calm or irritable); its emotional regulation, exploration of the environment, but also on the quality of sleep and dietary diversity [5].

The current view of ASD baby-to-be-centered research methods is that there are three main methods [6]:

The retrospective method consists of retracing the history of the neurodevelopmental disorder on the basis of precursor clues to the domains or altered functions. It is mainly based on the use of family films and information collected during parental interviews.

The prospective method consists of targeting certain areas of development such as motor skills, language, the sensory or emotional area, and identifying the child's development in these areas, while identifying the times when deviations from typical development appear.

The predictive method: a method currently being tested in psychopathology and child psychiatry, which has already brought results in certain areas such as the early detection of skin cancers for example. The experimental approach aims to first check whether the six entities that make up the neurodevelopmental disorders will be found or not, then to take into consideration the network of neurons with all the parameters that can influence this network as well as the trajectory of the child's development, namely genetic, epigenetic, sociological, psychological, neuropsychological but also environmental and familial. Then in a last step, make predictions and deduce the evolution of the most relevant functional areas [6].

More and more studies are focusing on the question of identifying the first signs of ASD [7, 8]. This orientation is largely explained by the challenge of identification and early diagnosis in the implementation of support projects and interventions adapted to ASD, in order to reduce additional disabilities. It is therefore essential to follow very closely the development of children in whom communication is not established in an ordinary way in order not to delay a possible diagnosis and to allow early treatment [9] .

Adrien [10] uses the term "functional and developmental dysregulation" to describe the developmental characteristics of babies at risk because we notice at a very early age a disharmony concerning all psychological functions. Deegenne [11] and his collaborators conducted research on the early detection of autism, and more specifically on the interrelational sphere of the infant, focusing on the period from birth to 6 months, which they consider to be a little investigated period, yet it is fundamental for the subsequent development of the child. Compared with normal children, the analysis of home movies highlights the presence of an early interactive dysfunction in infants later diagnosed with autism, from the first month of life (commitment and visual attention, deficit in tonic-postural dialog, deficit in emotional expression) [11].

The concerns of parents appear in the majority of cases early. Indeed, DiLalla and Rogers [12] point out that 38% of parents of children with ASD worry toward the end of the first year, 41% during the second year, 16% identify abnormalities between the second and the third year, and finally, 5% from 3 years. De Giacomo and Fombonne [13] conducted a study on the nature of the first signs suspected by parents. They have indeed found that it is the delay in the appearance of language that is the anomaly most often identified initially (53.7% of cases) and that the particularities of interactive and social responses are identified in 17% of cases.

2. Research problem and objectives

This research focuses on the study of the age of identification of the first signs of autism spectrum disorder by parents.

It aims to answer the following question: are there variations in the age of detection of the first autistic signs by parents?

We also sought to answer the following questions:

- What is the nature of the first signs reported by the parents (signs relating to non-verbal communication, verbal communication, motor skills, etc.)?

- Does the age of detection of the first signs by the parents depend on certain characteristics such as their economic level?

3. Hypotheses

We hypothesize that the average age of recognition of the first signs by parents is around 18 months. Similarly, we assume that the nature of the first signs mainly concerns the sphere of non-verbal communication such as response to the name, eye contact, joint attention, etc. Finally, we expect the age of onset of the first signs to be correlated with the socioeconomic level of the parents. In other words, the higher the socioeconomic level of the parents, the earlier the age of detection of the first signs.

4. Method and tools

4.1 Population

Our research was carried out in Tlemcen (Algeria) in a psychiatry and psychotherapy office. It is a private practice in which a psychiatrist, two psychologists, and a speech therapist practice. Consultations are conducted with adults with various psychiatric and psychological pathologies, but also with parents with children who have psychological developmental disorders and more particularly neurodevelopmental disorders (ASD, learning disabilities, ADHD, etc.)

	Boys	Girls
Sex (N)	92	28
Chronological age (average in months)	48	38
	Fathers	Mothers
Sex (N)	60	60
Average chronological age year month)	42 (504)	35 (420)

Table 1.
Population characteristics.

The study therefore focuses on an analysis of data collected as part of a prospective study. The latter was carried out on the basis of evaluation files carried out in the context of consultations with parents who suspected an autistic disorder in their children. The study population is an Algerian population, which consists of 120 parents of children at risk whose chronological age varies from 15 to 60 months (**Table 1**).

4.2 Tools

A data collection grid was designed for this research. This grid includes several parameters that can provide information on the child but also his entourage. Among these parameters, we can cite:

- General information about the child.
- Information about parents.
- Anamnesis.
- Information on screening or diagnosis.

The variables retained for this study are: the age of identification of the first signs by the parents, the nature of the signs observed, and the socioeconomic level of the parents.

For parents whose screening has not yet been carried out, we relied on two instruments used to identify signs related to Autism Spectrum Disorder: the M-CHAT and the ADOS-2.

The M-CHAT (Modified Checklist for Autism in Toddler) is an instrument that can detect the first signs of autism. It is aimed at parents with children aged 16–30 months and includes a set of questions (23) that cover several areas of development. A first screening test for autism, the CHAT (Checklist for Autism in Toddlers), was proposed and validated in the 1990s by a team of researchers including Simon Baron-Cohen. The M-CHAT is passed through a structured interview with the parents. The latter must answer yes or no, depending on the current behavior of their child. There are six key items in this test:

- Item 2: Interest in other children.

- Item 7: Proto-declarative pointing (pointing to indicate interest in something).
- Item 9: Bringing objects to parents.
- Item 13: Imitation.
- Item 14: Child's response to first name when called.
- Item 15: Ability to follow the adult's score.

If the child fails two or three of the items considered predictive of autism spectrum disorder, follow-up and further evaluation should be considered.

The ADOS-2 Autism Diagnostic Observation Schedule or Observation Scale for the Diagnosis of Autism developed by Catherine Lord in 1989 in the United States. This is the second version of a semi-structured tool, which makes it possible to observe the socio-communicative behavior of the child, and this, through a succession of playful scenes making it possible to evaluate the quality of the social openings but also the emotions and the level of imagination.

4.3 Procedure

The study took place over a period of approximately 2 years. The first year was devoted to data collection.

The procedure went through two main stages:

4.3.1 Reception of parents who have suspected abnormalities in their children

This process was carried out within the framework of consultations within a medical office of psychiatry and psychopathologies. It was about collecting through the grid we designed; information on the child, on his family and to trace the history of his development, and this, within the framework of a semi-structured interview with both parents.

4.3.2 Passing the M-CHAT and/or the ADOS-2

This step mainly focused on the child since a direct observation of his behavior was made, supplemented by a handover of ASD screening tools. The aim was to ensure that these were children at risk for Autism Spectrum Disorder and not another developmental disorder.

4.3.3 Data collection, tabulation, and analysis

Data from 120 children were collected, analyzed, and then categorized. The age in months of detection of the first anomalies by the parents was retained as well as the nature of these anomalies. Codes were assigned according to the altered domain. In other words, we have divided all the warning signs according to two main categories: negative signs, which include delays in the field of non-verbal communication, verbal communication, motor skills, sociability and emotions; and positive signs, which refer to behavioral particularities and sensory.

Levels	Professions	Fathers	Mothers
Superior (N)	Employers, freelancers, senior executives	22	13
Medium (N)	Middle manager, worker, employee	58	27
Low (N)	Laborer, personnel in transit, inactive	40	80

Table 2.
Categorization of parental economic levels.

The socioeconomic level of both parents was also taken into consideration. Indeed, the professions of each parent were categorized according to (**Table 2**).

5. Results and discussion

5.1 Results

Remember that the main objective of this research is to first identify the average age of detection of the first signs of ASD by parents and then identify the nature of these signs. In other words, we seek to identify what is the area most identified by parents. Statistical analysis was performed using SPSS software. The results are presented in the following tables:

5.1.1 Average age of recognition of the first signs by the parents

Table 3 shows that the average age of identification of the first signs of autism by parents is around 19 months.

5.1.2 Nature and percentage of signs reported by parents

Figure 1 shows that the highest number of parents report signs that relate to verbal communication with a percentage of 30.50%; 28.81% of them first identify signs related to non-verbal communication; 12.71% identify social and emotional abnormalities; 11.86% of parents identify sensory particularities; 11.2% are alarmed by behavioral particularities; and finally, 5.06% of them identify motor specificities.

5.1.3 Identification of warning signs of ASD and economic level of parents

An analysis of variance was carried out in order to know if a difference exists between the different economic levels of the parents in the age of the identification of the first signs.

	N	Minimum	Maximum	Average (Months)
Age of the identification of the first signs	120	0	48	18,96

Table 3.
Average age of detection of the first abnormalities by the parents.

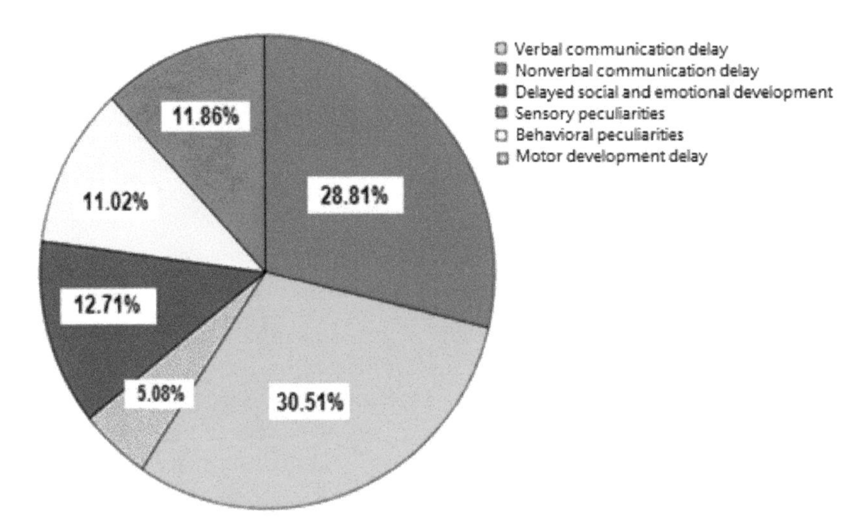

Figure 1.
Percentage of different warning signs reported by parents.

5.1.4 Economic level of fathers

Table 4 shows that the p-value (0.48) is greater than 0.05. These results indicate that there is no significant difference between the economic levels of the fathers in the age of detection of the first signs of ASD. However, the descriptive analysis shows that fathers with a high socioeconomic level detect precursor signs earlier than parents with medium and low socioeconomic levels (mean, standard deviation 21 (8.78)).

5.1.5 Economic level of mothers

Table 5 indicates that the p-value (0.31) is greater than 0.05. This result reveals that there is no statistically significant difference between the economic levels of the mothers and the age of detection of the first signs of ASD by the parents. On the other hand, the descriptive analysis highlights that mothers with a low economic level detect the warning signs earlier than mothers with a higher and average level (mean, standard deviation (10.27)).

5.2 Discussion

There is a consensus on the question of the need to spot and identify early the developmental particularities that could evolve into a neurodevelopmental disorder.

	N	Economic level of fathers Mean (standard deviation)			F test	P value
		High level	Medium level	Low level		
Age of detection of first signs	120	21 (8.78)	18.79 (10.3)	17.83 (10.01)	0.75	0.48

Table 4.
Economic level of fathers and age of detection of first signs.

	N	Economic level of fathers Mean (standard deviation)			F test	P value
		High level	Medium level	Low level		
Age of detection of first signs	120	15.23 (8.99)	8.55 (9.09)	19.70 (10.27)	1.17	0.31

Table 5.
Economic level of mothers and age of detection of first signs.

Pry [6] points out that this question of identifying signs is based on both theoretical and practical reasons. The theoretical reasons consist of saying that TND (neuro-developmental disorders) in particular Autism Spectrum Disorder is of early and neurodevelopmental origin, the first behaviors tend to change in meaning but also in function with the advancement in age. The practical reasons relate primarily to aspects of early interventions that aim to change the developmental trajectory of these behavioral formulations.

Therefore, this study focused on the question of the identification of early signs by parents. This is therefore a "retrospective" study based on data from interviews with parents, the main objective of which was to estimate the average age at which parents identify the warning signs of ASD, but also to identify the signs most reported by parents (concerns relating to motor, verbal, emotional, social development, etc.).

The results of our study show that the first signs of ASD are on average identified by parents around 19 months. In other words, it is only from the age of one and a half that parents begin to observe particular behavioral formulations. Thus, the calculation of the percentage of signs indicates that the most reported signs concern the field of communication, first "verbal" (30.51%), then "non-verbal" (28.81%).

The results obtained are in agreement with certain studies, notably that of Rogers [14] according to which the majority of parents (41%) identify the first signs during the second year. Most of the research on this subject emphasizes that parental concerns appear around the second year Guinchat et al. [8].

Concerning the origin of the first concerns, it is mainly about the delay in the development of the language [7, 13, 15].

These results can be partly explained by the involvement of certain factors, in particular the cultural and social factor. Indeed, parents may not be sensitive to the typical development of intentional communicative acts addressed to the environment and its deviations such as gazing, sharing attention, or pointing. These acts of course precede the appearance of the first words. Therefore, the concerns are quite late because the parents mainly wait for the age when the expressive language (first words) is supposed to appear to be alarmed. The knowledge of the parents on the early psychological development of the child and more particularly, the sociocommunicative development, is probably not sufficient to be able to detect its anomalies, delays, or deviations.

We also note that only 5.08% of the signs relate to motor behavior, except that several studies confirm that the first manifestations relating to developmental disorders concern motor development with atypical ocular motor skills, asymmetrical postures, or even particularities of the spontaneous movements [16]. These relatively late concerns can also be explained by the number and position of the child among the siblings. Indeed, during the interviews within the framework of consultations with the parents, we noted that having only one child or when it was the first child in the siblings, the parents had difficulty in evoking information related to the early

DOI: http://dx.doi.org/10.5772/intechopen.108000

development of the child because of the lack of a possibility of comparison with children of the same age. This situation can lead parents to miss a set of early signs, including signs relating to motor or sensory development.

A third element that can be used for interpretation consists of taking into consideration the "regressive" process usually cited in research on the baby to become of ASD. Indeed, the data of the literature underline the presence in certain cases of a regression or even a loss of communicative and language skills between 16 and 20 months. This phenomenon may explain the relatively late identification of the first signs.

We have also sought to study the factors that may possibly influence the age of identification of the first signs, in particular the socioeconomic factor of the parents, first of the fathers and then of the mothers.

The statistical analysis reveals an absence of significant link between the socioeconomic levels of the parents and the age of the identification of the first signs. In other words, the social and economic level of the parents has no influence on the precocity or not of the identification of the first signs of ASD. Parents with a higher level are not necessarily able to detect the first anomalies early.

One way to interpret this result is to say that the profession of parents with a higher level leads them not to spend a lot of time with their children, and therefore, they have less opportunity to carefully observe the appearance of the first signs.

This observation was assessed during the interviews with the parents and confirmed by the descriptive analysis concerning the economic level of the mothers. Indeed, the results of our study tell us that mothers with a low economic level (generally inactive mothers) tend to spot the first signs well before mothers with a higher to average level.

6. Conclusion

Autism is an early-onset neurodevelopmental disorder, the first behavioral expressions of which are the subject of several studies. A broad consensus exists on the need to identify the first behavioral deviations as early as possible. The interest of this approach consists of answering the following problem: can early interventions (educational, developmental, behavioral, or others) possibly modify the evolutionary course of the child, but also what is the most that makes it possible to modify the child's development as quickly as possible (before school age).

This work shows that Algerian parents detect the signs of autism during the second year of life (19 months) and that the signs reported relate mainly to nonverbal communication (pointing, gaze, gestures) language skills (delay appearance of language). Thus, the socioeconomic level of the parents is not linked to the age of detection of the first signs.

Parents should therefore be encouraged to carefully observe the child's developmental sequences in order to be able to identify developmental deviations earlier, which may relate to a set of areas (other than the area of non-verbal communication and verbal) such as motor development but also emotional or sensory.

Acknowledgements

We would like to thank all the people who contributed to the realization of this work.

First of all, we would like to express our gratitude to the parents of children with autism for their patience and availability to answer our questions.

We would also like to thank Doctor Lotfi Bendiouis for giving us the opportunity to carry out this work in the field by welcoming us to his psychiatry and psychotherapy practice.

Acronyms and abbreviations

DSM-V	diagnostic and statistical manual of mental disorders, fifth edition.
HAS	high authority of health.
ASD	autism spectrum disorder.

Author details

Yamina Hammas* and Sarah Bendiouis
University of Tlemcen, Tlemcen, Algeria

*Address all correspondence to: mounabendiouis3@gmail.com

References

[1] American Psychiatric Association. Diagnostic and Statistical Manual of Mental Disorders. Fifth ed. Arlington, VA: American Psychiatric Publishing; 2013. pp. 24-27

[2] Haute Autorité de Santé. Trouble du Spectre de l'Autisme - Signes D'Alerte, Repérage, Diagnostic Et Évaluation Chez L'Enfant Et L'Adolescent. Saint-Denis La Plaine: HAS; 2018

[3] De Hemptinne D, Fallourd N, Madieu E. Aider son enfant autiste. Paris: Deboeck; 2007. pp. 9-15

[4] Pry R. 100 idées pour accompagner un enfant avec autisme dans un cadre scolaire. de la maternelle, au college; Slovénie; 2021. pp. 17-19

[5] Haute Autorité de santé Troubles du Spectre de l'Autisme: signes d'alerte, repérage, diagnostic, et évaluation chez l'enfant et l'adolescent. 2018

[6] Pry R. Six leçons sur les troubles du neurodéveloppement. Vol. 107. Paris: Tom Pousse; 2018

[7] Coonrod E, Stone WL. Early concerns of parents of children with autistic and nonautistic disorders. Illnfants and Young Children. 2004;**17**(3):258-268. DOI: 10.1097/00001163-200407000-00007

[8] Guinchat V, Chamak B, Bonniau B, Bodeau N, Perisse D, Cohen D, et al. Very early signs of autism reported by parents include many concerns not specific to autism criteria. Research in Autism Spectrum Disorders. 2012:589-601

[9] Cousineau D, Mottron L. Les troubles envahissants du développement: De maladie à différence. Le medecin du Quebec. 2010;**45**(2):45-49

[10] Adrien J. Autisme du jeune enfant: Développement psychologique et régulation de l'activité. Paris: Expansion Scientifique Française; 1996

[11] Deegenne C. Etude préliminaire des troubles des interactions et de la motricité chez le bébé. Devenir; 2009. pp. 265-294

[12] DiLalla DL, Rogers SJ. Domains of the Childhood Autism Rating Scale: Relevance for diagnosis and treatment. Journal of Autism and Developmental Disorders. 1994;**24**(2):115-128. DOI: 10.1007/BF02172092. PMID: 8040157

[13] De Giacomo A, Fombonne E. Parental recognition of developmental abnormalities in autism. Eur Child Adolesc Psychiatry. Sep 1998;**7**(3):131-136. DOI: 10.1007/s007870050058. PMID: 9826299

[14] Rogers SJ. Brief report: Early intervention in Autism. Journal of Autism and Developmental Disorders. 1996;**26**(2):243-246

[15] Howlin P, Asgharian A. The diagnosis of Autism and Asperger syndrome: Findings from a survey of 770 families. Development Medicine and Child Neurology. 1999;**41**(12):834-839. DOI: 10.1017/s0012162299001656. PMID: 10619282

[16] Mitchell P, Mottron L, Soulières I, Ropar D. Susceptibility to the Shepard illusion in participants with autism: Reduced top-down influences within perception? Autism Respective. 2010;**3**(3):113-119. DOI: 10.1002/aur.130. PMID: 20575110

Chapter 4

Stigma: An Investigative Analysis of the Irish Public's Knowledge and Perception of Autism

April Hargreaves, David Mothersill and Gerard Loughnane

Abstract

Levels of stigma toward autism have greatly reduced over the past two decades, particularly since the introduction of various anti-stigma and educational campaigns. However, stigma does remain negatively impacting the lives of people with autism, despite attempts to educate the public about the condition. One country in which this is apparent is Ireland, where, although various autism campaigns have been implemented, and there is evidence of improved attitudes and behavior toward individuals with autism, there still remains a lack of knowledge and understanding with regard to the condition. This chapter presents some novel findings regarding the knowledge, attitudes, and behavior of the Irish public toward autism. In an exploratory analysis, results demonstrate that whilst the Irish public professes an awareness of autism, a deep understanding of the condition is not present. There is also confusion regarding factors that contribute to autism. Reassuringly, there is little evidence of discrimination toward autistic individuals, but there are elements of prejudice that still exist. Details of these findings are outlined and discussed.

Keywords: stigma, knowledge, prejudice, discrimination, autism, Ireland

1. Introduction

Public stigma is defined as interrelated problems of knowledge (ignorance), attitudes (prejudice), and behaviors (discrimination) [1]. The negative impact of such stigma is multifaceted, posing real-life problems, such as difficulties with employment and access to accommodation [2, 3], reduced access to mental and physical health care [3], reduced life expectancy [4], and self-stigma, low self-esteem, and self-confidence [5, 6]. It has been argued that the emotional impact of stigma can contribute to the physical, psychological, and social burden inherent in many conditions, and can be as great a source, if not a greater source, of suffering than the manifestation of the condition itself [7].

Stigma, by its nature, leads to "othering." This is evident in Link and Phelan's [8] description of stigma, which involves labeling, stereotyping, status loss, rejection, and cognitively separating into "us" and "them" groups. Such "othering" takes place in the context of power inconsistencies that allow one group to successfully devalue another. Stigmatized people are often seen as incompetent. They are blamed for their suffering. They are socially marginalized in ways that could be considered ableist [9].

Over the past couple of decades, the public's conception of autism, and with it, levels of public stigma toward autism, has undergone a monumental shift. Autism was originally defined in the 1940s as a mental illness, a form of childhood schizophrenia and the result of cold parenting. It was viewed as rare and profoundly disabling. More recently, however, this view has changed. The 1980s saw autism described as a pervasive developmental disorder, recognizing the biological underpinnings of the condition. The 1990s introduced the idea that autism exists on a spectrum, from mild to severe. This decade also saw the emergence of the neurodiversity movement. Indeed, the term neurodiversity was coined in 1997 by sociologist Judy Singer, who is herself autistic. Through this lens autism is no longer considered an illness or disability; rather the autistic brain is said to be "wired" differently, leading to an alternative way of viewing and experiencing the world. In essence, it has now been assigned a comparatively positive social value.

To aid this newer understanding of autism, various public educational programs and campaigns have emerged over the past two decades, instructing the public about autism and neurodivergence. These include, amongst others, the "Too Much Information" campaign in the UK, "Say Yes to Autism Acceptance" in Ireland, "Autism Speaks" in the USA and Canada, "ASD Awareness Campaign" in Romania, and "Change Your Reactions" in Australia. The impact of campaigns such as these is positive and noteworthy. Public awareness of Autism has improved in many parts of the world. This is demonstrated by surveys conducted in, for example, the UK [10], France, [11], the USA, Canada [12], Australia [13], and Ireland [14].

However, despite this progress in awareness and education, stigma toward autism still exists. Whilst these surveys demonstrate that the public possesses a basic knowledge of autism, and professes positive attitudes toward people with autism, results also reflect persistent misconceptions about autistic people, and an ensuing desire to distance themselves from autistic individuals [15].

It would thus appear that neither awareness nor scientific advances have fully eradicated the stigma attached to autism, whether explained via conventional psychosocial and psychoanalytic frames or the more recent neurobiological models. It may be that knowledge, in and of itself, is insufficient to shift the deeply entrenched beliefs and associations the public hold toward autism. Instead, perhaps what we need is a deeper understanding and acceptance of the differences observable in autistic people.

Gray [16] considered that autism has uniquely stigmatizing traits due to the atypical social behaviors associated with autism, coupled with a lack of any obvious physical explanation for these behaviors. This in effect confuses people, feeds into the "us and them" mentality outlined by Link and Phelan [8], and potentially leads to a belief that autistic people are somehow responsible for their atypical behaviors. Many studies have corroborated this idea, finding that atypical verbal and nonverbal communication behaviors displayed by autistic people are associated with negative first impressions and reduced intentions to pursue social interaction with the autistic individual [17, 18].

Similarly, stereotypes of autism are predominantly negative. In Wood and Freeth's [19] study, students were asked to list all of the characteristics/traits that society associates with autism. Eight of the 10 most commonly listed traits were negative and included (1) poor social skills, (2) introverted and withdrawn, (3) poor communication, (4) difficult personality or behavior, (5) poor emotional intelligence, (6) awkward, (7) obsessive, and (8) low intelligence. The only two positive traits listed in the most frequent 10 traits were special abilities and high intelligence. Interestingly, five of the eight negative traits mentioned refer directly to observable communicative behaviors, affirming Sasson's 2017 and 2019 findings [17, 18]. Wood and Freeth's study is not the only study to demonstrate the association between autism and negative stereotypes. The "same chance report" conducted by the autism advocate group "As I Am" in Ireland found that 6 in 10 people associate negative connotations with autism.

So, as anti-stigma campaigns are raising awareness of autism, and improving attitudes toward autism, they are not improving the entrenched negative stereotypes that the public hold about autism. One reason for this might be the methods used by autistic individuals to deal with such stereotypes and stigma—many people strategically use concealment and masking in an attempt to pass as neurotypical. Autistic masking or camouflaging is the conscious or unconscious suppression of natural responses and adoption of alternatives across a range of domains, including social interaction, movement, and behavior [20]. Whilst this often works as an effective coping mechanism against stigma in the short term, it has been associated with late/missed diagnosis, mental health issues, burnout, and suicidality [20]. It also limits public exposure to typical autistic behavior, which limits familiarity. Familiarity is important, as it has been shown to decrease stigma [21]. People like and accept what's familiar [22]. Familiarity has been defined as the interpersonal knowledge of another individual, but it also comprises affective and behavioral components [23]. As such it is separate from factual knowledge—the kind of knowledge typically imparted in the type of educational campaign that we have seen in support of autism over the past two decades.

When we examine levels of autism knowledge globally, we see vast differentiation between countries. Research shows that public knowledge of autism is particularly poor in Saudi Arabia [24], China [25, 26], and Pakistan [27], but much better in countries, such as Australia [28], USA [25, 29], Northern Ireland [30], and the UK [31]. Interestingly the countries that present with the greatest knowledge levels are the same countries in which autism education campaigns have been run, affirming the use and effectiveness of such campaigns. One notable exception to this is Ireland. According to the same chance report, in 2022 only 4 in 10 Irish people claim to have a "good" understanding of autism. In our own recent study, comparing knowledge, attitudes, and behaviors toward autism, schizophrenia, and bipolar disorder in Ireland, we found that compared to schizophrenia and bipolar disorder, the Irish public's knowledge of autism was lacking, even though their attitudes and behaviors toward autistic people were largely positive [14].

This paper is thus a deeper dive into the data gathered on autism in that study, in an attempt to understand what elements of knowledge were proving particularly problematic for the Irish public. Is it awareness of autism, understanding of autism, or stigmatizing beliefs, that are present amongst the Irish public, and what does this mean for autism stigma going forwards?

2. Methods

2.1 Participants

307 participants were recruited via online sites, including social media (such as Twitter and Facebook). Demographic information was gathered on place of residence, gender, age (in 5 years groupings), socioeconomic status (according to the occupation of the head of household), income, education, marital status, and

family structure. Participation was voluntary and anonymous and occurred only after informed consent was obtained. All assessments were conducted in accordance with the National College of Ireland ethics committees' approval, and participants did not receive compensation for participation in the study. On completion of the questionnaire, participants were debriefed and provided with the contact details of the researcher should they have any follow-up questions. In total, participation took approximately 10 minutes.

2.2 Measures

All participants completed an online survey titled "Perceptions and representations of mental illness" adapted from research by Durand-Zaleski *et al.* (2012). The questionnaire had 22 questions that asked participants about their knowledge, attitudes, and behaviors toward mental disorders in general, and specifically toward schizophrenia, bipolar disorder, and autism. The data presented in this chapter draws solely on the responses about autism. A detailed description of the questionnaire employed can be found in our previously published paper titled "Knowledge, attitudes and behaviors toward schizophrenia, bipolar disorder and autism in Ireland: A pilot study [14]."

In brief, the questionnaire aims to explore whether individuals understand the "terminology" of autism and what actually constitutes the condition.

The survey comprised questions designed to capture data on key themes examined in previously published questionnaires exploring knowledge, attitudes, and beliefs [32–38]. Key domains targeted include:

Knowledge explored participants' knowledge of autism in terms of (a) prevalence (b) causes (e.g., genetic vulnerability, external stressors), (c) controllability (by the individual themselves or via different treatments), and (d) stability and predictability.

Attitudes were explored using questions that assessed autism terminology.

Behavior was explored using questions about participants' reactions, such as avoidance or social distancing.

The items were formatted to include "yes/no/do not know" questions, rank ordering of statements, or Likert scale ratings. Likewise, some questions about predicted behaviors (e.g., would the respondent be prepared to work alongside someone with bipolar disorder, schizophrenia, or autism) assessed differences in reaction to, or degree of discrimination toward, each disorder.

2.3 Design

This study used a cross-sectional design. The three stigma components of knowledge, attitudes, and behaviors were examined. Participants were given a score of 1 for each correct answer to five questions asking about knowledge and these were summed to calculate an overall knowledge score. Participants were given a score of one-to-three based on whether they agreed or disagreed with each of eight statements about attitudes, and these were summed to calculate an overall attitudes score. Participants were also given a score of one-to-three based on whether they agreed or disagreed with each of three statements about behaviors, and these were summed to calculate an overall behaviors score. For knowledge, a higher score meant greater knowledge of a particular diagnosis. For both attitudes and behaviours, a higher score meant greater positivity toward a particular diagnosis. Further details of how the total scores were calculated can be found in the appendices.

2.4 Procedure

Study participants completed the survey online using Google Forms. Responses were saved as a Microsoft Excel .xlsx file, which was then converted to an IBM SPSS statistics .sav file for descriptive statistics and calculation of variables of interest.

3. Results

3.1 Sample characteristics

The sample was 75% female, 23% male, and 2% who identified as other (see **Table 1**). 42% of respondents were under the age of 25, 45% of respondents were aged between 26 and 49, and 13% of respondents were aged over 50. About 60% of respondents had received tertiary education, and a quarter of respondents had an income level of between 1000 and 2500 euro. The majority of this sample were single, employed, and had no children living at home.

Demographic		Frequency	Percent
Gender	Male	70	23
	Female	231	75
	Other	6	2
Age	18–25	124	40
	26–35	65	21
	36–49	77	25
	50–65	37	12
	66+	4	1
Occupation	Employed	165	54
	Student	85	28
	Student & employed	4	1
	Homemaker	18	6
	Unemployed	28	9
	Retired	3	1
Marital status	Single	177	58
	In a relationship	12	4
	Cohabiting	12	4
	Married	86	28
	Separated	6	2
	Divorced	9	3
	Widowed	5	2

Demographic		Frequency	Percent
Family structure	No children at home	181	59
	1–2 under 15	77	25
	1–2 over 15	21	7
	3+ under 15	12	4
	3+ over 15	14	5
Level of education	Primary	45	15
	Junior certificate	13	4
	Leaving certificate	53	17
	Certificate/Diploma	5	2
	Degree	108	35
	Masters	73	24
	PhD	5	2
Income level	0	19	6
	Social welfare	43	14
	10,000–25,000	78	25
	26,000–35,000	54	18
	36,000–50,000	47	15
	51,000–99,000	37	12
	100,000+	11	4
	Retired	1	1

Table 1.
Sociodemographic characteristics of sample, N = 316. Missing responses from each category are those that preferred not to answer that question.

3.2 Awareness of autism

Awareness of autism was measured by asking the following question: For autism, please tick one of the following options: (a) you know the name and are able to describe it, (b) you know the name without being able to describe it, or (c) you have never heard of the illness. Results demonstrate that 99% of respondents recognized the term autism. However, when respondents were asked if they could describe some of the characteristics of autism, the proportions decreased to 76%.

To understand whether a particular subset of the sample might have less awareness of autism than the rest, associations between awareness and demographic variables were assessed via a series of Pearson chi-square tests. We found no association between awareness of autism and the demographic variables of education, income level, and family structure. However, an association was found between awareness of autism and the demographic variables of gender, age, and marital status, as depicted in **Table 2**, with males, younger age groups, and single people demonstrating less awareness of autism. It should be noted that age and marital status are associated (Pearson chi-square: 179.928; $p = <0.001$), most likely accounting for the marital status finding.

Demographic variable	Pearsons chi-square	P value	Category that demonstrated significantly less awareness of autism
Gender	25.159	<0.001	Males
Age	31.497	0.002	18–25 years
Marital status	35.87	0.007	Single people

Table 2.
Demographic variables positively associated with awareness of autism.

3.3 Understanding of autism

As can be seen in **Table 3**, the majority of participants believe that autism is not contagious, does not worsen with time, involves lifelong treatment, causes motor disabilities, and expresses in young adults. The majority of participants did not know that autism could be diagnosed early. There was also confusion over the hereditary nature of the condition, and whether or not autism could be categorized alongside other conditions.

Responses to the question of autism prevalence can be found in **Table 4**, with the majority of participants believing that autism occurs at a prevalence of 10%.

3.4 Perception of factors that contribute to autism

As can be seen in **Table 5**, despite confusion in the previous question regarding the hereditary nature of autism, most participants believe that genetics contribute to the condition (63%). Other non-environmental factors, age and gender, are also chosen quite often as contributory factors. Many participants believe that the environmental factors of "conditions of life" and "parent/child relationships" contribute to autism, whilst fewer participants think that environmental factors, such as psychological or emotional shock, drugs, alcohol, and food, play a role in the condition.

Autism	Agree n (%)	Disagree n (%)	Do not know n (%)
Is contagious	5 (2)	299 (95)*	7 (2)
Worsens with time	45 (15)	200 (64)*	63 (20)
Can be diagnosed early	0*	10 (3)	304 (96)
Is a condition with which you can live normally with treatment	183 (58)*	90 (29)	39 (12)
Involves lifelong treatment	219 (70)	53 (17)*	37 (12)
Is hereditary	103 (33)*	119 (38)	87 (28)
Is a condition like any other	124 (40)*	129 (41)	55 (18)
Often causes motor disabilities	165 (52)*	77 (25)	68 (22)
Expresses in young adults	218 (69)	59 (19)*	33 (11)

**This denotes the correct answer.*

Table 3.
Participants' understanding of autism (1% of participants did not answer all questions).

In your opinion, what percentage of Irish people have been, are or will 1 day be affected by autism	1% n (%)	10% n (%)	25% n (%)	50% or more n (%)
Autism	72 (23)*	148 (47)	67 (21)	19 (6)

**Denotes the closest to the correct answer. In 2022, the official percentage in Ireland is 1.5%.*

Table 4.
Understanding of the prevalence of autism.

Factors that contribute to autism	n(%)
Genetic factors	198 (63)
Food	38 (12)
The conditions of life (living environment, lifestyle, etc.)	107 (34)
The parent/child relations	91 (29)
Age	86 (27)
The sex of the individual	68 (22)
Psychological or emotional shock	59 (19)
Drug or alcohol	55 (17)
You do not know	45 (14)

Table 5.
Number of participants who believe the factors listed contribute to autism (percentages are rounded to the nearest whole number).

3.5 Attitudes toward people with autism

Overall participants demonstrate a positive attitude toward autism. Most participants feel that people with autism are able to assume the responsibility of a family. The majority of participants also disagree that people with autism are left numbed by their treatment, cannot live with a partner, must be isolated from society, require daily assistance, cannot hold down a job, and represent a danger to self and others. See **Table 6** for further details.

3.6 Behavior toward people with autism

Very little discrimination toward people with autism was demonstrated in the sample (see **Table 7**). Most participants would happily work with, live with, and allow children to receive education with someone who had Autism.

3.7 Opinion on source of autism information

Participants are dissatisfied with the level of information they are getting from the media, their doctor, the medical community, and governmental agencies, generally feeling either too informed or not informed enough by these sources. In particular, participants want to hear more from governmental agencies and the media and less from the medical community, including their doctor (see **Table 8**).

A person with Autism...	Agree n (%)	Disagree n (%)	Do not know n (%)
...Is able to assume the responsibility of a family	163 (52)	93 (29)	56 (18)
...Must follow treatments that leave them numbed	36 (11)	207 (66)	65 (21)
...Cannot live with a partner	20 (6)	249 (79)	39 (12)
...Cannot live in society, must be isolated	12 (4)	289 (92)	8 (3)
...Needs to be assisted in his/her life everyday	110 (35)	159 (50)	40 (13)
...Cannot hold down a job	28 (9)	247 (78)	32 (10)
...Represents a danger to self (suicide, prison, indebtedness...)	34 (11)	241 (76)	35 (11)
...Often represents a danger to others (murder, rape, violence...)	19 (6)	253(80)	37 (12)

Table 6.
Participants' perception of social handicap associated with autism (2% of participants did not answer all ques; percentages are rounded to nearest whole number).

Question	Yes happily n (%)	Yes if I had to n (%)	Absolutely not n (%)
Would you work with someone who had autism:	249 (79)	57 (18)	5 (2)
Would you allow your children to be in the same class as a child with autism	264 (84)	42 (13)	6 (2)
Would you live under the same roof as a loved one with autism	246 (78)	57 (18)	7 (2)

Table 7.
Acceptance level of autism as measured by behavior toward people with autism.

Do you think you are too informed, adequately informed, or not informed enough about autism by ...	Too informed n (%)	Sufficiently informed n (%)	Not informed enough n (%)
The media	30 (10)	114 (36)	166 (53)
Your doctor	146 (46)	23 (7)	140 (44)
The medical community	147 (47)	21 (7)	142 (45)
Governmental agencies	96 (30)	7 (2)	206 (65)

Table 8.
Perceptions of information sources on autism.

3.8 Correlation between knowledge, attitudes, and behavior toward autism

Finally, we analyzed via Pearson's correlation coefficient, whether there was a correlation between the variables of knowledge, attitudes, and behaviours toward autism. We were interested in this because participants appeared to perform least well on questions of knowledge, and better on question relating to attitudes and behavior.

Measure	1	2	3
1. Knowledge	1	.143*	.145*
2. Attitude	.143*	1	.402**
3. Behavior	.145*	.402**	1

*Correlation is significant at the 0.05 level (2-tailed).
**Correlation is significant at the 0.01 level (2-tailed).

Table 9.
Correlation between the variable knowledge, attitude, and behavior toward autism.

We wanted to know if this poor knowledge was likely to impact subsequent attitudes and behavior. To test this, we used the total scores of these variables, as outlined in the methods section under "design" for this analysis. All three variables correlated with each other, as can be seen in **Table 9**.

4. Discussion

This study examined the knowledge, attitudes, and behaviors of 307 adults in the Republic of Ireland toward autism. Overall, the findings reveal a gap in knowledge about the condition, leading to the formation of certain unhelpful attitudes, although attitudes overall were positive. Future intended behavior toward autistic people were also very positive, with 98% of respondents stating they would be happy to work, live, and educate their children, with someone with autism. As the element of stigma that was most obviously impaired in our sample was knowledge, much of this discussion will be spent in consideration of these knowledge findings and what they mean for stigma and autism going forward.

In considering participant demographics and autism knowledge, we found that young single men have less knowledge on autism than other demographic groups. This discovery corroborates other findings in the literature. Previous research demonstrates that females are more aware of autism than males [24]. One possible reason for this is that females are more interested in studying medical information than males [13, 28, 39, 40], leading to a substantial difference in knowledge between males and females, as well as a stronger knowledge of specific illnesses and conditions in females [28]. Women speak to each other more about medical matters and are more engaged in using the internet for health-related information searching, using it for social motives and enjoyment. They also judged the usability of the internet medium and of the information gained by health information searches higher than men did. Overall, the research suggests that women have a higher personal disposition of being well-informed on medical matters [40, 41]. This might also partially explain why young single men have the least knowledge of autism in our study. Men who are in relationships, particularly long-term relationships (which are naturally associated with age) are more likely to enter into discussions on health-related matters with their partner, thus acquiring knowledge. Outside of relationship status, however, age and gender have both been reported as determinants of health-related knowledge, as have education and income (SES), which are of course associated with age [42].

Interestingly, when asked about preference for a source of autism information, participants as a whole expressed a preference for hearing from governmental agencies and the media. Almost half of the respondents also indicated that they receive too much information from the medical community. Together, these findings might suggest that people want to hear less medical-related facts and information, and more person-centered information; the kind of knowledge gained from hearing personal stories. Storytelling has been touted as the best way to make the leap from information to knowledge, and as the best way to capture and transfer tacit knowledge [43]. Ramasubramanian [44] confirms that storytelling in news-related media has a positive impact on reducing negative stereotypes in readers, and recent research confirms that storytelling narratives, particularly those constructed with the first-person point of view, are effective in reducing stigma [45, 46]. There is still a body of work to be done in understanding which elements of storytelling are most impactful, and how government agencies and the media can best employ storytelling narratives when presenting information on autism, but it is a promising avenue for increasing autism knowledge in the future.

If we delve deeper into the type of knowledge questions participants struggle with in our study, a general picture of an autistic person emerges as a youth who has motor difficulties, requires lifelong treatment, and is impacted by factors, such as genetics, their relationship with their parents, their living conditions, gender, and age. Certain facets of this description are likely to be hangovers from past misinformation. Autism was originally viewed as profoundly disabling and the result of cold parenting. Also, much of what society at large learns about autism is produced by representations of autism in novels, TV series, movies, or autobiographies [47], and many of these representations are misleading. Cognitive psychology informs us that when asked about a topic with which we lack familiarity, our brains tend toward cognitive biases, which are unconscious and automatic processes designed to make decision-making quicker and more efficient. They are, however, erroneous in nature, leading to information misinterpretation and reduced accuracy [48]. One such bias is the availability heuristic. According to Tversky and Kahneman [49], the availability heuristic occurs when people judge the frequency of events in the world by the ease with which examples come to mind. As such, if a certain message is frequently promulgated, then that is what our brain will latch on to when we think of any given concept, even if the message is incorrect. In this way, repeatedly hearing that parenting is associated with autism, for example, makes the connection between autism and parenting stronger and more easily accessible. Thus, to eradicate these errant messages, we must either cease their production or increase the output of correct information.

After all, information not only impacts our thoughts and beliefs, it impacts our attitudes and behaviors also. As our study demonstrates, knowledge (ignorance) is correlated with attitudes (prejudice) and behavior (discrimination). This correlation finding is not novel, having been reported by numerous studies across various domains [50–52]. Although we found all three factors to be intercorrelated, many studies report that the strongest associations lie between knowledge and attitudes and attitudes and behavior [53, 54]. This is interesting, because we found of the three, knowledge was the poorest in our sample, followed by attitudes. Behavior was actually very positive, with only 2% of participants reporting negative intended behavior toward autistic people. Indeed, we can see the connection between knowledge and attitudes in our sample by looking closely at the attitude statements that participants agree with and comparing them to knowledge gaps. For example, only half of the respondents feel that autistic people can assume responsibility for a family and a full 35% believe that autistic people need to be assisted in their life every day. This corresponds with knowledge gaps or beliefs that autistic people require lifelong treatment, and that autism is somehow different from other types of conditions.

One limitation of this study relates to sample demographics. Most of the participants had an income less than or equal to €25,000 (44%) and were aged between 18 and 25 (40%). As such, the sample is not fully representative of the Irish public as a whole. To address this, we are currently running a full-scale, population-representative study in Ireland, investigating the public's knowledge, attitude, and behavior toward various conditions, including autism. This will hopefully shed light on some of the unanswered questions remaining after this initial exploratory analysis.

5. Conclusions

In conclusion, this study showed that in our young Irish sample, whilst attitudes and behaviors toward autistic people are largely positive, there is evidence of knowledge gaps that should be addressed, as they are potentially impacting attitudes toward the condition. Respondents relayed a desire to learn more information from governmental agencies and the media, and many felt that too much information was received from medical quarters. As such, stigma policy and campaigns targeted toward young people, and young men in particular, could benefit from a focus on increasing familiarity and understanding, possibly through the medium of storytelling and personal narrative. It is yet unclear whether these same educational approaches are desired across the Irish population as a whole. To answer this, we are currently conducting a full-scale, population-representative study further examining autism stigma in an Irish context.

Acknowledgements

We would like to acknowledge Ms. Gabriela Grasso for her contribution to the study in uploading the questionnaire to an online format for use in the survey. We would also like to acknowledge our host institution, National College of Ireland, which is a designated autism friendly campus and very supportive of autism research, and autistic students and staff. Finally, we would like to acknowledge the Stigma and Mental Health Ireland (SAMI) research laboratory for continued engagement in stigma research.

A. Appendices Procedure for calculating total scores for knowledge, attitudes, and behavior

To calculate knowledge, participants were given a score of 1 for each correct answer to the following sub-questions.

Autism...:

1. .... Is contagious (false).

2. .... Is a condition with which one can live normally, with treatments (true).

3. .... Involves lifelong treatment (false).

4. .... Is a hereditary condition (true).

5. .... Is a condition like any other (true).

Where participants gave an incorrect answer or said "I do not know," they were given a score of 0. Correct scores were added to give a total knowledge score.

To calculate attitudes, each of the sub-questions was used:

A person with autism...

1. ... Is able to assume the responsibility of a family
2. ... Must follow treatments that leave them numbed
3. ... Cannot live with a partner
4. ... Cannot live in society, must be isolated
5. ... Needs to be assisted in his/her life everyday
6. ... Cannot hold down a job
7. ... Represents a danger to herself (suicide, prison, and indebtedness)
8. ... Often represents a danger to others (murder, rape, violence ...)

For sub-question 1, a higher agreement was recorded as a higher score, with "Agree" recorded as 3, "I do not know" recorded as 2, and "Disagree" recorded as 1.

For sub-questions 2 to 8, a lower agreement was recorded as a higher score, with "Agree" recorded as 1, "I do not know" recorded as 2, and "Disagree" recorded as 3. Scores were added to give a total attitudes score.

To calculate behavior, Questions 12, 13, and 14 of the questionnaires were used:

12. Would you work with someone who had autism?

13. Would you allow your children to be in the same class as a child with autism?

14. Would you accept to live under the same roof as a loved one if s/he had autism?

Higher agreement was recorded as a higher score, with "Yes happily" recorded as 3, "Yes if I had to" recorded as 2, and "Absolutely not" recorded as 1. Scores were added to give a total behaviors score.

Author details

April Hargreaves*, David Mothersill and Gerard Loughnane
National College of Ireland, Dublin, Ireland

*Address all correspondence to: april.hargreaves@ncirl.ie

References

[1] Gaiha SM, Salisbury TT, Koschorke M, Raman U, Petticrew M. Stigma associated with mental health problems among young people in India: A systematic review of magnitude, manifestations and recommendations. BMC Psychiatry. 2020;**20**:1-24. DOI: 10.1186/s12888-020-02937-x

[2] Stuart H. Mental illness and employment discrimination. Current Opinion in Psychiatry. 2006;**19**:522-526. DOI: 10.1097/01.yco.0000238482.27270.5d

[3] World Health Organization. Mental health action plan 2013-2020. Available from: https://www.who.int/publications/i/item/9789241506021. [Accessed: 11 June 2021]

[4] Gissler M, Laursen TM, Ösby U, Nordentoft M, Wahlbeck K. Patterns in mortality among people with severe mental disorders across birth cohorts: A register-based study of Denmark and Finland in 1982-2006. BMC Public Health. 2013;**13**:1-11. DOI: 10.1186/1471-2458-13-834

[5] Corrigan PW, Bink AB, Schmidt A, Jones N, Rüsch N. What is the impact of self-stigma? Loss of self-respect and the "why try" effect. Journal of Mental Health. 2016;**25**:10-15. DOI: 10.3109/09638237.2015.1021902

[6] Pasmatzi E, Koulierakis G, Giaglis G. Self-stigma, self-esteem and self-efficacy of mentally ill. Psychiatriki. 2016;**27**:243-252. DOI: 10.22365/jpsych.2016.274.243

[7] Weiss MG, Ramakrishna J, Somma D. Health-related stigma: Rethinking concepts and interventions. Psychology, Health & Medicine. 2006;**11**:277-287. DOI: 10.1080/13548500600595053

[8] Link BG, Phelan JC. Conceptualizing stigma. Annual Review of Sociology. 2001;**27**:363-385. DOI: 10.1146/annurev.soc.27.1.363

[9] Grinker RR. Autism, "Stigma", disability – A shifting historical terrain. Current Anthropology. 2020;**61**(s21). DOI: 10.1086/705748

[10] Cage E, Di Monaco J, Newell V. Understanding, attitudes and dehumanisation towards autistic people. Autism. 2019;**23**(6):1373-1383. DOI: 10.1177/1362361318811290

[11] Durand-Zaleski I, Scott J, Rouillon F, Leboyer M. A first national survey of knowledge, attitudes and behaviours towards schizophrenia, bipolar disorders and autism in France. BMC Psychiatry. 2012;**12**:1-8. DOI: 10.1186/1471-244X-12-128

[12] Mitchell GE, Locke KD. Lay beliefs about autism spectrum disorder among the general public and childcare providers. Autism. 2015;**19**(5):553-561. DOI: 10.1177/1362361314533839

[13] Jones SC, Akram M, Gordon CS, Murphy N, Sharkie F. Autism in Australia: Community knowledge and autistic people's experiences. Journal of Autism and Developmental Disorders. 2021;**51**(10):3677-3689. DOI: 10.1007/s10803-020-04819-3

[14] Mothersill D, Loughnane G, Grasso G, Hargreaves A. Knowledge, attitudes, and behaviours towards schizophrenia, bipolar disorder, and autism: A pilot study. Irish Journal of Psychological Medicine. 2021;**3**:1-7. DOI: 10.1017/ipm.2021.81

[15] Han E, Scior K, Avramides K, Crane L. A systematic review on autistic

people's experiences of stigma and coping strategies. Autism Research. 2021;**15**(1):12-26. DOI: 10.1002/aur.2625

[16] Gray DE. Perceptions of stigma: The parents of autistic children. Sociology of Health & Illness. 1993;**15**:102-120. DOI: 10.1111/1467-9566.ep11343802

[17] Sasson NJ, Faso DJ, Nugent J, Lovell S, Kennedy DP, Grossman RB. Neurotypical peers are less willing to interact with those with autism based on thin slice judgments. Scientific Reports. 2017;**1**(7):40700. DOI: 10.1038/srep40700

[18] Sasson NJ, Morrison KE. First impressions of adults with autism improve with diagnostic disclosure and increased autism knowledge of peers. Autism. 2019;**23**(1):50-59. DOI: 10.1177/1362361317729526

[19] Wood C, Freeth M. Students' stereotypes of Autism. Journal of Educational Issues. 2016;**2**(2):131-140. DOI: 10.5296/jei.v2i2.9975

[20] Pearson A, Rose K. A conceptual analysis of autistic masking: Understanding the narrative of stigma and the illusion of choice. Autism in Adulthood. 2021:52-60. DOI: 10.1089/aut.2020.0043

[21] Corrigan PW, Nieweglowski K. Difference as an indicator of the self-stigma of mental illness. Journal of Mental Health. 2021;**30**(4):417-423. DOI: 10.1080/09638237.2019.1581351

[22] Hansen J, Wänke M. Liking what's familiar: The importance of unconscious familiarity in the mere-exposure effect. Social Cognition. 2009;**27**(2):161-182. DOI: 10.1521/soco.2009.27.2.161

[23] Rockett TL, Okhuysen GA. Familiarity in groups: Exploring the relationship between inter-member familiarity and group behavior. In: Sondak H, editor. Toward Phenomenology of Groups and Group Membership. Elsevier Science; 2002. pp. 173-201. DOI: 10.1016/S1534-0856(02)04008-2

[24] Alyami HS, Naser AY, Alyami MH, Alharethi SH, Alyami AM. Knowledge and attitudes toward autism spectrum disorder in Saudi Arabia. International Journal of Environmental Research and Public Health. 2022;**19**(6):3648. DOI: 10.3390/ijerph19063648

[25] Yu L, Stronach S, Harrison AJ. Public knowledge and stigma of autism spectrum disorder: Comparing China with the United States. Autism. 2020;**24**(6):1531-1545. DOI: 10.1177/1362361319900839

[26] Liu Y, Li J, Zheng Q, Zaroff CM, Hall BJ, Li X, et al. Knowledge, attitudes, and perceptions of autism spectrum disorder in a stratified sampling of preschool teachers in China. BMC Psychiatry. 2016;**16**:142. DOI: 10.1186/s12888-016-0845-2

[27] Anwar MS, Tahir M, Nusrat K, Khan MR. Knowledge, awareness, and perceptions regarding autism among parents in Karachi, Pakistan. Cureus. 2018;**10**(9):e3299. DOI: 10.7759/cureus.3299

[28] Kuzminski R, Netto J, Wilson J, Falkmer T, Chamberlain A, Falkmer M. Linking knowledge and attitudes: Determining neurotypical knowledge about and attitudes towards autism. PLoS One. 2019;**14**(7):e0220197. DOI: 10.1371/journal.pone.0220197

[29] Stronach S, Wiegand S, Mentz E. Brief report: Autism knowledge and stigma in university and community samples. Journal of Autism

and Developmental Disorders. 2019;**49**(3):1298-1302. DOI: 10.1007/s10803-018-3825-1

[30] Dillenburger K, Jordan JA, McKerr L, Devine P, Keenan M. Awareness and knowledge of autism and autism interventions: A general population survey. Research in Autism Spectrum Disorders. 2013;**7**:1558-1567. DOI: 10.1016/j.rasd.2013.09.004

[31] Shand A, Close S, Shah P. Greater autism knowledge and contact with autistic people are independently associated with favourable attitudes towards autistic people. Experimental Results. 2021;**1**:E46. DOI: 10.1017/exp.2020.46

[32] Angermeyer MC, Matschinger H. The stigma of mental illness: Effects of labelling on public attitudes towards people with mental disorder. Acta Psychiatrica Scandinavica. 2003 Oct;**108**(4):304-309. DOI: 10.1034/j.1600-0447.2003.00150.x

[33] Corrigan PW, River LP, Lundin RK, Penn DL, Uphoff-Wasowski K, Campion J, et al. Three strategies for changing attributions about severe mental illness. Schizophrenia Bulletin. 2001;**27**(2):187-195. DOI: 10.1093/oxfordjournals.schbul.a006865

[34] Griffiths KM, Nakane Y, Christensen H, Yoshioka K, Jorm AF, Nakane H. Stigma in response to mental disorders: A comparison of Australia and Japan. BMC Psychiatry. 2006;**6**:21. DOI: 10.1186/1471-244X-6-21

[35] Jorm AF. Mental health literacy. Public knowledge and beliefs about mental disorders. The British Journal of Psychiatry. 2000;**177**:396-401. DOI: 10.1192/bjp.177.5.396

[36] Kelly CM, Jorm AF. Stigma and mood disorders. Current Opinion in Psychiatry. 2007;**20**(1):13-16. DOI: 10.1097/YCO.0b013e3280113cf5

[37] Link BG, Yang LH, Phelan JC, Collins PY. Measuring mental illness stigma. Schizophrenia Bulletin. 2004;**30**(3):511-541. DOI: 10.1093/oxfordjournals.schbul.a007098

[38] Wolff G, Pathare S, Craig T, Leff J. Public education for community care. A new approach. British Journal of Psychiatry. 1996;**168**(4):441-447. DOI: 10.1192/bjp.168.4.441

[39] Alsehemi MA, Abousaadah MM, Sairafi RA, Jan MM. Public awareness of autism spectrum disorder. Neurosciences (Riyadh). 2017;**22**(3):213-215. DOI: 10.17712/nsj.2017.3.20160525

[40] Bidmon S, Terlutter R. Gender differences in searching for health information on the internet and the virtual patient-physician relationship in germany: Exploratory results on how men and women differ and why. Journal of Medical Internet Research. 2015;**17**(6):e156. DOI: 10.2196/jmir.4127

[41] Ek S. Gender differences in health information behaviour: A finnish population-based survey. Health Promotion International. 2015;**30**(3):736-745. DOI: 10.1093/heapro/dat063

[42] Beier ME, Ackerman PL. Determinants of health knowledge: An investigation of age, gender, abilities, personality, and interests. Journal of Personality and Social Psychology. 2003;**84**(2):439-448. DOI: 10.1.1.1010.8824&rep=rep1&type=pdf

[43] LeBlanc SM, Hogg J. Storytelling: A Practical Method for Facilitating Knowledge Management. Vol. 2. AECT 29th Annual Proceedings; 2006. Available from: https://

members.aect.org/pdf/Proceedings/proceedings06/2006I/06_32.pdf

[44] Ramasubramanian S. Media-based strategies to reduce racial stereotypes activated by news stories. Journalism & Mass Communication Quarterly. 2007;**84**(2):249-264. DOI: 10.1177/107769900708400204

[45] Zhuang J, Guidry A. Does storytelling reduce stigma? A meta-analytic view of narrative persuasion on stigma reduction. Basic and Applied Social Psychology. 2022;**44**(1):25-37. DOI: 10.1080/01973533.2022.2039657

[46] Fong THC, Mak WWS. The effects of internet-based storytelling programs (Amazing Adventure Against Stigma) in reducing mental illness stigma with mediation by interactivity and stigma content: Randomized controlled trial. Journal of Medical Internet Research. 2022;**24**(8):e37973. DOI: 10.2196/37973

[47] Draaisma D. Stereotypes of autism. Philosophical Transactions of the Royal Society of London. Series B, Biological Sciences. 2009;**364**(1522):1475-1480. DOI: 10.1098/rstb.2008.0324

[48] Tversky A, Kahneman D. The framing of decisions and the psychology of choice. Science. 1981;**211**:453-458. DOI: 10.1126/science.7455683

[49] Tversky A, Kahneman D. Availability: A heuristic for judging frequency and probability. Cognitive Psychology. 1973;**5**(2):207-232. DOI: 10.1016/0010-0285(73)90033-9

[50] Devkota HR, Sijali TR, Bogati R, Clarke A, Adhikary P, Karkee R. How does public knowledge, attitudes, and behaviors correlate in relation to COVID-19? A community-based cross-sectional study in Nepal. Frontiers in Public Health. 2021;**8**:589372. DOI: 10.3389/fpubh.2020.589372

[51] Bettinghaus EP. Health promotion and the knowledge-attitude-behavior continuum. Preventive Medicine. 1986;**15**(5):475-491. DOI: 10.1016/0091-7435(86)90025-3

[52] Ul Haq N, Hassali MA, Shafie AA. A cross sectional assessment of knowledge, attitude and practice towards Hepatitis B among healthy population of Quetta, Pakistan. BMC Public Health. 2012;**12**:692. DOI: 10.1186/1471-2458-12-692

[53] Fabrigar LR, Petty RE, Smith SM, Crites SL Jr. Understanding knowledge effects on attitude-behavior consistency: The role of relevance, complexity, and amount of knowledge. Journal of Personality and Social Psychology. 2006;**90**(4):556-577. DOI: 10.1037/0022-3514.90.4.556

[54] Marklinder I, Eskhult G, Ahlgren R, Blücher A, Börjesson SE, Moazzami M, et al. A structural equation model demonstrating the relationship between food safety background, knowledge, attitudes and behaviour among Swedish students. Food. 2022;**11**(11):1595. DOI: 10.3390/foods11111595

Section 2

Neural Perspectives and Etiology

Chapter 5

Neural Structure and Function in Autism Spectrum Disorder

Tânia Plens Shecaira, Thais Miriã da Silva Santos, Nayara Barbosa Lopes, Leonardo Ribeiro Miedes, Fabrício Porto Matrone and Nathalia Bernardes

Abstract

Autism spectrum disorder (ASD) refers to a group of neurodevelopmental disorders characterized by changes in communication, social interaction, and repetitive behavior, recognized as a public health problem with a sharp increase in its prevalence in the world population. It is known that brain functioning in individuals with ASD presents important deficits. It is essential to understand these deficits to identify and promote new management strategies for the development of this population with ASD. In this sense, the objective of this chapter is to present, through a literature review, the main risk factors that make up ASD, by showing classic and current findings based on neurophysiological changes and treatments.

Keywords: autism spectrum disorder, neurophysiology, neuropathology, polymorphism, learning disabilities

1. Introduction

Autism spectrum disorder (ASD) is a set of heterogeneous conditions of neurological development and encompasses a series of invasive disorders, characterized by the early onset of social communication deficits and restricted and repetitive patterns of sensorimotor behaviors, interests, or activities, associated with important genetic and environmental factors [1].

The prevalence of ASD has increased globally, with the number of diagnoses of children with ASD tripling in the last three decades [2]. In this sense, recent studies by the Centers for Disease Control and Prevention in the United States have shown a prevalence of the disorder in 1 out of every 59 born children [3].

ASD is often comorbid with other disorders such as anxiety, attention-deficit/hyperactivity disorder, and intellectual disability, and some affected individuals also suffer from gastrointestinal, immune, and sleep disorders, suggestive of systemic dysregulation [4].

Autism severity levels may vary widely, with some cases presenting only mild deficits in social interactions, while other cases exhibit severe deficits in social behaviors [5]. These symptoms are present from childhood to adulthood [6].

IntechOpen

Although there is a lot of research on the etiology of ASD, this disorder is still a challenge, being considered a multifactorial impairment, with the influence of genetics, epigenetics and environmental factors in its genesis [7, 8]. Individually or in a combination of the factors mentioned above, these disturbances can alter the function of genes and neural tissue in ASD [9].

Recent research on ASD has gained prominence in the scientific community with regard to neurophysiology. Trying to understand the factors that can trigger this disability is of fundamental importance for advancing the comprehension of such a disorder. Therefore, it is of paramount importance not only for the knowledge of traditional ASD concepts, but also for the study of new concepts that previously could not be achieved [10], the study of neurophysiology, which is the science that addresses neuronal physiology and the factors involved that alter synapses, such as genetic, epigenetic, and environmental ones.

Advances in this area of science have been a major challenge for researchers around the world, as the prevalence of ASD has been increasing every year. However, the evolution of neurophysiology in terms of neurogenetics, neuropathology, animal studies, neuroanatomy, and psychophysics has now allowed the clinical staff new tools for the diagnosis and treatment of ASD, such as gene therapies, transcranial electrical stimulation, and cannabis/cannabidiol [11].

2. Genetic and environmental contributors

The etiology of autism is heterogeneous. In the scientific literature, there is convincing evidence that the disorder is influenced by environmental and genetic factors in its pathogenesis; however, genetic factors seem to be predominant [12]. Although not all causes of ASD are known yet, it is estimated that up to 40% of cases related to genetic influences can be identified [13, 14]. The remaining percentage is possibly a result of other factors such as prenatal, perinatal, and postnatal environmental factors [15].

In this sense, the causes of ASD might be considered highly genetic due to multiple patterns of family inheritance and the occurrence of many variations. It is currently known that men have a higher incidence of ASD, about four times more than women [16].

Experimental and clinical studies have identified more than 800 genes related to ASD, making it one of the most complex neurophysiological disorders [17]. In this sense, there is evidence of the importance of complex genetic factors composed of different forms of genetic variation in the etiology of ASD [18]. These include genes involved in intellectual disabilities, neuropsychiatric disorders, common pathways, ASD risk genes, multigene contributions from rare or common variations, DNA mutations, and environmental effects on gene expression and/or protein function [19].

The most affected genes encode proteins that are involved with chromatin remodeling and transcriptional regulation, cell proliferation, and mainly synaptic architecture and functionality [17].

An important study elucidated several genetic and non-genetic factors related to ASD. The genetic causes can be several, but the authors have highlighted the following characteristics: new mutations, rare and common genetic alterations, and also polymorphisms. The study states that several genes associated with ASD have already been listed. These genes listed by *SAFARI* (Simons Foundation Autism Research Initiative) are classified according to the risk of causing ASD and are subdivided into four different categories, according to the number of new mutations reported in the literature, namely syndromic S, category 1, category 2, and category 3 [20].

According to the number of new mutations, the first category to be listed is syndromic (S), which includes genes whose mutations carry a substantial risk for the occurrence of ASD, and other characteristics present in other disorders that can predict ASD. Category 1 predicts a high risk for the onset of ASD and is characterized by having at least three new mutations reported in the literature. Category 2 genes are those that have a strong risk of association with ASD and include at least two new mutations. Finally, category 3 genes are those that include the vast majority of genes and that may or may not be suggestive of the onset of ASD, having at least one new mutation [21].

While there are different mechanisms through which genetic factors may influence autistic behaviors and clinical variants of ASD, inflammation and immune activation, oxidative stress, hypoxia, and endocrine disorders are likely the most important contributors to atypical neurodevelopment [22]. In fact, the relevance of these factors may not be of the direct cause, and thus, sometimes they may be confused with genetic factors. Furthermore, current understanding is limited due to a paucity of research examining gene–environment interactions.

On the other hand, there is a growing awareness of the potential of environmental influences on ASD, which stands out as a topic of great current scientific interest. In this regard, researchers have investigated several environmental risk factors that correlate with this pathology, including maternal and paternal age, fetal environment, perinatal and obstetric events, medications, nutritional events, smoking, and alcohol use [22].

With regard to biological environmental factors, the important factor of advanced paternal age (APA) has been associated with the reduced cortical thickness of the right posterior ventral cingulate cortex in ASD descendants [23].

Experiments performed in murine models confirmed that APA is associated with the development of ASD-like symptoms in offspring and with altered cortical morphology in male mice with APA [24, 25].

ASD-related behaviors were also observed in second-generation mice with older grandparents, indicating that APA-associated genetic and epigenetic changes are heritable [25].

Among the most researched environmental risk factors in ASD, perinatal ones are among the most difficult factors to be determined and predicted in advance. In the available literature, two comprehensive meta-analyses examined 60 obstetric factors and found statistically significant associations between the risk of ASD and umbilical cord complications, birth injury or trauma, multiple births, maternal hemorrhage, low birth weight, and neonatal anemia [26].

There is also evidence of the association between increased risk of autism and different factors, including cesarean delivery, induced delivery, fetal age less than 36 weeks, and fetal distress [15].

Such facts surely contribute to a better understanding of ASD during the first years of life, because derived from them, new biomarkers and new concepts in the neuropathology of ASD are possible to be observed in case ASD is considered to be a multifactorial disorder that affects several neuronal regions, and that will probably get worse, if not diagnosed during childhood.

3. Neurophysiology in ASD

The complex "machine" that orchestrates the entire body ordering is governed by active cells and neural circuits responsible for sensitivity, motricity, thoughts, ideas and feelings, among others, and such functions are fully realized, enabling the totality of cognitive and motor movements. This complex system leads to the synaptic cleft, whose communication is not primarily electrical, but chemical. The neuron releases substance at its end to the bottom of the synaptic cleft, thus generating the so-called synapse, which is the chemical communication of neurons [27].

Substances that may act in different brain regions, such as acetylcholine, serotonin, and glutamate that enter the synaptic cleft are neurotransmitters that have different excitatory or inhibitory actions, critically involving impairments in particular aspects of inhibitory gamma-aminobutyric acid (GABA). In fact, in a study carried out with animal models was shown that there is a dysfunction in the signaling involving GABA, which is known to be the most important inhibitory neurotransmitter in the adult mammalian brain, possibly contributing to the clinical symptoms found in autistic patients [28].

GABA can inhibit neuronal excitation by activating two main receptors: GABAA, which are integral membrane ion channels, and GABAB, which are G protein-coupled ion channels. In patients diagnosed with Autism Spectrum Disorder, brain tissues show a reduction in the density of GABAA and GABAB receptors in the cingulate cortex region, and alterations in the morphology of the tracings, being related to a GABAergic imbalance between excitation and inhibition, involving the senses, memory, social and emotional processes [28].

GABA levels are relevant factors when referring to ASD, and polymorphisms in the receptors of GABA may be an explanation for this relationship. By evaluating the serum levels of GABA together with the genetic variants of GABAA receptor, it is possible to ascertain a strict agreement between high serum levels of GABA and the etiology of ASD [29]. Although it is embryonic, polymorphisms found in the GABAA receptors in the GABRB3, GABRG3, and GABRA5 subunits may be related to the appearance of ASD. Especially the mutations found in the rs4906902G and rs140679T subunits can confer substantial risk for the appearance of at least one deficit associated with ASD since these mutations alter the expression of these receptors [30].

GABAB receptors, on the other hand, play an important role in brain development. The activation of presynaptic receptors of this type is related to the inactivation of neurotransmitters and neuropeptides in the synaptic cleft. Moreover, GABAB receptors postsynaptic activation is related to the slow and long inhibition of the action potential. In autistic individuals, the amount of these receptors is reduced, which can cause a deficit in the migration and differentiation of new neurons, as well as a decrease in their production during corticogenesis. Another relevant factor is that the decrease in the expression of GABAB receptors also diminishes the protection they provide against insulin-like growth factor 1 (IGF-1), which can cause apoptosis of neurons, explained by the mechanism of autophosphorylation inhibition of the IGF-1 receptor and PI3 kinase/Akt inactivation [31].

Glutamate, on the other hand, known to be the most important excitatory neurotransmitter in the central nervous system, and to be associated with the regulation of excitatory/inhibitory balance, also plays an important role in neuronal migration and differentiation, as well as in synaptogenesis. There are three main receptors associated with glutamate, but evidence suggests that α-amino-3-hydroxy-5-methyl-4-isoxazolepropionic acid receptors (AMPARs) and N-methyl-D-aspartate receptors (NMDARs) when mutated are strongly related to the appearance of ASD. Overexpression of the NR2A and NR2B subunits of the NMDAR receptor has been demonstrated in association with autism since such subunits cause excessive excitation of synaptic currents in the receptors, which may increase postsynaptic plasticity, causing an imbalance in the E/I system. In the second receptor reported, AMPAR, modifications were identified in the AMPAR GluA2 subunit, which also causes excessive excitability when associated with ASD. In other words, a high release of glutamate in the synaptic cleft may be strongly associated with ASD [32].

Still, glutamate is related to memory functions and cognitive performance; as a confirmation of this relation, however, its excess has been reported to act as a potent neurotoxin that might cause neuronal death and may also be related to neurological disorders [33]. Through a meta-analysis, a brief relationship was found between high levels of glutamate and ASD, as autistic symptoms were more evident in patients with high levels of glutamate, demonstrating, thus, that glutamate is a potent biomarker for the disorder [34].

Another system related to changes that can be associated with ASD corresponds to the serotonergic system. Serotonin or 5-HT is an important neurotransmitter in neuronal growth, synaptogenesis, differentiation, as well as neurogenesis [35]. 5-HT can be produced essentially in two identified places in the organism: in the central nervous system (CNS), by the serotonergic neurons of the raphe nucleus, and in the gastrointestinal tract by the enterochromaffin cells. Serotonin produced by enterochromaffin cells is predominantly the so-called peripheral serotonin, 99% of which is stored inside platelets with the help of the 5-HT transporter (SERT), and then stored in vesicles by the vesicular monoamine transporter (VMAT2). Both transporters are modulated by protein complexes present in the blood, such as αIIbβ3 and 5-HT2A receptors [36].

The marked effects of serotonin on the CNS are already well known in the literature, such as mood control, states of happiness, sleep modulation, and changes in pain perception; therefore, changes that affect serotonergic neurotransmission and cause a decrease in serotonin bioavailability are strongly associated with disorders such as depression and anxiety [37].

Interestingly, in autistic individuals, especially children, there are many reports of hyperserotonemia, characterized by an elevated amount of serotonin, mainly peripheral. This factor may lead to changes in the growth trajectory of serotonin synthesis in the brain [38]. Such a condition may be associated with an increased plasma concentration of SERT in platelets, as well as changes in affinity for 5-HT receptors [38].

In experimental models of ASD, it has been observed that cases of hyperserotonemia worsen cognitive deficits and behavioral patterns, and they may also affect immunomodulatory function, significantly increasing brain inflammation and oxidative stress. Such effects are reported because serotonin directly or indirectly impacts the levels of substances such as BDNF, pCREB/CREB, IL-10, GSH, TNF-α, IL-6, and TBARS, associated with inflammation and oxidative stress [39].

3.1 New concepts of ASD Neuropathology

Inserted into the traditional concepts of ASD, new updates appear on the subject, which improves the understanding and how the treatment will be given to the patient with ASD. Performing a brief search in the Medline/Pubmed database up to August 2022, there were 49,828 articles published in the last 5 years with the descriptor (autism spectrum disorder), but when the advanced search was used to describe the pathology of ASD, 2141 results were found in the same period of publication, what demonstrates the scientific community's great interest in understanding the factors that trigger this disorder.

As of 2017, new concepts emerged for ASD analysis that could not be accessed only with neuroimaging studies, such as differentiation and migration processes, neuronal morphology, and cytoarchitectural changes in the nervous system. Based on this, it was elucidated that there are disorganizations in the white and gray matter of the brain and that they are associated with cognitive and judgment difficulties. In individuals with ASD, these changes cause dysplasia and heterotopia, which can be detected concurrently or in isolation [40]. Furthermore, in this group there is a decrease in the expression of reelin, a protein necessary for maturation and migration during cortical lamination [41].

Regarding brain cytoarchitecture, there is an age-dependent increase in brain circumference size. In younger individuals, this macrocephaly may be related to mini-columnopathy, that is, to an abnormal number of connections that neurons make with the neocortex. In patients with ASD, a greater number of minicolumns can be found, but with reduced size in 9, 21, and 22 Brodmann's areas; however, these changes are visible in the primary visual cortex, suggesting that they are regionally specific. Finally, there is also a significant increase in neuropil, non-myelinated axons, synapses, and glial cells in the frontopolar region, but not in the motor and somatosensory cortex [42].

Relating these facts, it could be verified that neuropathological disorders are linked to dysfunctions in the membrane of neurons and autophagy, caused by defects in the synthesis of GTPases, induced by Xq28 mutations located in the RAB39B gene. Such changes are related to defects in neuronal development, what can lead to macro-cephaly, Parkinson's, and ASD [43].

Corresponding to this, a review published in the International Journal of Molecular Sciences tried to discuss the genetic, epigenetic, and environmental factors that may contribute to the pathogenesis of ASD, and how these factors alter brain neurophysiology. The authors confirm what has already been elucidated about changes in synaptic cytoarchitecture and their functions. These Changes, in turn, are mainly related to the formation of dendritic spines [17].

Dendritic spines are small actin-rich membranous protrusions present on a dendrite, responsible for the postsynapse of various excitatory impulses. Therefore, alterations that cause an increase or decrease in its size, or even alterations in the production of actin, can be the factors that alter the normal functioning of synapses, and consequent learning and memory mechanisms, that is, they can be a risk and can be observed in patients with neurological disorders such as ASD. Furthermore, it has been elucidated that those alterations in postsynaptic density proteins, which include cell adhesion proteins and cytoskeletal proteins, may be associated with ASD [17].

Neurexins (NRXN) and neuroligins (NLGN) are adhesion proteins between cells, present in the membrane of presynaptic neurons and which are crucial for the functioning of the synapses; however, in individuals with ASD there is a loss in the function of the NRX1 protein variant, what was confirmed in a study in animals, as they presented symptoms common to ASD [44]. In addition, there is a decrease in the amount of an adhesion protein between glia cells and neurons, CNTNAP2, which according to a study in mice, is also related to ASD [45].

Another group of proteins that may be related whenever variants arise are the scaf-fold proteins. Scaffold proteins or SHANK proteins are dense postsynaptic proteins that connect neurotransmitter receptors, ion channels, and other membrane proteins to the actin cytoskeleton and signaling proteins. Deletions that occur, therefore, in the genes that synthesize these proteins can cause malfunction or even shut down in their synthesis. These deletions in the proteins of the SHANK family, in turn, determine the Phelan–McDermid syndrome, and are characterized by cognitive problems, epilepsy, and ASD. It was also identified that in individuals with ASD, loss of protein function due to mutations in the SHANK3 gene is more frequent than in other family genes [46]. Finally, in patients with ASD, there are mutations that can affect ion channels. The most common mutations occur in the following genes: CACNA1C, CACNB2, SCN1A, VDAC, and also in genes encoding potassium channels [47].

By utilizing recent studies, an interesting systematic review elucidated the role of microglia in brain development and how its dysfunctions may be important in the development of brain disorders, such as ASD, which demonstrates another factor to be considered for the diagnostic evaluation of the disease. However, further studies are still needed to confirm this event [48].

Another review was discussed about the neuronal imaging research from a structural, functional, and molecular perspective in order to have a more accurate diagnosis of ASD. Based on the evaluation of several studies, four main association factors were identified, namely exaggerated synaptic pruning, anomalous gyrification, interhemispheric connectivity, and glutamate/GABA imbalance. These factors, according to the researchers, are mitigated factors, but they make a difference in the multifactorial analysis of the disease, what can be a tool to improve the diagnosis in the future and how the pharmacological intervention will take place [49].

From a genetic point of view, researchers have demonstrated progress by using brain organoids to elucidate the genetic basis of certain neurodevelopmental disorders, such as ASD [50].

Organoid models of the human brain tried to identify and specify the development of disorders resulting from three risk genes for ASD: SUV420H1, ARID1B and CHD8, by using RNA sequence for the analysis of these cells. All three of these induced mutations confer the asynchronous development of two main neuronal lineages in GABA release and deep layer excitatory projection neurons, which according to the study, were contributing factors in the neuropathology of ASD [51].

In experimental research, researchers evaluated the mutations in an induced model of ASD and whether the displayed phenotypes are consistent with the symptoms of ASD. In this sense, a critical risk of these genetic factors for the etiology of ASD was suggested. Furthermore, applied neuroimaging identified common synaptic deficiencies in the neocortex, with specific mutations in neural circuitry [52].

With the neuroimaging analysis performed on human babies, it is possible to identify that in groups with ASD, there are smaller bilateral accumbens nuclei and larger cerebral ventricles. In addition, less thickness has been identified in the caudal anterior cingulate cortex and greater thickness in the right medial orbitofrontal cortex. These factors are independent of age, gender, and gestational age, suggesting that there are magnetic resonance imaging biomarkers that can predict the development of ASD, and that can help in a better diagnosis of the disorder [53].

Based on new advances and what has been elucidated here, new biomarkers have arisen for a better understanding of ASD neuropathology. It is worth mentioning that recent research in the area does not invalidate or discredit previous well-designed concepts about ASD. New concepts involving ASD neurophysiology are added to those already described, so that a more effective diagnosis of the disorder is expected, as well as more integrative and efficient forms of treatment.

4. Updates on ASD Treatments

The diagnosis of ASD is predominantly based on the observation of atypical behaviors, with criteria of persistent deficits in social communication and restricted and repetitive behavior patterns [19, 54].

Four criteria have been considered for the diagnosis of ASD: persistent impairment in social communication and social interaction (Criterion A), restricted and repetitive patterns of behavior, interests, or activities (Criterion B). These symptoms are present from early childhood and limit or impair daily functioning (Criteria C and D). The classification is made by the level of severity of the disorder, according to the criteria mentioned above, and through the necessary support to the person with ASD [6].

Intellectual disability is present in 70% of the population with ASD, with 29.3% of individuals having mild/moderate disability and 38.5% having severe/profound disability [55]. Diagnosis occurs from 3 years of age, but therapeutic measures should be taken whenever marked changes are observed by the multidisciplinary team [56].

With the advent of new research and technologies, recent studies on ASD have gained prominence in the scientific community, regarding management and treatments for this population. In this sense, transcranial direct current electrical stimulation (tDCS) proved to be a safe, well-tolerated, and low-cost technique with tDCS occurring through scalp electrodes that modulate regional cortical excitability [57].

A study with 18 autistic 6–14-year-old children, analyzed the effects of tDCS in improving balance and found that those who received about 1.5 m over the left M1 for 20 minutes in conjunction with motor exercises, considerably increased the static and dynamic balance in a few weeks [58].

Another study, involving 6 adults with ASD in ages ranging from 18 to 58 years, with the anode electrode being placed over the right parietal temporal lobe (PC6), revealed that there was a more significant improvement in the emotional verbal fluency of the individuals [59].

Another promising research proceeds from gene therapy to help elucidate and look for new treatments in the future. An important factor is that ASD may have a single clinical or syndromic phenotype. In the latter case, ASD is indicative of a developmental disorder that includes different phenotypes, such as epilepsy, intellectual disability, and dimorphic aspects [60]. For non-syndromic ASD, there is genetic evidence for a polygenic or multifactorial architecture, and disease risk is expected to be determined by a combination of multiple environmental and genetic reasons [61].

In a recent study, 11 single-gene ASD syndromes were selected, validated by animal models, and current gene therapies. Due to the wide range of possibilities, it was decided on the gene and mutation therapy study. Gene therapies that have a transient effect, including ASOs, ncRNA, and RNA-editing leave the genome unedited and will require repeated dosing; nevertheless, they may have the primacy of being controllable and reversible. The accurate diagnosis of DNA and, consequently, the accurate prediction of the consequences of the mutation will hopefully be able to elucidate and help in gene therapies soon [62].

In parallel to this, some treatments are already widely discussed or are already available at the population level. In this sense, recent research on ASD has gained prominence in the scientific community regarding treatments with cannabidiol.

Cannabidiol comes from *Cannabis sativa*, a plant that contains two main cannabinoids: tetrahydrocannabinol (THC) and cannabidiol (CBD). THC is psychoactive and can cause anxiety and psychosis. CBD is non-psychoactive and has anxiolytic, antipsychotic, anti-inflammatory and antioxidant potential, with a high threshold of toxicity [63]. Cannabidiol has multiple targets, regulating the performance of glutamate and GABA, thus, influencing the excitatory and inhibitory signaling pathways, respectively [64].

In fact, there is a growing interest in the use of Cannabis, and particularly cannabidiol, as a treatment for mental health and neurodevelopmental disorders, such as

ASD. In this regard, cannabidiol is known to have important neuroprotective effects on addiction, cognition, and negative affect [65].

The use of cannabidiol for the treatment of ASD has been reported as a well-tolerated, safe, and effective option for the relief of symptoms, including seizures, stereotypies, depression, restlessness, and aggression [66].

According to a recent study, more than 80% of children with ASD treated with cannabidiol had significant or moderate improvement in symptoms and cognitive difficulties [67].

In this sense, researchers evaluated the intervention with Cannabis rich in cannabidiol, in 60 children with ASD, who had severe behavioral problems. After treatment with 10 mg/kg/day of Cannabis oil, behavioral flare-ups improved in 61% of patients [68]. In another recent study, 53 children were given Cannabis extract for 66 days, and attacks of self-harm and anger improved by 67.6%, hyperactivity improved by 68.4%, sleep problems improved by 71.4%, anxiety by 47.1%, and adverse effects such as drowsiness and change in appetite were mild. Thus, the authors suggest that cannabidiol may be effective in improving ASD symptoms [69].

The new treatments, whether with the use of electrostimulation technologies, or with the use of phytotherapy drugs, are shown today to be effective and safer alternatives for patients with ASD, which demonstrates great benefit, as it is possible to guarantee a better quality of life, an element that traditional pharmacological therapies might not achieve.

5. Conclusion

ASD is a set of heterogeneous conditions of neurological development, whose elucidation is still partial in the scientific/medical literature. With the constant increase in diagnosed cases, research has been carried out in human and experimental models. In fact, findings on risk factors and neurophysiological functioning in ASD are fundamentally important to understand this disorder and to enable innovation in satisfactory interventions. There are significant advances in etiology, diagnosis, and neural functions in ASD, as well as effective and promising treatments such as gene therapies, transcranial direct current electrical stimulation (tDCS), and the use of cannabis/cannabidiol.

While there are clear challenges with regard to elucidating the complex neurophysiology of autism, it is also clear that surprising advances are being made, as shown in the contributions of this chapter. Such findings could potentially contribute to new intervention research looking forward to alleviating symptoms in the ASD population.

Conflicts of interest

The authors declare no conflicts of interest.

Author details

Tânia Plens Shecaira[1], Thais Miriã da Silva Santos[2], Nayara Barbosa Lopes[2], Leonardo Ribeiro Miedes[2], Fabrício Porto Matrone[3] and Nathalia Bernardes[2]*

1 Physiology Exercise Laboratory, Department of Physiology, Federal University of Sao Paulo (UNIFESP), São Paulo, Brazil

2 Human Movement Laboratory, Sao Judas Tadeu University (USJT), Sao Paulo, SP, Brazil

3 Laboratory of Physiology and Metabolism Applied to Physical Activity, City University of Sao Paulo (UNICID), Sao Paulo, SP, Brazil

*Address all correspondence to: nbernardes@outlook.com

References

[1] Lord C, Elsabbagh M, Baird G, Veenstra-Vanderweele J. Autism spectrum disorder. Lancet. 2018;**392**:508-520. Available from: https://pubmed.ncbi.nlm.nih.gov/30078460/. [Accessed August 23, 2022]

[2] Fusar-Poli L, Cavone V, Tinacci S, Concas I, Petralia A, Signorelli MS, et al. Cannabinoids for people with ASD: A systematic review of published and ongoing studies. Brain Sciences. 2020;**10**:1-18. Available from: https://pubmed.ncbi.nlm.nih.gov/32825313/. [Accessed August 23, 2022]

[3] Baio J, Wiggins L, Christensen DL, Maenner MJ, Daniels J, Warren Z, et al. Prevalence of autism spectrum disorder among children aged 8 years – Autism and Developmental Disabilities Monitoring Network, 11 Sites, United States, 2014. Morbidity and Mortality Weekly Report. 2019;**67**:1-23. Available from: https://www.cdc.gov/mmwr/volumes/67/ss/ss6706a1.htm. [Accessed August 23, 2022]

[4] Reynoso C, Rangel MJ, Melgar V. El trastorno del espectro autista: aspectos etiológicos, diagnósticos y terapéuticos. Revista Médica del Instituto Mexicano del Seguro Social. 2017;**55**:214-222

[5] Hu VW, Devlin CA, Debski JJ. ASD phenotype—genotype associations in concordant and discordant monozygotic and dizygotic twins stratified by severity of autistic traits. International Journal of Molecular Sciences. 2019;**20**:3804-3804. Available from: /pmc/articles/PMC6696087/. [Accessed August 23, 2022]

[6] American Psychiatric Association, editor. DSM-5 - Manual Diagnóstico e Estatístico de Transtornos Mentais. 5th ed. Arlington, TX: Artmed: American Psychiatric Association; 2013

[7] Matsuzaki H, Iwata K, Manabe T, Mori N. Triggers for autism: Genetic and environmental factors. Journal of Central Nervous System Disease. 2012;**4**:27. Available from: /pmc/articles/PMC3619552/. [Accessed August 23, 2022]

[8] Posar A, Visconti P. Autismo em 2016: necessidade de respostas. Jornal de Pediatria. 2017;**93**:111-119. Available from: http://www.scielo.br/j/jped/a/WWH8xDrXxL3KTLFhL7vX9Px/abstract/?lang=pt. [Accessed August 23, 2022]

[9] Ribeiro I, Freitas M, Oliva-Teles N. As Perturbações do Espectro do Autismo – Avanços da Biologia Molecular. Nascer e Crescer. 2013;**22**(1):19-24. Available from: http://repositorio.chporto.pt/handle/10400.16/1487. [Accessed August 23, 2022]

[10] Prochazka A. Neurophysiology and neural engineering: A review. Journal of Neurophysiology. 2017;**118**:1292-1309. Available from: https://pubmed.ncbi.nlm.nih.gov/28566462/. [Accessed August 23, 2022]

[11] Foxe JJ, Molholm S, Baudouin SJ, Wallace MT. Explorations and perspectives on the neurobiological bases of autism spectrum disorder. The European Journal of Neuroscience. 2018;**47**:488-496. Available from: https://onlinelibrary.wiley.com/doi/full/10.1111/ejn.13902.[Accessed August 23, 2022]

[12] Nadia B, Ridha M, B. Ahlem, Mohamed Bechir H, Habiba C. Autism: An overview of genetic aetiology. Tunis Med. 2008;**86**:573-578

[13] Froehlich-Santino W, Londono Tobon A, Cleveland S, Torres A,

Phillips J, Cohen B, et al. Prenatal and perinatal risk factors in a twin study of autism spectrum disorders. Journal of Psychiatric Research. 2014;**54**:100-108. Available from: https://pubmed.ncbi.nlm.nih.gov/24726638/. [Accessed August 23, 2022]

[14] Hallmayer J, Cleveland S, Torres A, Phillips J, Cohen B, Torigoe T, et al. Genetic heritability and shared environmental factors among twin pairs with autism. Archives of General Psychiatry. 2011;**68**:1095-1102. Available from: https://pubmed.ncbi.nlm.nih.gov/21727249/. [Accessed August 23, 2022]

[15] Wang C, Geng H, Liu W, Zhang G. Prenatal, perinatal, and postnatal factors associated with autism: A meta-analysis. Medicine. 2017;**96**:e6696-e6696. Available from: /pmc/articles/PMC5419910/. [Accessed August 23, 2022]

[16] Tran KT, Le VS, Bui HTP, Do DH, Ly HTT, Nguyen HT, et al. Genetic landscape of autism spectrum disorder in Vietnamese children. Scientific Reports. 2020;**10**:1-11. Available from: /pmc/articles/PMC7081304/. [Accessed August 23, 2022]

[17] Masini E, Loi E, Vega-Benedetti AF, Carta M, Doneddu G, Fadda R, et al. An overview of the main genetic, epigenetic and environmental factors involved in autism spectrum disorder focusing on synaptic activity. International Journal of Molecular Sciences. 2020;**21**:1-22. Available from: /pmc/articles/PMC7663950/. [Accessed August 29, 2022]

[18] Devlin B, Scherer SW. Genetic architecture in autism spectrum disorder. Current Opinion in Genetics & Development. 2012;**22**:229-237. Available from: https://pubmed.ncbi.nlm.nih.gov/22463983/. [Accessed August 23, 2022]

[19] Masi A, DeMayo MM, Glozier N, Guastella AJ. An overview of autism spectrum disorder, heterogeneity and treatment options. Neuroscience Bulletin. 2017;**33**:183. Available from: /pmc/articles/PMC5360849/. [Accessed August 23, 2022]

[20] Sauer AK, Stanton JE, Hans S, Grabrucker AM. Autism Spectrum Disorders: Etiology and Pathology. In: Grabrucker AM, editor. Autism Spectrum Disorders [Internet]. Brisbane (AU): Exon Publications; 2021. Chapter 1

[21] Satterstrom FK, Kosmicki JA, Wang J, Breen MS, De Rubeis S, An JY, et al. Large-scale exome sequencing study implicates both developmental and functional changes in the neurobiology of autism. Cell. 2020;**180**:568. Available from: /pmc/articles/PMC7250485/. [Accessed August 23, 2022]

[22] Bölte S, Girdler S, Marschik PB. The contribution of environmental exposure to the etiology of autism spectrum disorder. Cellular and Molecular Life Sciences. 2018;**76**:1275-1297. Available from: https://link.springer.com/article/10.1007/s00018-018-2988-4. [Accessed August 29, 2022]

[23] Kojima M, Yassin W, Owada K, Aoki Y, Kuwabara H, Natsubori T, et al. Neuroanatomical correlates of advanced paternal and maternal age at birth in autism spectrum disorder. Cerebral Cortex. 2019;**29**:2524-2532. Available from: https://academic.oup.com/cercor/article/29/6/2524/5003434. [Accessed August 23, 2022]

[24] Foldi CJ, Eyles DW, McGrath JJ, Burne THJ. Advanced paternal age is associated with alterations in discrete behavioural domains and cortical neuroanatomy of C57BL/6J mice. The European Journal of Neuroscience. 2010;**31**:556-564. Available from:

https://pubmed.ncbi.nlm.nih.gov/20105239/. [Accessed August 23, 2022]

[25] Sampino S, Juszczak GR, Zacchini F, Swiergiel AH, Modlinski JA, Loi P, et al. Grand-paternal age and the development of autism-like symptoms in mice progeny. Translational Psychiatry. 2014;**4**:e386. Available from: https://www.nature.com/articles/tp201427. [Accessed August 23, 2022]

[26] Gardener H, Spiegelman D, Buka SL. Prenatal risk factors for autism: Comprehensive meta-analysis. The British Journal of Psychiatry. 2009;**195**:7-14. Available from: https://www.cambridge.org/core/journals/the-british-journal-of-psychiatry/article/prenatal-risk-factors-for-autism-comprehensive-metaanalysis/0D63EE57942E9A0CC312EA30025A9DD2. [Accessed August 23, 2022]

[27] Lopes ACP, Rosa LC, De R, Beleboni O, Pereira RNR, De Vasconcelos CAC, et al. Aspectos moleculares da transmissão sináptica. Medicina (Ribeirão Preto). 1999;**32**:167-188. Available from: https://www.revistas.usp.br/rmrp/article/view/12692. [Accessed August 29, 2022]

[28] Kerche-Silva LE, Camparoto ML, Rodrigues FV. As alterações genéticas e a neurofisiologia do autismo. SaBios - Revista de Saúde e Biologia [Internet]. 2020;15:40-56. Available from: https://revista2.grupointegrado.br/revista/index.php/sabios/article/view/2932. [Accessed August 29, 2022]

[29] Saha S, Chatterjee M, Dutta N, Sinha S, Mukhopadhyay K. GABA receptor SNPs and elevated plasma GABA levels affect the severity of the Indian ASD probands. Journal of Molecular Neuroscience. 2022;**72**:1300-1312. Available from: https://pubmed.ncbi.nlm.nih.gov/35562522/. [Accessed August 29, 2022]

[30] Adak P, Sinha S, Banerjee N. An association study of gamma-aminobutyric acid type A receptor variants and susceptibility to autism spectrum disorders. Journal of Autism and Developmental Disorders. 2021;**51**:4043-4053. Available from: https://pubmed.ncbi.nlm.nih.gov/33442857/. [Accessed August 29, 2022]

[31] Oblak AL, Gibbs TT, Blatt GJ. Decreased GABAB receptors in the cingulate cortex and fusiform gyrus in autism. Journal of Neurochemistry. 2010;**114**:1414. Available from: /pmc/articles/PMC2923229/. [Accessed August 29, 2022]

[32] Marotta R, Risoleo MC, Messina G, Parisi L, Carotenuto M, Vetri L, et al. The neurochemistry of autism. Brain Sciences. 2020;**10**:163-163. Available from: https://pubmed.ncbi.nlm.nih.gov/32182969/. [Accessed August 29, 2022]

[33] Yang P, Chang C-L. Glutamate-mediated signaling and autism spectrum disorders: Emerging treatment targets. Current Pharmaceutical Design. 2014;**20**:5186-5193. Available from: https://pubmed.ncbi.nlm.nih.gov/24410563/. [Accessed August 29, 2022]

[34] Zheng Z, Zhu T, Qu Y, Mu D. Blood glutamate levels in autism spectrum disorder: A systematic review and meta-analysis. PLoS One. 2016;**11**:158688. Available from: /pmc/articles/PMC4938426/. [Accessed August 29, 2022]

[35] Howes OD, Rogdaki M, Findon JL, Wichers RH, Charman T, King BH, et al. Autism spectrum disorder: Consensus guidelines on assessment, treatment and

research from the British Association for Psychopharmacology. Journal of Psychopharmacology. 2018;**32**:3. Available from: /pmc/articles/PMC5805024/. [Accessed August 29, 2022]

[36] Gabriele S, Sacco R, Persico AM. Blood serotonin levels in autism spectrum disorder: A systematic review and meta-analysis. European Neuropsychopharmacology. 2014;**24**:919-929. Available from: https://pubmed.ncbi.nlm.nih.gov/24613076/. [Accessed August 29, 2022]

[37] Apresentada D, Maria P, Glória BA. Determinação de precursores da serotonina - triptofano e 5-hidroxitriptofano - em café por clae-par iônico. Universidade Federal de Minas Gerais; 2008. Available from: https://repositorio.ufmg.br/handle/1843/MBSA-7JZM6L. [Accessed August 29, 2022]

[38] Katsui T, Okuda M, Usuda S, Koizumi T. Kinetics of 3H-serotonin uptake by platelets in infantile autism and developmental language disorder (including five pairs of twins). Journal of Autism and Developmental Disorders. 1986;**16**:69-76. Available from: https://pubmed.ncbi.nlm.nih.gov/3957859/. [Accessed August 29, 2022]

[39] Luhach K, Kulkarni GT, Singh VP, Sharma B. Effect of papaverine on developmental hyperserotonemia induced autism spectrum disorder related behavioural phenotypes by altering markers of neuronal function, inflammation, and oxidative stress in rats. Clinical and Experimental Pharmacology & Physiology. 2021;**48**:614-625. Available from: https://pubmed.ncbi.nlm.nih.gov/33480092/. [Accessed August 29, 2022]

[40] Pagnamenta AT, Wing K, Akha ES, Knight SJL, Bölte S, Schmötzer G, et al. A 15q13.3 microdeletion segregating with autism. European Journal of Human Genetics. 2009;**17**:687-692. Available from: https://pubmed.ncbi.nlm.nih.gov/19050728/. [Accessed August 29, 2022]

[41] Camacho J, Ejaz E, Ariza J, Noctor SC, Martínez-Cerdeño V. RELN-expressing neuron density in layer I of the superior temporal lobe is similar in human brains with autism and in age-matched controls. Neuroscience Letters. 2014;**579**:163-167. Available from: https://pubmed.ncbi.nlm.nih.gov/25067827/. [Accessed August 29, 2022]

[42] Varghese M, Keshav N, Jacot-Descombes S, Warda T, Wicinski B, Dickstein DL, et al. Autism spectrum disorder: Neuropathology and animal models. Acta Neuropathologica. 2017;**134**:537. Available from: /pmc/articles/PMC5693718/. [Accessed August 29, 2022]

[43] Tang BL. RAB39B's role in membrane traffic, autophagy, and associated neuropathology. Journal of Cellular Physiology. 2021;**236**:1579-1592. Available from: https://pubmed.ncbi.nlm.nih.gov/32761840/. [Accessed August 29, 2022]

[44] Südhof TC. Neuroligins and neurexins link synaptic function to cognitive disease. Nature. 2008;**455**:903-911. Available from: https://pubmed.ncbi.nlm.nih.gov/18923512/. [Accessed August 29, 2022]

[45] Peñagarikano O, Abrahams BS, Herman EI, Winden KD, Gdalyahu A, Dong H, et al. Absence of CNTNAP2 leads to epilepsy, neuronal migration abnormalities, and core autism-related deficits. Cell. 2011;**147**:235-246. Available from: https://pubmed.ncbi.nlm.nih.gov/21962519/. [Accessed August 29, 2022]

[46] Leblond CS, Nava C, Polge A, Gauthier J, Huguet G, Lumbroso S, et al.

Meta-analysis of SHANK mutations in autism spectrum disorders: A gradient of severity in cognitive impairments. PLoS Genetics. 2014;**10**:e1004580-e1004580. Available from: https://pubmed.ncbi.nlm.nih.gov/25188300/. [Accessed August 29, 2022]

[47] Schmunk G, Gargus JJ. Channelopathy pathogenesis in autism spectrum disorders. Frontiers Media. 2013;**4**: 222-222. Available from: /pmc/articles/PMC3817418/. [Accessed August 29, 2022]

[48] Lukens JR, Eyo UB. Microglia and neurodevelopmental disorders. Annual Review of Neuroscience. 2022;**45**: 425-445. Available from: https://pubmed.ncbi.nlm.nih.gov/35436413/. [Accessed August 29, 2022]

[49] Rafiee F, Rezvani Habibabadi R, Motaghi M, Yousem DM, Yousem IJ. Brain MRI in autism spectrum disorder: Narrative review and recent advances. Journal of Magnetic Resonance Imaging. 2022;**55**:1613-1624. Available from: https://pubmed.ncbi.nlm.nih.gov/34626442/. [Accessed August 29, 2022]

[50] Trujillo CA, Muotri AR. Brain organoids and the study of neurodevelopment. Tendências em Med Mol. 2018;**24**:982-990. Available from: https://pubmed.ncbi.nlm.nih.gov/30377071/

[51] Paulsen B, Velasco S, Kedaigle AJ, Pigoni M, Quadrato G, Deo AJ, et al. Autism genes converge on asynchronous development of shared neuron classes. Nature. 2022;**602**:268-273 Available from: https://pubmed.ncbi.nlm.nih.gov/35110736/ [Accessed August 29, 2022]

[52] Terashima H, Minatohara K, Maruoka H, Okabe S. Imaging neural circuit pathology of autism spectrum disorders: Autism-associated genes, animal models and the application of in vivo two-photon imaging. Reproductive System and Sexual Disorders. 2022;**71**:I81-I99. Available from: https://pubmed.ncbi.nlm.nih.gov/35275183/. [Accessed August 29, 2022]

[53] Shiohama T, Ortug A, Warren JLA, Valli B, Levman J, Faja SK, et al. Small nucleus accumbens and large cerebral ventricles in infants and toddlers prior to receiving diagnoses of autism spectrum disorder. Cerebral Cortex. 2022;**32**:1200-1211. Available from: https://pubmed.ncbi.nlm.nih.gov/34455432/. [Accessed August 29, 2022]

[54] Muotri AR. Autism spectrum disorders: Challenges and perspectives. Developmental Neurobiology. 2018;**78**:431-433. Available from: https://pubmed.ncbi.nlm.nih.gov/29516662/

[55] De Moura M, Evêncio K, Cristina H, Menezes S, George Fernandes P. Transtorno do Espectro do Autismo: Considerações sobre o diagnóstico / Autism spectrum disorder: Diagnostic considerations. Revista de psicologia. 2019;**13**:234-251. Available from: https://idonline.emnuvens.com.br/id/article/view/1983. [Accessed August 24, 2022]

[56] Pinho Costa JLG, Maia LO, Orlandi-Mattos P, Villares JC, Fernandez Esteves MA. Neurobiologia da Cannabis: do sistema endocanabinoide aos transtornos por uso de Cannabis. Jornal Brasileiro de Psiquiatria. 2011;**60**:111-122. Available from: http://www.scielo.br/j/jbpsiq/a/sjLsV6Qg3S7YtQWnKqwnjWv/?lang=pt. [Accessed August 29, 2022]

[57] Hameed MQ, Dhamne SC, Gersner R, Kaye HL, Oberman LM, Pascual-Leone A, et al. Transcranial magnetic and direct current stimulation in children. Current Neurology and Neuroscience Reports. 2017;**17**:11-11. Available from: https://pubmed.ncbi.

nlm.nih.gov/28229395/. [Accessed August 24, 2022]

[58] Mahmoodifar E, Sotoodeh MS. Combined transcranial direct current stimulation and selective motor training enhances balance in children with autism spectrum disorder. Perceptual and Motor Skills. 2020;**127**:113-125. Available from: https://pubmed.ncbi.nlm.nih.gov/31744385/. [Accessed August 24, 2022]

[59] Esse Wilson J, Trumbo MC, Wilson JK, Tesche CD. Transcranial direct current stimulation (tDCS) over right temporoparietal junction (rTPJ) for social cognition and social skills in adults with autism spectrum disorder (ASD). Journal of Neural Transmission. 2018;**125**:1857-1866. Available from: https://pubmed.ncbi.nlm.nih.gov/30341695/. [Accessed August 24, 2022]

[60] Buescher AVS, Cidav Z, Knapp M, Mandell DS. Costs of autism spectrum disorders in the United Kingdom and the United States. JAMA Pediatrics. 2014;**168**:721-728. Available from: https://pubmed.ncbi.nlm.nih.gov/24911948/. [Accessed August 24, 2022]

[61] LeClerc S, Easley D. Pharmacological therapies for autism spectrum disorder: A review. Pharmacology & Therapeutics. 2015;**40**:389. Available from: /pmc/articles/PMC4450669/. [Accessed August 30, 2022]

[62] Weuring W, Geerligs J, BPC K. Gene therapies for monogenic autism spectrum disorders. Genes (Basel). 2021;**12**:1667-1667. Available from: https://pubmed.ncbi.nlm.nih.gov/34828273/. [Accessed August 29, 2022]

[63] Campos AC, Fogaça MV, Scarante FF, Joca SRL, Sales AJ, Gomes FV, et al. Plastic and neuroprotective mechanisms involved in the therapeutic effects of cannabidiol in psychiatric disorders. Frontiers in Pharmacology. 2017;**8**:269-269. Available from: https://pubmed.ncbi.nlm.nih.gov/28588483/. [Accessed August 29, 2022]

[64] Pretzsch CM, Freyberg J, Voinescu B, Lythgoe D, Horder J, Mendez MA, et al. Effects of cannabidiol on brain excitation and inhibition systems: A randomised placebo-controlled single dose trial during magnetic resonance spectroscopy in adults with and without autism spectrum disorder. Neuropsychopharmacology. 2019;**44**:1398-1405. Available from: https://pubmed.ncbi.nlm.nih.gov/30758329/. [Accessed August 29, 2022]

[65] Chadwick B, Miller ML, Hurd YL. Cannabis use during adolescent development: Susceptibility to psychiatric illness. Frontiers in Psychiatry. 2013;**4**:129-129. Available from: https://pubmed.ncbi.nlm.nih.gov/24133461/. [Accessed August 29, 2022]

[66] Oliveira ALM de, Shecaira TP, Rodrigues LM, Bueno GC, Bernardes N. Transtorno do espectro autista e tratamento com canabidiol: uma revisão bibliográfica / Autism spectrum disorder and cannabidiol treatment: A literature review. Brazilian Journal of Development; 2021 ;7:39445-39459. Available from: https://brazilianjournals.com/ojs/index.php/BRJD/article/view/28355. [Accessed August 30, 2022]

[67] Bar-Lev Schleider L, Mechoulam R, Saban N, Meiri G, Novack V. Real life experience of medical cannabis treatment in autism: Analysis of safety and efficacy. Scientific Reports. 2019;**9**:200-200. Available from: https://pubmed.ncbi.nlm.nih.gov/30655581/. [Accessed August 29, 2022]

[68] Barchel D, Stolar O, De-Haan T, Ziv-Baran T, Saban N, Fuchs DO, et al. Oral cannabidiol use in children with

autism spectrum disorder to treat related symptoms and co-morbidities. Frontiers Media. 2018;**9**:1521-1521. Available from: /pmc/articles/PMC6333745/. [Accessed August 29, 2022]

[69] Aran A, Cassuto H, Lubotzky A, Wattad N, Hazan E. Brief report: Cannabidiol-rich cannabis in children with autism spectrum disorder and severe behavioral problems–A retrospective feasibility study. Journal of Autism and Developmental Disorders. 2019;**49**:1284-1288. Available from: https://pubmed.ncbi.nlm.nih.gov/30382443/. [Accessed August 29, 2022]

Chapter 6

Perspective Chapter: Rethinking Autism Assessment, Diagnosis, and Intervention within a Neurodevelopmental Pathway Framework

Marion Rutherford and Lorna Johnston

Abstract

The neurodiversity paradigm is reshaping how we understand, use language, interpret and undertake research, and support autistic people and those with related neurodevelopmental differences across the lifespan. Multi-disciplinary teams are seeking new ways to operationalise deficit focussed diagnostic criteria, to reflect the preferences of autistic people and the wider neurodiversity movement. In this chapter, we explore what the neurodiversity paradigm could mean in practice and how to reconcile the position that autism is a difference not a deficit and therefore individuals do not need to be "fixed" or "cured," with the continued importance of timely diagnosis and the very real impact on participation, engagement, and wellbeing of autistic individuals and their families, within the environments of home, education, community, employment, and care. We present work underway to move from "single condition" pathways to neurodevelopmental pathways and new approaches which consider co-occurring conditions in a single process, involve autistic people as partners and value differences.

Keywords: autism, neurodevelopmental pathways, assessment, diagnosis, intervention

1. Introduction

Internationally recognised diagnostic criteria for Autism Spectrum Disorder (ASD) are provided in the Diagnostic and Statistical Manual of Mental Disorders (5th ed.; DSM-5) [1] and the International Classification of Diseases, Eleventh Revision (ICD-11) [2], under a newly included category of "neurodevelopmental disorders," which are lifelong and not episodic mental health conditions. The behaviourally defined criteria continue to be "impairment" or "deficit" focused and diagnostic terms use the language of "disorder," which might be considered to be at odds with social models of disability, realistic medicine, and the neurodiversity paradigm [3].

There is clear evidence that different neurodevelopmental conditions defined as they are currently, usually co-occur and overlap [4] and it is often the combination

IntechOpen

of individual profile or "neurotype" together with the environment, that determines support needs rather than diagnosis. One consequence of this development in diagnostic criteria, is that it supports the shift in clinical practice, away from a "single condition" focus towards "neurodevelopmental" pathways [5] and a diversification of our approach to assessment, diagnosis, and intervention.

From the historical point when autism began being diagnosed [6], the single-condition approach has been positive in raising the profile and need for autism assessment. It has led to the development of accessible and focussed, evidence-based clinical guidelines [7]; together with evidence about what leads to effective and efficient pathways [8] and accessibility of professional learning frameworks and resources to help multi-disciplinary teams develop shared and specialist skills and to learn from experiences of those waiting for and taking part in assessment [9].

The challenges with a single condition approach at this point are: firstly, it limits what is considered in an assessment and clinicians tend to find what they are looking for. With the binary option of "is it autism or not?," we fail to identify important neurodevelopmental differences or diagnoses, out with our current lens. Secondly, even where we do not find autism but suspect another condition, for example, ADHD, the individual must rejoin a new waiting list and see a new set of people, who often ask very similar questions, with a similar binary focus.

As services evolve towards the adoption of a "neurodevelopmental" approach [5] which sets out with different questions and a different underlying philosophy, there is a need for practical tools and an iterative process of evaluation in partnership with neurodivergent people.

2. Evolving paradigms

Evolving paradigms support changes in the way we think, question, communicate, and act. The reality is that there is overlap, complexity, and nuance in how core theories are applied in practice.

Medical model paradigms broadly focus on "within-person" disease, disorder, or disability. Autism research within this paradigm has mostly been led by non-autistic people and outcome measures are usually skills based rather than focussed on the preferences of the individual. This model has been criticised by many within the autistic community for being deficit focussed, so that observed and reported "signs" are seen as pathologised and the focus of intervention is on "treatment" or "cure" of the person who has this "functional impairment" problem [10]. The model has also underpinned valuable scientific development in understanding the genetic, neurodevelopmental, and cognitive explanations for the differences we see in individuals [11]. Often for people with ADHD, the medical model of "treatment" is still sought after and reported to be effective in improving outcomes.

Within a social paradigm or social model of disability, there is a rejection of the deficit model and recognition of the relationship between the environment and individuals. Since the 1970s, the "biopsychosocial model" has underpinned clinical practice within mental health services [12]. Diagnostic assessment includes consideration of the physical and social environment (e.g., home, education, employment, community environments, and the attitudes and actions of people in them) and how these result in a positive or negative impact on people with neurodevelopmental differences. Strengths and differences in thinking style are recognised, although the focus may still be on problems arising and autism may still be described from the view of observers rather than the autistic person's experience. Within this model, there is acknowledgement that autistic masking [13] and/or supportive environments may result in less obvious presentation and an adapted approach to diagnostic assessment is applied. Interventions may involve people around the autistic person making changes rather than "fixing" the person. Outcomes reported may relate to skills, participation, functioning, or quality of life but may have arisen from neurotypical "societal norms." Measurement of factors and outcomes important to autistic people and their families can also be considered. In line with this paradigm, Autism and ADHD clinical guidelines [14–17] now recommend environmental modifications as a first line of intervention.

One interpretation of this model from a professional perspective can be that diagnosis does not matter because the focus should be on supporting needs identified, with the assumption that this will happen. Consequently, the power over who decides whether diagnosis matters or not lies with professionals. People may end up waiting until they hit a crisis before diagnosis is considered necessary or receive inappropriate supports which do not fully account for an understanding of the importance of diagnosis for identity or other understanding of neurodevelopmental differences. This way of thinking is criticised by some autistic people who share their experience that diagnosis can be transformational and barriers to accessing diagnostic assessment exacerbate stress.

3. The neurodiversity paradigm

The clinical application of the neurodiversity paradigm [18] is still in its infancy but has the potential to provide an important additional layer to the social model. From just one academic publication including the word "neurodiversity" in 2010, there were 33 in 2020 [11] and we can foresee an escalation of this field. Practice based on this paradigm offers subtle but important differences in language, mindset, and actions. The following perspective is that of neurotypical authors who are practitioners and researchers seeking to understand what needs to change and how we could play a role in that change through understanding and actions.

3.1 Nothing about us without us

A vital shift is the involvement of neurodivergent people in setting priorities, for research, service provision, and individual support, and in balancing power between professionals and those who might be seen as "neurominorities." Historical research evidence that has previously been seen as robust, is now being questioned with the lens of this paradigm. What we view as evidence-based practice requires re-evaluation in relation to its acceptance to neurodivergent communities. Future research in this paradigm will include autistic people as leaders and partners, at all stages, from setting the research priorities and questions [19] to delivery and reporting of research [20]. Future development of assessment tools and supports or interventions will be centred around perspectives and experiences of neurodivergent people.

3.2 Language and mindsets matter

Preferred language and terminology in relation to autism and other neurodevelopmental conditions is to some extent culturally determined and continue to evolve

[21]. In English-speaking countries, research highlights a preference for "identity first" language and reference to "autistic people," however a review of Dutch people, reported a preference for person first language—referring to "people with autism" [22]. In our own community in Scotland, autistic people have shared with us how important their autistic identity is and how much language matters [23]. The neurodivergent people we spoke to expressed a range of preferences and told us that it is important to ask people about their preferences, particularly in professional relationships. However, it is not just the language people use but the mindset behind it that matters. The neurodiversity paradigm encourages professionals to find out about and be mindful of neurodiversity-affirming language and approaches in all interactions. Application of a neurodiversity-affirming approach is currently a new and emerging concept in research and practice [24].

3.3 Difference not deficit

Within the neurodiversity paradigm, autistic or neurodivergent identity is understood as a welcome and important part of a neurodiverse society. People are seen as different, not impaired or disordered and this will require a big shift in the language we use in assessment tools, processes, and diagnostic reports. As the next iterations of DSM and ICD are a few years off, clinicians are trying to translate deficit focussed criteria into strengths focussed language in assessments, conversations, written reports, and information provided. It is possible to describe the same actions, responses, and preferences that define what it means to be autistic or neurodivergent, with a new lens. Outcome measures used to define success can start with this new lens of "what is important to autistic individuals and the autistic community?"

3.4 Does diagnosis matter?

With the understanding that we live in a neurodiverse society and that diversity is to be welcomed—a key question is then why do we need diagnosis at all? The reason is that autistic people tell us that it does matter, whether diagnosed early in childhood [25], or in adulthood [26]. In societies constructed to provide resources to meet needs according to diagnosis, lack of diagnosis is an immediate barrier to accessing support and information. Even where legislation and policy advise that no support is diagnosis dependent, diagnostic labels are a shorthand for understanding the types of adaptations and supports in the present environments and importantly when there is a transition to a different level of independence, autonomy, or life stage, where demands placed on the person change. Further key benefits of diagnosis are self-understanding or identity and access to peers with shared experience [27].

Although some would argue that diagnoses can be stigmatising, it is clear that stigma and discrimination happen anyway in societies lacking in acceptance and understanding of diversity. Individual differences are there anyway, and it is not the diagnosis that makes people different. The decision and power about whether or not to disclose diagnosis in different contexts, should lie with the individual [28].

3.5 If it's just a difference why is support needed?

Within this paradigm, it is acknowledged that being a neurominority in a largely neurotypical world can still lead to difficulties for individuals at different times in life. This might be a direct difficulty in daily life or indirectly in response to masking or camouflaging [13] to try to fit in. Difficulties described might arise with, for example, sensory processing, feeling overwhelmed, being able to use communication to express the range of things you want to say, understanding or predicting social expectations, being able to initiate, plan and organise or responding to disrupted expectations or unpredictable situations. When a difficulty is experienced, a key difference is that this is understood in the context of the 24 hour environment and in the context of neurotype. When a person is no longer described as having "challenging behaviour" but their actions, responses, distress, and stress are understood, we are better placed to meet individual needs.

4. Neurodevelopmental pathways

The neurodiversity paradigm and neurodevelopmental pathways are different constructs in development. Each can inform but is not dependent on the other.

Chris Gillberg and researchers in Sweden have highlighted the co-occurrence of neurodevelopmental conditions and advocated a neurodevelopmental and multi-disciplinary approach for more than a decade [4, 29], this is now beginning to be applied more widely in Scotland. Care pathways are applied internationally as a way of planning and delivering individualised support to specified groups of people through multidisciplinary team working [30]. Within the last decade, evidence has become available to inform standards and practice in pathways for assessment and diagnosis of autism in children and adults [8, 9, 31].

4.1 Children and young people

As services evolve, there is a move in Scotland towards developing neurodevelopmental pathways and service providers have a need for evidence-informed guidance. In 2021, the Scottish Government National Autism Implementation Team published the first children's neurodevelopmental pathway guidance in the UK [5] and the Scottish Government published a national neurodevelopmental specification: principles and standards of care [32]. In 2022, 50% of children's health board areas in Scotland are implementing neurodevelopmental pathways and the other 50% are undertaking work to move in this direction, in partnership with education and social care partners, with the aspiration of taking an integrated approach to support according to need before, during and after diagnosis.

4.2 Adults

The adult service context in Scotland is quite different and there is currently no formal adult neurodevelopmental pathway guidance. The development of adult autism services has taken place in intellectual disability and adult mental health services [33]. Within these services, co-occurrence of autism and ADHD is recognised but services are not always planned in partnership with neurodivergent people, they may not be "neurodevelopmentally informed" nor do they give routine consideration of other co-occurring neurodevelopmental conditions. Demand for provision often exceeds capacity to meet needs.

Under-ascertainment of adults with ADHD and a dearth of services has been highlighted [34]. A feasibility study was undertaken in response to this challenge [35]. It makes recommendations that neurodevelopmental approaches be developed through a stepped care model [36]. Stepped care approaches are used within mental health services to deliver care in a range of settings depending on needs, risk, and complexity [37]. New ways of working with a broader multidisciplinary team have the potential to deliver services more suited to neurodivergent people. Practitioners leading change in adult neurodevelopmental pathways need access to evidence-informed approaches, professional learning, and resources.

We give consideration below to the ways a neurodiversity paradigm could inform future pathways for children and adults.

5. Assessment

There is a need for the development of evidence-based neurodevelopmental and neurodiversity-affirming assessment tools for children, adolescents, and adults.

5.1 Diagnostic tools

Tools recommended in single-condition clinical guidelines for identification and diagnostic assessment of autism (e.g., ADOS and ADI-r) [38] and even tools designed to take a neurodevelopmental perspective (e.g., ESSENCE) [4], all use the deficit focussed language of diagnostic criteria. There are no self-report tools recommended for young people or adults that use neurodiversity-affirming language. We hope that this is something that changes in the next decade and that in future, clinicians can map the conversations we should be having to criteria in a robust way.

5.2 Assessment approaches

There are some approaches to contextual assessment and planning which are not standardised or mapped to diagnostic criteria but may have a better fit within the neurodiversity paradigm. They consider individual preferences, factors facilitating participation and engagement in naturally occurring environments. Some examples of these are:

The SCERTS framework [39], which can be applied in a neurodiversity-affirming way but is not designed as a diagnostic tool. A key element of the assessment is the consideration of "within child" developmental stage, together with assessment of "transactional supports" which are the things people around the child do and the adjustments put in place in the environment or learning materials. The focus is on the child being able to do things, when the adults do particular things and not on "fixing the child" or their "behaviour." Predictability and desirability in everyday environments are used to support emotional regulation and social communication.

The Person in Context tool [40] was developed with neurodivergent people and is designed to gather information about how an individual experiences aspects of themselves without reference to context and then with consideration of experiences in different environments.

Peter Vermeulen's "Autism Good Feeling Questionnaire" [41] can be used through a structured conversation with an autistic person to find out what is most likely to make them happy. This approach helps "flip the narrative" within a neurodiversity paradigm.

The School Participation Questionnaire [42] supports teachers to consider the ways a child participates and inclusive environmental supports in place to facilitate active engagement.

Our literature review did not identify published or standardised neurodiversity-affirming assessment tools and we do not know of clinical guidelines which have reviewed or recommended such tools. This is clearly an area in need of development.

6. Interventions and supports

In a systematic review of research priorities of the autistic community, Roche et al. [19] identified the request for research that will lead to real-world changes in the daily lives of the autism community. Neurodiversity-affirming approaches are not yet widely defined and researched but health and education professionals and allies are interested in how to take these on board. It is clear that there is no single approach or intervention for all autistic or neurodivergent people in all contexts. Aspects of different approaches may be relevant at different times and the neurodiversity paradigm offers a new perspective in decision-making.

There is research evidence of the benefits of inclusive environments in naturally occurring environments of education, employment, and home but what makes them neurodiversity affirming is as much about appropriate and informed choices and how the approach is used, as it is about which approaches work. The following examples are a selection of commonly reported "interventions" and supports, recommended in clinical guidelines. We provide examples of ways they can be considered from the perspective of a neurodiversity paradigm. This is by no means a complete list and we would advise that practitioners can reflect on any approach used currently in a similar way.

6.1 Behaviour focussed interventions

Outdated "fix the person" interventions are rejected by the neurodiversity movement [43] and by professional allies working within the neurodiversity paradigm. The negative view of behaviourist or behaviourally focussed approaches is widely known [44]. As Amy Laurent highlights, within a neurodiversity paradigm, "Compliance is not the goal" [45]. New goals do not seek to use external rewards to encourage people to mask and do things they find distressing but rather seek to provide intrinsically motivating experiences to reduce distress. Even commonly used interventions like Cognitive Behavioural Therapy recommended in clinical guidelines [15] can be re-evaluated within the neurodiversity paradigm. They can clearly benefit some people in some circumstances but are problematic when offered as the only option to people who might benefit from other types of support. Until there is better evidence about acceptability to the autistic community and potential risks, they should be used with caution [46], due to a lack of autism and neurodevelopmentally informed knowledge amongst CBT practitioners and the lack of alternatives to psychological therapies being offered.

6.2 Parent-mediated interventions

Parent-mediated interventions are recommended in autism clinical guidelines [14, 16]. Rather than seeking to "fix the child" they can support parents and carers to better understand their child's developmental stage and preferences. Such interventions are applied in naturalistic settings and have been found to reduce parent and family stress and improve communication experiences for autistic individuals [47].

We have not identified any which explicitly state that they are positioned within a neurodiversity paradigm, however, some existing programmes take a child-led, relationships focussed approach rather than a behaviourist, or reward-based approach. They could be delivered in a neurodiversity-affirming way, particularly those that take account of sensory, play, and communication preferences, motivation, and support parents to understand how to adapt communication and naturally occurring opportunities to meet their child's needs [48]. Within these programmes, a neurodiversity-affirming approach honours autistic communication, recognises the communicative intent behind echolalia, never forces eye contact or touch and values passions and self-regulation actions, such as stimming.

6.3 Supporting social communication

Social skills interventions are criticised for positioning neurotypical responses and actions as correct and encouraging masking of natural and authentic ways of being for neurodivergent people. This in turn can reduce mental well-being [13]. Within the neurodiversity paradigm, there can be an acknowledgement that autistic people in a neurotypical world may need help to understand social actions and expectations in day to day environments. However crucially, there should be no expectation that neurodivergent people adopt neurotypical behaviours. The onus for changing lies with the neurotypical majority. Awareness and nuanced understanding of "double empathy" changes the way we think about autistic communication styles being different and not wrong [49]. Do we need to stop supporting all autistic people in understanding social expectations because historical methods are problematic? or do we need to reconsider why and how we do this?

Most interventions recommended in clinical guidelines [50] are based on evidence gathered without reference to the neurodiversity paradigm or the views of the autistic community [51]. A recent systematic review of 26 social skills intervention studies published in the past 20 years, highlighted that only 4 involved autistic people in their design and less than half sought feedback from participants [52]. This study highlights the importance of applying evaluation of social validity in future evidence reviews and reports of whether interventions are recommended.

Some researchers and intervention developers are seeking to update historical practice, to reflect the neurodiversity paradigm, respect neurodiversity, and acceptability of approaches to supporting social understanding to the neurodivergent community. For example, authors of the PEERS programme [53] and Social Thinking Methodology [54] have taken explicit steps to reflect their awareness of and support for neurodiversity affirming ways of applying approaches to support social understanding for those who wish to engage in these approaches, without the expectation that autistic people adopt a neurotypical communication style. As with CBT, it is possible that these approaches have something to offer in facilitating autonomy and confidence in aspects of social interaction in the neurotypical world, for some people, if they can be used in ways which value neurodivergent communication preferences and thinking styles as different, not wrong.

Over time, we anticipate partnerships between autistic and non-autistic people can support access to a nuanced and shared understanding, a difference not deficit mindset and neurodiversity affirming adaptations and supports in naturally occurring environments of home, school, further education, work, and in the community.

6.4 Visual supports

Developmentally relevant visual supports [55] also come recommended in clinical guidelines [14–16]. These are good example of an approach that can be applied flexibly and which can be implemented through a medical, social, or neurodiversity paradigm.

One more controversial type of visual support for communication amongst the autistic community is The Picture Exchange Communication System or PECS [56]. It has been reported to be effective for autistic people, in providing a means of expression which does not rely on speech or pointing but the use of ABA methods to support communication is problematic within the neurodiversity paradigm. The question for speech and language therapists and teachers is—do we need to stop using Picture Exchange as a communication support, if we want to work within a neurodiversity paradigm? Or can we modify the way we support people to understand and be motivated to use picture exchange when it is developmentally relevant for them? Is it enough to change the focus from only requesting objects, to also adding socially and personally motivating and useful language, like people's names and verbs? Should we adapt the games we use to introduce and practice picture exchange, to ensure they are intrinsically desirable rather than coerced or prompted? There is work ahead to revisit the outcome measures used, so that they focus on outcomes valued by autistic people.

6.5 Intervention and support in naturally occurring environments

A disproportionate number of exclusions and anxiety-related absence from school affect autistic learners [57, 58], and in the UK only 22% of autistic people are in employment [46]. Naturally occurring environments of school, further education, or work have not always met the needs of autistic people [59–61], however relevant adjustments in physical and social environments have the potential to be powerful interventions within a neurodiversity paradigm. Within this paradigm difference and diversity are expected and daily environments are designed to be inclusive; people in these environments are the agents of change, through adapting their own assumptions, expectations, and communication and modelling neurodiversity-affirming words and actions.

What can employers and educators do? A key issue arising in conversations with autistic people is the need for access to high-quality professional learning, which is co-created with autistic people, to support practitioners to put neurodiversity-affirming ways of working into practice. Recognised approaches might include: taking an anticipatory approach rather than reacting when things go wrong; recognising, valuing, and celebrating a wide range of strengths and achievements; considering individual needs to feel well-regulated in structured and unstructured times (e.g., needs for quiet spaces, movement needs, needs for information and avoidance of disrupted expectations and knowing that good things should just happen); finding meaningful ways for autistic people to feel listened to and to have their experiences and preferences taken into account. In schools, this might be involving young people in planning to meet their needs. In the workplace, this might be providing opportunities to reflect on what's going well and whether there are reasonable adjustments the autistic individual would like.

In school settings, the biggest reason for challenges arising is the mismatch between an individual's developmental stage and expectations of others. We can consider how to make learning meaningful, so that individuals see the point in what they are expected to do. Adults can look for ways to infuse the day with predictable and desirable experiences. For example, instead of using rewards to encourage a child to remain seated in assembly, the adults can consider sensory and communication preferences and adapt assembly to make it intrinsically enjoyable, so that the individual wants to stay. Teams can reflect on language and mindsets in relation to distress. Instead of talking about "behaviour that is challenging," consider how situations are experienced by the individual, which explains their responses and actions.

While environmental modifications are recommended and may be well understood in some professional groups, there are practitioners working in more medical or biopsychosocial paradigms who remain uncertain of how to support people to access this support. There is a need to prioritise research about approaches set in naturally occurring environments, to give clarity to what works, for whom in what circumstances, and what is valued by autistic people.

7. A neurodiversity-affirming professional and ally

Neurodivergent people and professional allies are engaged in thought and debate about how to evolve mindsets and practice, reflecting on how neurotypical people can work positively in partnership with neurodivergent friends, family, and people at work and in our community. We propose that a neurodiversity-affirming approach:

- is based on listening to individuals and their preferences
- provides developmentally relevant support for understanding and expression
- seeks to understand differences rather than labelling deficits
- does not focus on fixing the person or making them perform in a neurotypical way
- prioritises approaches designed and developed in partnership with neurodivergent people
- takes account of elements of the physical and social environment that can be adapted and made inclusive
- honours communication, sensory, and play/leisure preferences
- understands the preferences for predictability or other aspects of daily life
- recognises the need for processing time and safe spaces
- recognises difficulties experienced and seeks to address these in partnership with the individual and their family
- offers access to timely diagnostic assessment
- enables opportunities to engage with a community of people with shared interests and experiences

- encourages stimming and safe self-regulation strategies
- uses neurodiversity affirming language and mindsets and normalises conversations about diversity and difference
- flips the narrative to celebrate the value of a neurodiverse society
- focusses on opportunities for meaningful participation and active engagement in day to day life

8. Conclusion

We conclude this chapter on a hopeful note. The neurodiversity paradigm is here to stay and we have foundations to build upon, to develop an evidence base led by and developed with the autistic and neurodivergent community. Researchers and practitioners have reported a range of elements core to neurodiversity-affirming practice. There is a real desire for change and a need for practical, evidence-informed guidance, tools, and resources for students, new practitioners, and people in leadership roles. By thinking in a neurodevelopmentally informed way, individuals of all ages, with all neurotypes can be better understood and many adjustments could become second nature. The complex shift from single-condition approaches to neurodevelopmental pathways is happening and is only possible because it is built upon several decades of evolution in how we think about and understand autism and other neurodevelopmental differences from the medical, social, and neurodiversity perspectives.

Acknowledgements

The authors are members of the National Autism Implementation team, funded by the Scottish Government. We would like to acknowledge the whole team and autistic, non-autistic and people of all neurotypes who we work alongside, who support and challenge us, and who are passionate about improving experiences of neurodivergent people now and in the future.

Conflict of interest

The authors declare no conflict of interest.

Author details

Marion Rutherford* and Lorna Johnston
Queen Margaret University, School of Health Sciences, Queen Margaret University Drive Musselburgh, UK

*Address all correspondence to: mrutherford@qmu.ac.uk

References

[1] American Psychiatric Association. Diagnostic and Statistical Manual of Mental Disorders: DSM-5. 5th ed. Washington, DC: American Psychiatric Publishing; 2013

[2] World Health Organisation. International Classification of Diseases, Eleventh Revision (ICD-11), World Health Organization (WHO). 2019/2021. Available from: https://icd.who.int/browse11

[3] Jellett R, Muggleton J. Implications of applying "clinically significant impairment" to autism assessment: Commentary on six problems encountered in clinical practice. Journal of Autism and Developmental Disorders. 2022;**52**(3):1412-1421

[4] Gillberg C. The Essence of Autism and Other Neurodevelopmental Conditions: Rethinking Co-Morbidities, Assessment, and Intervention. London, Philadelphia: Jessica Kingsley Publishers; 2021

[5] Rutherford M, Maciver D, Johnston L, Prior S, Forsyth K. Development of a pathway for multidisciplinary neurodevelopmental assessment and diagnosis in children and young people. Children. 2021 Nov 11;**8**(11):1033

[6] Silberman S. Neurotribes: The Legacy of Autism and How to Think Smarter About People Who Think Differently. London: Atlantic Books; 2017

[7] Penner M, Anagnostou E, Andoni LY, Ungar WJ. Systematic review of clinical guidance documents for autism spectrum disorder diagnostic assessment in select regions. Autism. 2018 Jul;**22**(5):517-527

[8] Abrahamson V, Zhang W, Wilson PM, Farr W, Reddy V, Parr J, et al. Realist evaluation of Autism ServiCe Delivery (RE-ASCeD): Which diagnostic pathways work best, for whom and in what context? Findings from a rapid realist review. BMJ Open. 2021;**11**(12):e051241

[9] Rutherford M, Burns M, Gray D, Bremner L, Clegg S, Russell L, et al. Improving efficiency and quality of the children's ASD diagnostic pathway: Lessons learned from practice. Journal of Autism and Developmental Disorders. 2018 May;**48**(5):1579-1595

[10] Anderson-Chavarria M. The autism predicament: Models of autism and their impact on autistic identity. Disability & Society. 2021 Jan;**37**:1321-1341

[11] Pellicano E, den Houting J. Annual research review: Shifting from 'normal science' to neurodiversity in autism science. Journal of Child Psychology and Psychiatry. 2022 Apr;**63**(4):381-396

[12] Benning TB. Limitations of the biopsychosocial model in psychiatry. Advances in Medical Education and Practice. 2015;**6**:347

[13] Sedgewick F, Hull L, Ellis H. Autism and Masking: How and Why People Do It, and the Impact It Can Have. London: Jessica Kingsley Publishers; 2021

[14] National Institute for Health and Care Excellence. Autism Spectrum Disorder in Under 19s: Recognition, Referral and Diagnosis (CG128). London, UK; 2011. pp. 1-45

[15] National Institute for Health and Care Excellence. Autism: Recognition, Referral, Diagnosis and Management of Adults on the Autism Spectrum (CG142). London: National Institute for Health and Care Excellence; 2012 [Online]. Available from: https://www.nice.org.uk/guidance/cg142

[16] Scottish Intercollegiate Guidelines Network: SIGN 145 Assessment, Diagnosis and Interventions for Autism Spectrum Disorders, Edinburgh; 2016

[17] NICE. Attention Deficit Hyperactivity Disorder: Diagnosis and Management [NG87]. Published: 14 March 2018.

[18] Bölte S, Lawson WB, Marschik PB, Girdler S. Reconciling the seemingly irreconcilable: The WHO's ICF system integrates biological and psychosocial environmental determinants of autism and ADHD: The International Classification of Functioning (ICF) allows to model opposed biomedical and neurodiverse views of autism and ADHD within one framework. BioEssays. 2021 Sep;**43**(9):2000254

[19] Roche L, Adams D, Clark M. Research priorities of the autism community: A systematic review of key stakeholder perspectives. Autism. 2021 Feb;**25**(2):336-348

[20] Fletcher-Watson S, Adams J, Brook K, Charman T, Crane L, Cusack J, et al. Making the future together: Shaping autism research through meaningful participation. Autism. May 2019;**23**(4):943-953. DOI: 10.1177/1362361318786721

[21] Botha M, Hanlon J, Williams GL. Does language matter? Identity-first versus person-first language use in autism research: A response to Vivanti. Journal of Autism and Developmental Disorders. 2021 Jan 20:1-9

[22] Buijsman R, Begeer S, Scheeren AM. 'Autistic person' or 'person with autism'? Person-first language preference in Dutch adults with autism and parents. Autism. Aug 2022;**0**(0):1-8. DOI: 10.1177/13623613221117914

[23] National Autism Implementation Team, Newsletter. 8, Apr 2022:5-7. Available from: https://www. thirdspace. scot/wp-content/ uploads/2022/04/ NAIT-Newsletter-8- April-2022.pdf

[24] Guyon K. Perspectives about neurodiversity-affirming practices.

[25] Guilbaud J, Vuattoux D, Bezzan G, Malchair A. Autism spectrum disorder: Ethiopathogenesis and benefits of early diagnosis. Revue Médicale de Liège. 2021 Sep 1;**76**(9):672-676

[26] de Broize M, Evans K, Whitehouse AJ, Wray J, Eapen V, Urbanowicz A. Exploring the experience of seeking an autism diagnosis as an adult. Autism in Adulthood. 2022 Jun 1;**4**(2):130-140

[27] Crane L, Hearst C, Ashworth M, Davies J, Hill EL. Supporting newly identified or diagnosed autistic adults: An initial evaluation of an autistic-led programme. Journal of Autism and Developmental Disorders. 2021 Mar;**51**(3):892-905

[28] Thompson-Hodgetts S, Labonte C, Mazumder R, Phelan S. Helpful or harmful? A scoping review of perceptions and outcomes of autism diagnostic disclosure to others. Research in Autism Spectrum Disorders. 2020 Sep 1;**77**:101598. DOI: 10.1016/j.rasd.2020.101598

[29] Gillberg C. The essence in child psychiatry: Early symptomatic syndromes eliciting neurodevelopmental clinical examinations. Research in Developmental Disabilities. 2010 Nov 1;**31**(6):1543-1551

[30] Vanhaecht K, Coeckelberghs E. Interprofessional team working: The case of care pathways. In: Implementation Science. Routledge; 2022. pp. 185-187. Ebook ISBN 9781003109945 1st edition

[31] Wigham S, Ingham B, Le Couteur A, Wilson C, Ensum I, Parr JR. A survey

of autistic adults, relatives and clinical teams in the United Kingdom: And Delphi process consensus statements on optimal autism diagnostic assessment for adults. Autism. Nov 2022;**26**(8):1959-1972. DOI: 10.1177/13623613211073020

[32] Scottish Government Children and young people - national neurodevelopmental specification: principles and standards of care. September 2021. ISBN 9781802013276. Available from: https://www.gov.scot/publications/national-neurodevelopmental-specification-children-young-people-principles-standards-care/

[33] Rutherford M, Forsyth K, McKenzie K, McClure I, Murray A, McCartney D, et al. Implementation of a practice development model to reduce the wait for Autism Spectrum diagnosis in adults. Journal of Autism and Developmental Disorders. 2018 Aug;**48**(8):2677-2691

[34] Radley A, Melia B, Rutherford M, MacIver D, Boilson M Prescribing data shows under treatment of ADHD for people aged 10-59 years in Scotland.

[35] National Autism Implementation Team. National Clinical ADHD Pathway Feasibility Study. January 2021. Available from: https://www.thirdspace.scot/wp-content/uploads/2021/09/NAIT-Feasbility-Study-Report-2021-National-ADHD-Pathway.pdf

[36] National Autism Implementation Team. Adult Diagnosis Referral Thresholds, Stepped Care. January 2021. Available from: https://www.thirdspace.scot/wp-content/uploads/2021/09/NAIT-Adult-Diagnosis-Referral-Thresholds-Stepped-Care-Pathway-2021.pdf

[37] Mughal S, Salmon A, Churchill A, Tee K, Jaouich A, Shah J. Guiding Principles for Implementing Stepped Care in Mental Health: Aligning on the Bigger Picture. PsyArXiv Preprints. Available from: https://psyarxiv.com/2pazw/

[38] Lebersfeld JB, Swanson M, Clesi CD, O'Kelley SE. Systematic review and meta-analysis of the clinical utility of the ADOS-2 and the ADI-R in diagnosing autism spectrum disorders in children. Journal of Autism and Developmental Disorders. 2021 Nov;**51**(11):4101-4114

[39] Rubin E, Prizant BM, Laurent AC, Wetherby AM. Social communication, emotional regulation, and transactional support (SCERTS). In: Goldstein S, Naglieri JA, editors. Interventions for Autism Spectrum Disorders. Translating Science into Practice. New York, NY: Springer Science & Business Media. 3 Feb 2013. pp. 107-127

[40] Laurent A, Fede J. The PIC (Person In Context), Supports and resources. The Energy Regulation Suite. 2020. Available from: https://autismlevelup.com/the-pic-person-in-context/#:~:text=This%20support%20is%20designed%20to,are%20engaged%20(Energy%20Meter)

[41] Vermeulen P. The practice of promoting happiness in autism. In: Jones G, Hurley E, editors. Good Autism Practice: Autism, Happiness and Wellbeing. Birmingham: BILD Publications; 2014. pp. 8-17

[42] Maciver D, Tyagi V, Johnston L, Kramer JM, Richmond J, Todorova L, et al. Psychometric properties of the school participation questionnaire: Testing a measure of participation-related constructs. Developmental Medicine and Child Neurology. 2021;**64**(7):847-854. DOI: 10.1111/dmcn.15146

[43] Leadbitter K, Buckle KL, Ellis C, Dekker M. Autistic self-advocacy and the

neurodiversity movement: Implications for autism early intervention research and practice. Frontiers in Psychology. 2021;**12**(Article 635690):1-7. DOI: 10.3389/

[44] Chapman R, Bovell V. Neurodiversity, advocacy, anti-therapy. In: Matson JL, Sturmey P, editors. Handbook of Autism and Pervasive Developmental Disorder. Cham: Springer; 2022. pp. 1519-1536

[45] Laurent A. TED Talk, Compliance is not the goal. Letting go of control and rethinking support for autistic individuals, TEDXURI. 7 March 2019. Available from: https://www.ted.com/talks/amy_laurent_compliance_is_not_the_goal_letting_go_of_control_and_rethinking_support_for_autistic_individuals

[46] National Autism Implementation Team. Research Summary: Mental Health in Autistic Adults. 2021. Available from: https://www.thirdspace.scot/wp-content/uploads/2021/12/Research-Summary-Mental-Health-in-Autistic-Adults-2021-with-Appendices.pdf

[47] Rutherford M, Singh-Roy A, Rush R, McCartney D, O'Hare A, Forsyth K. Parent focused interventions for older children or adults with ASD and parent wellbeing outcomes: A systematic review with meta-analysis. Research in Autism Spectrum Disorders. 2019 Dec 1;**68**:101450

[48] Weitzman E. More than words—The Hanen Program for parents of children with autism spectrum disorder: A teaching model for parent-implemented language intervention. Perspectives on Language Learning and Education. 2013 Aug;**20**(3):96-111

[49] Mitchell P, Sheppard E, Cassidy S. Autism and the double empathy problem: Implications for development and mental health. British Journal of Developmental Psychology. 2021 Mar;**39**(1):1-8

[50] Hume K, Steinbrenner JR, Odom SL, Morin KL, Nowell SW, Tomaszewski B, et al. Evidence-based practices for children, youth, and young adults with autism: Third generation review. Journal of Autism and Developmental Disorders. 2021 Nov;**51**(11):4013-4032

[51] Curnow E, Rutherford M, MacIver D, Johnston L, Prior S, Boilson M, Shah P, Jenkins N, Williams T. Mental health in autistic adults: A rapid systematic review of prevalence and effectiveness of interventions within a neurodiversity informed paradigm.

[52] Monahan J, Freedman B, Pini K, Lloyd R. Autistic input in social skills interventions for young adults: A systematic review of the literature. Review Journal of Autism and Developmental Disorders. 2021 Jul 13:1-21

[53] Honan I, Sharp N, McIntyre S, Smithers-Sheedy H, Balde I, Quinn K, et al. Program evaluation of an adapted PEERS® social skills program in young adults with autism spectrum disorder and/or mild intellectual impairment and social skills difficulties. Journal of Evaluation in Clinical Practice. 4 Aug 2022:1-10. DOI: 10.1111/jep.13743

[54] Crooke P, Garci WM. Respecting Neurodiversityby Helping Social Learners meet their personal goals. 2022. Available from: https://www.socialthinking.com/Articles?name=respecting-neurodiversity-help-social-learners-meet-goals

[55] Rutherford M, Baxter J, Grayson Z, Johnston L, O'Hare A. Visual supports at home and in the community for individuals with autism spectrum disorders: A scoping review. Autism. 2020 Feb;**24**(2):447-469

[56] Pierson LM, Ganz JB. Does use of the Picture Exchange Communication System (PECS) and Focused Playtime

Intervention (FPI) improve the communication of children with autism spectrum disorder who are minimally verbal? Evidence-Based Communication Assessment and Intervention. 2019 Oct 2;**13**(4):200-203

[57] Johnston L, Rutherford M. Anxiety Related Absence Guidance, National Autism Implementation Team. 2020. Available from: https://www.thirdspace.scot/wp-content/uploads/2020/08/NAIT-Anxiety-Related-Absence-Guidance-2020.pdf

[58] Children in Scotland, The National Autistic Socity Scotland and Scottish Autsm are ther authors and publishers of the document entitled 'Not included, Not engaged, Not involved: A report on the experiences of autistic children missing school, published 25th September 2018. Available from: https://www.notengaged.com/download/SA-Out-Of-School-Report.pdf

[59] Wood R. Inclusive Education for Autistic Children: Helping Children and Young People to Learn and Flourish in the Classroom. London: Jessica Kingsley Publishers. 21 Aug 2019

[60] Anderson AH. Stephenson J, Carter M, Carlon S. A systematic literature review of empirical research on postsecondary students with autism spectrum disorder. Journal of Autism and Developmental Disorders. 2019 Apr;**49**(4):1531-1558

[61] Scott M, Milbourn B, Falkmer M, Black M, Bölte S, Halladay A, et al. Factors impacting employment for people with autism spectrum disorder: A scoping review. Autism. 2019 May;**23**(4):869-901

Chapter 7

Perspective Chapter: Autism Spectrum Disorder Neurophenotype with Preconceptional and Prenatal Alcohol Exposure – A Call for Industry Responsibility in Prevention

Susan D. Rich

Abstract

Preconceptional and prenatal alcohol exposure is a widespread, costly, and preventable influence on neurodevelopment contributing to Autism Spectrum Disorder. Neurodevelopmental Disorder associated with Prenatal Alcohol Exposure is a heterogeneous neurophenotype that underscores the importance of etiology in diagnosis, treatment, and prevention. Expanding upon previously published clinical implications, this perspective elucidates a phenomenology describing neurophenotypic heterogeneity leading to a range of clinical neurophenotypes including Autism Spectrum Disorder as well as neurodevelopmental issues and neuropsychiatric problems. Given that ND-PAE affects up to 1 in 20 people, a pandemic-level public health response is warranted to prevent and treat preconceptional and prenatal alcohol exposure. Given the widespread use of alcohol during reproductive years, governmental enforcement of industry responsibility in consumer protection should include point of sales labeling and risk reduction advertising about the reproductive effects of alcohol products. Widespread dissemination of public health information by physicians and allied health professionals would help improve awareness that use of the solvent (alcohol) can cause reproductive health effects to gametes, zygotes, embryos, and fetuses. Improvements in screening for ND-PAE, nonjudgmental discussions with biological parents about preconceptional alcohol use, pregnancy planning through contraceptive access, and marketing mandates may reduce unintentional exposures prior to pregnancy recognition.

Keywords: neurodevelopment, neurophenotype, neuroteratogen, alcohol, fetal alcohol syndrome, neurodevelopmental disorder associated with prenatal alcohol exposure, fetal alcohol Spectrum disorder, preconceptional health, contraception, contracept, FASD, autism Spectrum disorder, prenatal alcohol exposure, epigenetics, methylation

1. Introduction

Alcohol is a prevalent and potent neuroteratogen affecting as many as 1 in 20 Americans [1], and a worldwide cause of atypical neurodevelopment, particularly due to exposures in unplanned or mistimed pregnancies for "social drinkers" [2, 3]. Clinically, Neurodevelopmental Disorder associated with Prenatal Alcohol Exposure (ND-PAE) and Autism Spectrum Disorder (ASD) have overlapping clinical features [4], in part due to the symptom-based diagnostic paradigm of the Diagnostic and Statistical Manual of Psychiatric Disorders (DSM-5) [5], with few psychiatric symptoms being mutually exclusive to a single psychiatric condition. Since human neurodevelopment is complex and dependent on multifactorial processes, it is no wonder that we have such heterogeneity of expressed neurophenotypes. Alcohol as a solvent perhaps is perhaps the most quintessential neurodevelopmental teratogen known to mankind.

Effects of prenatal alcohol exposure (PAE) exist on a continuum, with milder cases exposed to as few as 7 drinks per week (1 serving per day on average) associated with attention deficits and as few as 4–5 consumed during the late 3rd to early 4th week post conception causing the full Fetal Alcohol Syndrome (FAS) [6]. Alcohol can affect human development at any point from preconceptionally (gametogenesis) to the first few weeks post conceptionally (neurulation and gastrulation through organogenesis) [7] through fetal development to birth. Lactation is also a time when the newborn and infant can be exposed to and affected by a mother's use of alcohol [8]. Neurodevelopmental effects of PAE involve brain functions as well as sensorium (cranial nerves and sensory neurons), motor neurons, autonomic regulation, and neurotransmitter systems. These effects have been described in the DSM-5 as ND-PAE, yet there remains a lack of acknowledgement, understanding, and recognition in the psychiatric community for this diagnosis. Nonetheless, scholars are attempting to highlight the link between PAE and neuropsychiatric illness [9].

Neurodevelopmental complexity of symptoms associated with prenatal alcohol exposure can lead to an ASD-like phenotype, including social communication deficits, neurocognitive issues (e.g., executive functions), sensory integration problems (e.g., interoception, hypo/hypersensitivities), motor deficits, and emotional dysregulation. All of the body systems can be affected by PAE, including immune, endocrine, reproductive, metabolic, cardiovascular, urinary, gastrointestinal, and integumentary. Alcohol affects both the developing sperm up to 3 months preconceptionally (DNA histone modifications) as well as beginning as early as weeks 2–3 post-conception. Research implicates alcohol consumption during adolescence with epigenetic effects on gametes, leading to alterations in the hypothalamic stress response system [10].

Likewise, Autism Spectrum Disorder (ASD) is a broad, umbrella term describing complex atypical neurodevelopment due to a wide array of multifactorial etiologies [11]. Williams and Lewis have developed a useful clinical screening tool for ASD [12]. As a neurophenotype [13], ASD has a wide range of symptoms which can be due to preconceptional epigenetic insults to gametes, *in utero* prenatal exposures to neuroteratogens, genetic (familial) hereditary anomalies, early neurologic birth traumas, and as yet unidentified causes [14]. The heterogeneity of ASD as well as the plethora of etiological factors are beyond the scope of this chapter. Given the range of unknown and otherwise as yet nonpreventable causes of ASD, any reductions in etiology due to a substance so ubiquitous as alcohol would reduce the societal burden of this otherwise complex, difficult to treat condition.

Since human neurodevelopment is multifactorial, with genetic, epigenetic, and environmental influences, exact etiological associations in each child difficult to elucidate. A proposed paradigm for atypical neurophenotypic development is described in **Figure 1**, which is adapted from Picci and Sherf [15]. The combination of preconceptional issues, genetics, epigenetics, and the prenatal environment are exacerbated by adverse childhood experiences (ACEs) and adolescent use of alcohol, tobacco and other drugs – which are cumulative effects to disrupt healthy neuronal development. This model shows prenatal alcohol exposure in the context of an individual zygote's biological background of epigenetic and/or genetic factors, such as familial autism traits and/or predisposition to effects of prenatal alcohol exposure (e.g., CYP-450 enzyme expression in the mother or fetus). The first preventable hit to neurodevelopment is preconceptional or prenatal use of alcohol, whereas the model assumes that the epigenetic and genetic background of the zygote may not be changed. In order to effectively prevent the first hit, one must contracept if using alcohol and must stop using alcohol up to 3 months preconceptionally in order to prevent epigenetic influences on spermatogenesis. The second hit, ACEs, is currently identified by childhood screening for abuse and neglect, though beyond the scope of this chapter. Further alterations in neurodevelopment happen when adolescent use of substances such as alcohol, tobacco and other drugs, often triggering psychosis, mania, or other severe and persistent mental illness. Hence, the term "*neurodevelopmental*" may be best understood in the context of the *neuro*logical *develop*ment of *mental* disorders.

Because DSM-5 is based on symptomatology, etiological factors of neurodevelopmental conditions are conceptualized by psychiatrists and mental health practitioners as secondary or inconsequential to diagnostic criteria and treatment paradigms. Co-morbidity of ASD and ND-PAE blurs the clinical picture, leaving psychiatrists, pediatricians, mid-level providers, and allied health professionals with a laundry list differential diagnoses and complex formulations. Individuals with prenatal alcohol exposure are at risk for many DSM-5 psychiatric and neurodevelopmental conditions [16]. Co-occurrence may be overlooked for affected children who may have been exposed prior to pregnancy recognition or who have preconceptional alcohol-induced epigenetic factors that would not show up on chromosomal karyotype or genetic

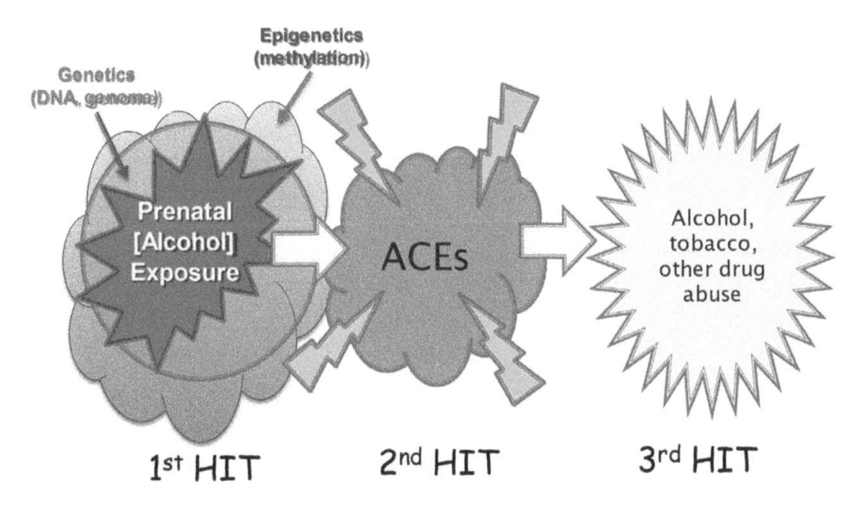

Figure 1.
3-hit model of "neuro-develop-mental" damage.

microarray analysis [17]. Neurobiology, neuropsychiatry, neuroimaging, and neurogenetics may assist in clarifying clinically overlapping phenotypes (i.e., co-morbid ASD and ND-PAE) when prenatal alcohol exposure is known.

2. Alcohol's impact on evolution, epigenetics, neurodevelopmental (functional) birth defects, and the etiology of ASD

The origins of the earliest fertile crescent agricultural settlements have been associated with the production of beer for feasting and celebrations as early as the pre-pottery neolithic age (PPNA) [18] approximately 11,500 to 11,000 years ago around the end of the last ice age. *Homo sapiens* is the only species to have fermented, distilled, and mass-produced alcohol for large scale population consumption and exposure to laboratory animals to study the effects. Alcohol is therefore the oldest and most pervasive recreationally used neurodevelopmental teratogen, affecting human neurodevelopment since the earliest known neolithic agricultural settlements. Hence, widespread use of our social drug of choice has influenced human evolution through preconceptional (epigenetic) and prenatal exposures since those ancient times. Alcohol metabolic variants have been found among Southeast Asian human populations [19], with their fermentation of rice and berry wines dating back to 6500 to 7000 BC [20]. Hence, alcohol's transgenerational effects for 10,000 years on our evolution as a species may account for metabolic and phenotypic variance in human populations.

Given the range of effects on developing limbic brain systems, some of our most severe mental illnesses can be traced to preconceptional and prenatal alcohol exposure. Many neuropsychiatric and neurodevelopmental conditions are reported to be familial and/or transmitted intergenerationally, most likely through epigenetic [21], multifactorial gene–environment interactions. Prenatal and preconceptional alcohol exposure result in genetic and epigenetic [22] variants, which also have been described in ASD [23], schizophrenia [24], as well as other neuropsychiatric conditions [25]. Further, genetic and epigenetic variants of serotonin, dopaminergic and norepinephrine metabolism may account for the clustering of mental health disorders such as schizophrenia and bipolar disorder in families with histories of alcohol abuse.

2.1 Epigenetics, teratogenicity, and neurodevelopmental (functional) birth defects

Neurodevelopmental teratogens are chemicals that cause functional birth defects in the developing zygote or embryo. In contrast to physical birth defects, functional (or neurodevelopmental) birth defects are those associated with changes in brain, central nervous system, sensorium, motor nerves, and somatosensory function [26]. Alcohol has long since been known to be a potent, prevalent and preventable neurodevelopmental teratogen leading to atypical social communication, neurocognitive processes, sensory integration and motor problems, and mood regulation/autonomic arousal. These children, adolescents, and young adults often have difficulty with adaptive functions (conceptual, social, and practical skills) despite a relatively normal intellect.

Neuroteratologists define functional birth defects as abnormalities in neurological, immune and endocrine systems, in contrast to physical anomalies such as phocomelia, cleft lip or palate, hypospadias or other structural malformations. Whereas structural problems may be identified at birth, functional abnormalities can take months or years to identify. Alcohol can cause physical birth defects but is more potent as a neurodevelopmental teratogen. An increased understanding of epigenetic effects on neurodevelopment may expand the definition of neuroteratogens to include chemicals that cause methylation effects in the gametes, not simply effects in the embryo, zygote and fetus.

Alcohol has long been described as a neurodevelopmental teratogen, affecting sperm beginning as early as 3 months preconceptionally (epigenetic) and within 2 to 3 weeks postconceptionally in the embryo (teratogenic). An array of *de novo* DNA damage (microdeletions, microinsertions, translocations) can happen as a result of alcohol's effects on the gamete, conceptus, zygote, early embryo and fetus. Carefully designed animal studies and epidemiological human studies have provided clues to the neurodevelopmental teratogenicity of alcohol – leading to many different types of *de novo* microdeletions, insertions, translocations, and epigenetic mechanisms for atypical development.

An appreciation of the epigenetic influence on ND-PAE begins before conception and embryonic neurodevelopment. Spermatogenesis takes 3 months for sperm maturation, during which time the male gametes are susceptible to a father's use of alcohol. Epigenetic effects mediated by histone protein methylation during spermatogenesis make the zygote and early embryo more susceptible to neuroteratogenic effects of prenatal alcohol exposure (i.e., maternal alcohol use) [27]. This epigenetic susceptibility of the zygote interacts with maternal factors (e.g., timing, duration, blood alcohol concentration, nutrition, metabolism, stress hormone secretion, other drug exposure) to worsen the prognosis.

2.2 ND-PAE as a preventable cause of ASD

Developmental deficits, executive functioning issues, neuropsychiatric sequelae, and adaptive functioning issues make ND-PAE a challenging, under-appreciated, and costly neurodevelopmental condition for the individual, family and society [28]. Given the association between prenatal alcohol exposure, neuroteratogenicity, and *de novo* genetic changes, our social drug of choice, alcohol may be the leading known and preventable cause of ASD. Gamete and embryonic exposure leading to microdeletions and insertions associated with autism features. As a solvent, alcohol is lipophilic – penetrating every barrier in the human body, from the blood–brain barrier to the maternal-fetal circulation, to the gut-circulatory system. Clinical overlap between symptoms necessitates a careful preconceptional and prenatal history to accurately identify patients with ND-PAE with or without comorbid ASD.

Despite public health warnings by the Centers for Disease Control and Prevention (CDC) for women to abstain from alcohol if pregnant or planning to be, and to contracept if using alcohol, the Fetal Alcohol Spectrum Disorder incidence has been reported to be as high as 1 in 20 grade school children in the United States. The simple fact that neuroteratogenic effects of prenatal alcohol exposure begins as early as the late 3rd to early 4th week post conception means that an unplanned pregnancy in a "social drinking" couple may be associated with exposure prior to pregnancy recognition. Recent reports indicate the convergence of two "perfect storm" situations: nearly 50% of pregnancies are mistimed or unplanned and drinking rates among childbearing age women has been steadily on the rise, exceeding that of males for some age groups.

Like other DSM-5 conditions, the diagnosis of Autism Spectrum Disorder (ASD) as a DSM-5 disorder is made based on symptoms rather than etiology, with a wide array of genetic and environmentally-acquired issues giving rise to the phenotypic expression. A number of neurodevelopmental teratogens have been identified in our human ecosystem, from petroleum derivatives, solvents, recreational substances, and pharmaceuticals. However, the heterogeneity of symptoms and difficulty with cause-effect clinical research has left large gaps in understanding etiology of autism spectrum disorder, outside of the known associated rare genetic disorders [29]. The American Academy of Child and Adolescent Psychiatry recommends genetic testing (chromosomes and a microarray) of individuals with ASD to rule out genetic variants associated with syndromic conditions. Findings may not be associated with any known clinical disorder because of the range of possible mutations that may lead to a phenotypic change.

3. A four domain clinical model

A previously published model describes four domains of clinical functioning impacting an individual's adaptive functions. These domains may be scaffolded by family, school, therapeutic, or community supports to improve an individual's adaptive functions. The clinical presentation may manifest as a plethora of externalizing neurobehavioral symptoms masking intrinsic neurodevelopmental deficit. This model can help elucidate the domains of functional deficits to help scaffold the child, adolescent, or young adult with appropriate systems of care to reduce their sensory overstimulation, social pragmatic issues, and/or frustration from neurocognitive issues to minimize outbursts. For example, a child may be having mood outbursts or rage due to hypersensitivity to crowded places (school bus, classroom, playground, lunchroom), people (facial expressions, voice tone, body odor, etc.), sounds (sirens, TV, voice frequency or volume, screechy noises, chalkboard, etc.), smells (food odors, body odor, smoke, decaying trash, sewer, public bathroom, etc.) (**Figure 2**).

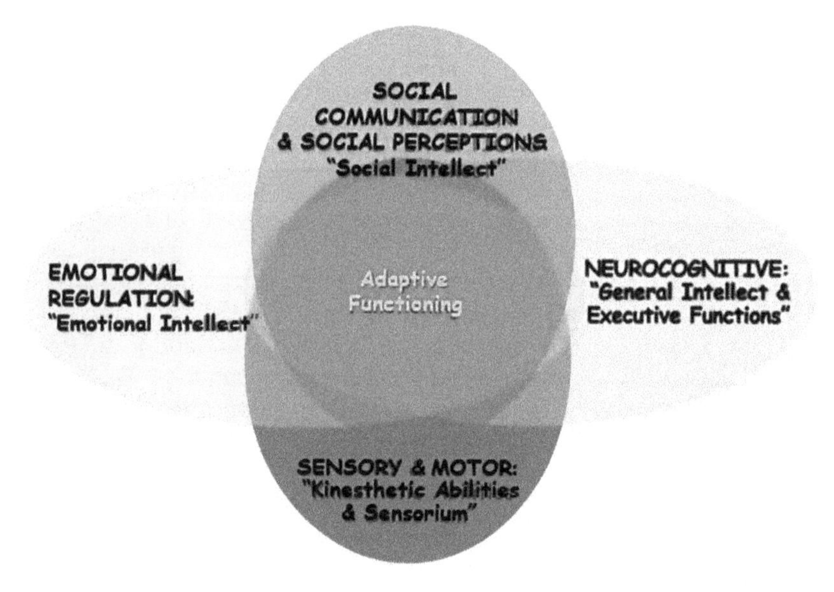

Figure 2.
Four domain model of neurodevelopmental issues.

3.1 Social communication (social intellect)

Speech and language pragmatics, receptive and expressive language deficits, nonverbal cue recognition, facial expressions, body language, and a variety of other social communication issues can be affected by prenatal alcohol exposure. Social misperceptions, suspiciousness, feeling judged and scrutinized by peers, misunderstanding constructive criticism, personalizing negative comments, over-reacting to social slights are common consequences of the miswiring of neural networks important in social cognition. From an early age, social communication issues are tied to maladaptive attachment behaviors as the individual may lack a social smile, eye contact, and typical attachment behaviors. During early childhood and latency years, these deficits leave the individual vulnerable to social problems and negative peer interactions. By middle school, atypical social interactions leave the adolescent vulnerable to bullying and harassment by peers who misunderstand their social deficits and mood dysregulation or have outpaced them in their social and emotional functioning. Affected individuals' atypical reactions to social slights may cause social disenfranchisement and maladaptive peer interactions (e.g., friends' anger and/or hurt feelings, estrangement from social groups, fear responses in peers, etc.). Often, alexithymia (difficulty recognizing their own emotions and that of others) and poor social perceptions lead family and friends feeling they lack empathy and compassion. Socially awkward facial expressions and nonverbal cues may lead others (e.g., teachers, principals, administrators) to feel they are narcissistic, callous and unemotional. Because of lack of understanding social risk and subtleties of community safety, often these individuals are at risk of having predatory behavior perpetrated against them. Their social dysmaturity makes relationships with younger individuals feel more comfortable, which can lead to inappropriate interactions with peers.

3.2 Neurocognitive (general intellect and executive functions)

Only 10–15% of individuals affected by prenatal alcohol exposure have intellectual disability (IQ at or below 75 per DSM-5) according to research by the National Institutes on Alcohol Abuse and Alcoholism. Executive functioning issues (organization, planning, time management, working memory, problem solving, visual spatial planning, etc.) are more common sequelae of prenatal alcohol exposure, with attention deficits associated with as little as 1 drink per day or up to 7 drinks per week. Hyperactivity and impulsivity (failure to inhibit unwanted behaviors) lead the individual to be seen as willful and destructive, immature or dysmature, and unable to self-regulate at home, in the classroom, and in the community. These subtle yet important neurodevelopmental functions leave the individual prone to learning challenges, academic failure, vocational problems, and difficulties transitioning into young adulthood. Often, their faulty ego strength masks their challenges, leading to a sense of "false bravado." The resulting subconscious over-inflation of their strengths to hide their challenges can lead the individual to appear haughty, grandiose, narcissistic, and flamboyant. Faulty information processing combined with impulsivity, deficits in consequential thinking and understanding social risk may lead the individual to confabulate, steal, cheat, or be vulnerable to predatory behavior.

3.3 Sensory and motor (sensorium and kinesthetic intellect)

Our somatosensory, cranial nerves, and voluntary nervous systems are as intricately wired and vulnerable to the effects of prenatal alcohol exposure as our higher-level brain functions. In fact, the midline brain defects linked to prenatal alcohol exposure from the neural crest cell migration all the way to development of the brain, cranial nerves, somatosensory and motor neurons can be affected by alcohol. Hence, hyper- and hyposensitivities to noise, texture, temperatures, and even interoceptive signals can lead to sensory integration issues. Interoceptive deficits can cause difficulty accurately perceiving signals from the digestive system (e.g., normal digestive sensations from peristalsis, gas, bloating, indigestion, stomach aches, hunger cues), rectum and bladder (defecation and urination signals). These interoceptive signaling issues often lead to emotional outbursts due to lack of understanding of the source of the discomfort and/or frustration/embarrassment due to voiding accidents. Children with interoceptive deficits may have delays in bowel and bladder control, nocturia, fecal smearing (caused by overflow incontinence), somatosensory complaints, and heightened stress response or mood dysregulation caused by hypersensitivities to environmental stimuli.

3.4 Emotional regulation (emotional quotient)

Prenatal alcohol exposure affects the sympathetic and parasympathetic nervous system, leading to emotional dysregulation, autonomic arousal (fight or flight response), sleep–wake cycle disturbances, and a variety of mood problems. Often, affected individuals are irritable, easily frustrated, annoyed, and provoked into heightened stress response by facial expressions, sensory overstimulation, or unpreferred activities. Their emotional dysmaturity leads them to seem years younger than their chronological age, to revert to more primitive mood states during stressful situations, and to be overreactive to discomfort and distress. They are perceived as infants and toddlers as emotionally dysregulated, fussy, hyper-reactive, clingy, and easily fatigued.

4. Patient perspective

A Patient presents for an intake assessment, which includes a comprehensive childhood history questionnaire complete with questions about intendedness of pregnancy (mistimed or unplanned), prenatal exposures, paternal use of substances. A very careful preconceptional and prenatal history may reveal unintentional exposures to alcohol or other drugs prior to pregnancy recognition. The history also includes history of neglect, abuse, and other adverse childhood experiences; developmental milestones (speech/language delays, social relatedness, gross/fine motor deficits, coordination problems, sensory hypo- or hypersensitivities, toileting issues). During the assessment, we find that the birth mother drank two glasses of wine per day up until week 7 post conception at the point of pregnancy recognition. The mother is Asian with alcohol dehydrogenase (ADH) enzyme variant leading to rapid metabolism of alcohol into acetaldehyde, a highly neurotoxic metabolite. Therefore, she would have higher blood acetaldehyde levels during gastrulation, neurulation, other critical points during neurogenesis, and a majority of organogenesis. Whereas she may have stopped drinking at the point she learned she was pregnant, much of neurodevelopment had already occurred at the time she stopped drinking. Her child at age 10 presents with years of distress in school due to inattention, hyperactivity, impulsivity; learning disabilities; sleep–wake cycle dysregulation; difficulty with fine and gross motor as well as coordination and balance; social communication issues (i.e., speech/language issues, pragmatic difficulties, nonverbal facial expression recognition, and decreased empathy), and sensory disintegration. There is no family history of similar problems, he has a neurotypical younger brother, and he had a normal karyotype analysis with reflex microarray. A discussion with his parents about the etiology of their son's neurodiversity helps convey a sense of responsibility on the part of the parents who had previously demeaned and demoralized the patient with statements like "You're a bad seed. Why can't you be like your brother? You need to try harder. You're stupid!" as a way to motivate better behavior.

The first step in assessing the child or adolescent with ND-PAE is to assess and treat underlying sleep issues. Psychoeducation for the child and parent on the importance of adequate sleep for mental, physical, social and academic functioning; reviewing sleep hygiene; and providing information about natural sleep aids such as melatonin, magnesium 400 mg, lavender 500 mg or chamomile tea 30 minutes before sleep can be helpful to minimize medications. By improving sleep, we can reduce reliance on medications and improve the patient's overall wellbeing. In the event these gentler approaches do not work, use of alpha adrenergic agonists like clonidine to down-regulate the sympathetic overdrive before sleep then the long-acting form (Clonidine ER 0.1 mg twice daily) to maintain sleep allows for a single medication to treat sleep, anxiety/heightened stress response, and ADHD symptoms. Other medications such as propranolol can be effective for sleep and anxiety but not necessarily for ADHD.

After the child is sleeping well, if regulation of mood is needed, an antiseizure medication such as lamotrigine or gabapentin can be helpful to reduce the seizure like irritability of the brain. Starting with a very low dose of lamotrigine 12.5 mg twice daily (or lamotrigine long acting 25 mg once daily after a meal) and gradually increasing by no more than a total of 25 mg per week until on 100–200 mg twice daily (depending on the age of the child) will reduce the frequency, duration, and intensity of the outbursts. It is necessary to have careful discussion with parents about the potential for rash and recommendation for them not to change any of their detergents, soaps, lotions or other hygiene products while the medication is being started and increased. In the event of poor response after a couple of months on the therapeutic dose, a transition to gabapentin or topiramate would be another choice to improve their symptoms.

Affected individuals have a hard time achieving Maslow's Hierarchy (food clothing, shelter; safety/security; love, belonging and sense of community; and meaning/purpose); therefore self-actualization is as challenging as basic practical life skills, social aptitude and integration of academic skills into daily life. Beginning at young ages, developing a sense of purpose through hands-on experiences in nature and with farm animals or other meaningful activities can improve their self-esteem. These multisensory experiences desensitize children to environmental stimuli, enhance their self-esteem through accomplishments caring for animals, and improve social relationships through attachments with animals. Addressing adoptive parental rights and the affected individual's rights to birth history exposure information will also improve outcomes for affected children by providing insight into etiology of their neurodevelopmental condition. Further, positive parenting approaches, self-regulation of adults around them, mindfulness, skill building and immersion in nature will create resiliency and a healthy sense of self.

5. The Industry's responsibility

Whereas alcohol taxes are embedded in most governmental gross domestic profits, the industry seems immune to mandated responsibility for health consequences due to its products (beer, wine, or liquor) [30]. Social responsibility should account for more than prevention efforts [31]. The pharmaceutical industry is required to make reparations for damage from its products, yet the alcohol industry has no financial or legal accountability for ND-PAE or other medical problems. Like big tobacco was sued by states for the Medicaid and Medicare costs of people with emphysema, cancers, and other medical conditions [32], perhaps states should consider the inordinate costs associated with preterm labor, infant morbidity, developmental services for infants and toddlers, special education, juvenile and criminal justice, productive life years lost, and health/human services costs from adults with disabilities due to prenatal alcohol exposure.

6. Conclusions

While much is known about the effects of alcohol on embryogenesis (prior to pregnancy recognition) and methylation effects to gametes, the alcohol industry has bore little responsibility in prevention or treatment. A plethora of research indicates embryos are more vulnerable to the mother's use of alcohol if the father also consumes alcohol during the 3 months preconceptionally. Little has been shared with the public about the implications of epigenetic methylation effects during spermatogenesis, likely due to the paucity of interest in the media. Further, the psychiatric community remains befuddled by the ND-PAE diagnosis, with clinicians using symptom clusters rather than etiology for diagnosis – largely based on the DSM-5 methodology. Clearly it would not be in the interest of alcohol manufacturers and distributers to have truth in labeling and advertising its product to include the warnings about epigenetic and early pregnancy effects. However, in the interest of public health, strong consistent messaging and warnings at every point of purchase as well as in marketing of alcohol would improve the knowledge of alcohol consumers and hopefully the use of contraceptives to prevent inadvertent exposures. Likewise, messaging in hospitals, health care facilities, physician offices, pregnancy test kits, and contraceptive packaging may improve the likelihood that couples would contracept if using alcohol and avoid alcohol if pregnant or planning to be, which is the 2016 revised CDC guidelines [33].

Problems in accurately diagnosing prenatal alcohol exposure as an etiological basis for autism spectrum stems from lack of understanding and recognition by geneticists, dysmorphologists, developmental pediatricians, neurologists, psychiatrists, and "mid-level providers" (nurses, physician assistants) and allied health professionals (social workers, speech/language pathologists, occupational therapists, physical therapists, applied behavioral analysts) who commonly see these children in practice. Additionally, research on the effects of prenatal alcohol exposure tend to be published in obscure research journals read by a paucity of clinicians (e.g., Alcohol Health and Research). Lack of appreciation for the numbers of affected children (1 in 20) by policymakers and legislatures may stem from financial incentives to overlook the influence of alcohol on many of our social ills (such as prenatal/preconceptional brain damage leading to the pipeline to prison). Political campaigns all the way back to our first President George Washington have been funded by the very drug causing many of these problems; therefore, it presents an ethical conundrum for policymakers and legislators.

DOI: http://dx.doi.org/10.5772/intechopen.108820

A neurodevelopmental approach to diagnosis and treatment enables specificity in surveillance efforts, improved prognosis through the life course, and prevention through preconceptional approaches. While neurodevelopment is multifactorial, distinguishing ND-PAE co-occurring with ASD (i.e., as an etiological subtype for some affected individuals, like genetic causes) would enable improved specificity of surveillance and targeted clinical trials of therapies for the underlying neurodevelopmental lesions, leading to improved treatment efficacy and clinical prognosis (i.e., possibly reducing the burden of severe and persistent mental illness such as schizophrenia for the individual). Elucidating etiology (i.e., prenatal alcohol exposure) identifies the individuals who may suffer from underlying cardiac defects, susceptibility to seizure disorders, metabolic anomalies, propensity to CYP-450 enzyme variants, and a variety of other underlying contraindications to certain medications. From a public health perspective, distinguishing prenatal alcohol exposure as a preventable cause of ASD would help improve policy and prevention efforts, given the concerns raised by policy makers and legislators about the impact of ASD on productive life years lost.

To appropriately prevent unintentional prenatal alcohol exposure prior to pregnancy recognition, public health approaches must include preconception health, pregnancy planning and contraception for alcohol consumers. A comprehensive, holistic approach to treatment for alcohol-exposed children, similar to the well accepted guidelines for ASD, may reduce the need for medication and improve prognosis. The clinical, public health, and therapeutic implications of this perspective will hopefully help motivate policy makers, legislators, educators, and mental health professionals to work proactively in consort with childbearing alcohol consumers, affected children, and parents to create lasting change.

Acknowledgements

I would like to recognize the contribution of my mentors from the University of North Carolina at Chapel Hill - Dr. Robert C. Cefalo, past Chairman of the Department of Obstetrics and Gynecology and Dr. Kathleen K. Sulik of the UNC Bowles Center for Alcohol Studies. Their insights into preconception health and teratology helped highlight the need for contraception and careful family planning for alcohol consumers to prevent alcohol exposure prior to pregnancy recognition.

Conflict of interest

The author declares no conflict of interest.

Notes/thanks/other declarations

I would especially like to thank my children who have tolerated "good enough mothering" while growing up on an inclusive green care farm animal sanctuary. They have been great traveling companions during international conferences in Toronto, Canada; Vienna, Austria; and Shanghai, China. My advocacy in raising awareness about ND-PAE in the psychiatric community are supported by my outpatient clinical practice, Therapeutic & Learning Centers, P-LLC (www.susandrich.com) and my nonprofit 501c3, 7th Generation Foundation, Inc. (www.7thGenerationFoundationInc.org).

Nomenclature

Neurodevelopmental Disorder
Atypical Neurodevelopment
Functional Birth Defect
Neurophenotype
Preconception Health
Epigenetics
Methylation

Author details

Susan D. Rich
7th Generation Foundation, Inc., Potomac, MD

*Address all correspondence to: dr.sdrich@gmail.com

References

[1] May PA, Chambers CD, Kalberg WO, et al. Prevalence of fetal alcohol Spectrum disorders in 4 US communities. Journal of the American Medical Association. 2018;**319**(5):474-482

[2] Greenwood M. Fetal Alcohol Exposure Data Underscore Need for Public Health Interventions. Yale News; 2021. Available from: https://news.yale.edu/2021/06/28/fetal-alcohol-exposure-data-underscore-need-public-health-interventions

[3] Yaesoubi R, Mahin M, Martin G, Paltiel AD, Sharifi M. Reducing the prevalence of alcohol-exposed pregnancies in the United States: A simulation modeling study. Medical Decision Making. 2022;**42**(2):217-227

[4] O'Malley KD, Rich SD. Clinical implications of a link between fetal alcohol Spectrum disorders (FASD) and autism or Asperger's disorder – A neurodevelopmental frame for helping understanding and management. In: Recent Advances in Autism Spectrum Disorders - Volume I. London, UK, London, UK: IntechOpen; 2013

[5] American Psychiatric Association. Diagnostic and Statistical Manual of Mental Disorders. Fifth ed. Washington, DC; 2013. pp. 86, 798-801

[6] Mattson SN, Bernes GA, Doyle LR. Fetal alcohol Spectrum disorders: A review of the neurobehavioral deficits associated with prenatal alcohol exposure. Alcoholism, Clinical and Experimental Research. 2019;**43**(6):1046-1062

[7] Wallén E, Auvinen P, Kaminen-Ahola N. The effects of early prenatal alcohol exposure on epigenome and embryonic development. Genes (Basel). 2021;**12**(7):1095

[8] Mennella J. Alcohol's effect on lactation. Alcohol Research & Health. 2001;**25**(3):230-234

[9] Briana Lees B, Mewton L, Jacobus J, Valadez EA, Stapinski LA, Teesson M, et al. Association of Prenatal Alcohol Exposure with psychological, behavioral, and neurodevelopmental outcomes in children from the adolescent brain cognitive development study. The American Journal of Psychiatry. 2020;**177**(11):1060-1072

[10] Asimes A, Torcaso A, Pinceti E, Kim CK, Zeleznik-Le NJ, Pak TR. Adolescent binge-pattern alcohol exposure alters genome-wide DNA methylation patterns in the hypothalamus of alcohol-naïve male offspring. Alcohol. 2017;**60**:179-189

[11] Verhoeff B. Fundamental challenges for autism research: The science–practice gap, demarcating autism and the unsuccessful search for the neurobiological basis of autism. Medicine, Health Care, and Philosophy. 2015;**18**(3):443-447. DOI: 10.1007/s11019-015-9636-7

[12] Williams, Z and Lewis, B. DSM-5 Symptom Checklist for Adult Autism Diagnosis. Available from: https://www.researchgate.net/publication/353909455_DSM-5_Symptom_Checklist_for_Adult_Autism_Diagnosis

[13] Jagaroo V, Santangelo S. Neurophenotypes: Advancing Psychiatry and Neuropsychology in the "OMICS" Era. 1st ed. Springer; 2017

[14] Bhandari R, Paliwal JK, Kuhad A. Neuropsychopathology of autism Spectrum disorder: Complex interplay of genetic, epigenetic, and environmental

factors. Advances in Neurobiology. 2020;**24**:97-141

[15] Picci G, Scherf KS. A two-hit model of autism: Adolescence as the second hit. Clinical Psychological Science. 2015;**3**(3):349-371

[16] Weyrauch D, Schwartz M, Hart B, Klug MG, Burd L. Comorbid mental disorders in fetal alcohol Spectrum disorders: A systematic review. Journal of Developmental & Behavioral Pediatrics. 2017;**38**(4):283-291

[17] Carpita B, Migli L, Chiarantini I, Battaglini S, Montalbano C, Carmassi C, et al. Autism Spectrum disorder and fetal alcohol Spectrum disorder: A literature review. Brain Sciences. 2022;**12**(6):792

[18] Dietrich O, Heun M, Notroff J, Schmidt K, Zarnkow M. The role of cult and feasting in the emergence of Neolithic communities. New evidence from Göbekli Tepe, South-Eastern Turkey. Antiquity. 2012;**86**(333):674-695

[19] Wall TL, Ehlers CL. Genetic influences affecting alcohol use among Asians. Alcohol Health and Research World. 1995;**19**(3):184-189

[20] McGovern PE, Zhang J, Tang J, Zhang Z, Hall GR, Moreau RA, et al. Fermented beverages of pre- and proto-historic China. Proceedings of the National Academy of Sciences of the United States of America. 2004;**101**(51):17593-17598

[21] Sweatt JD, Tamminga CA. An epigenomics approach to individual differences and its translation to neuropsychiatric conditions. Dialogues in Clinical Neuroscience. 2016;**18**(3):289-298

[22] Lussier AA, Bodnar TS, Matthew M, Morin AM, Martin H, Kobor MS, et al. Prenatal alcohol exposure: Profiling developmental DNA methylation patterns in central and peripheral tissues. Frontiers in Genetics. 2018;**9**

[23] Wiśniowiecka-Kowalnik B, Nowakowska BA. Genetics and epigenetics of autism spectrum disorder—Current evidence in the field. Journal of Applied Genetics. 2019;**60**:37-47

[24] van de Leemput J, Hess JL, Glatt SJ, Tsuang MT. Genetics of schizophrenia: Historical insights and prevailing evidence. Advances in Genetics. 2016;**96**:99-141

[25] Kuehner JN, Bruggeman EC. Wen Zhexing, Yao Bing. Epigenetic regulations in neuropsychiatric disorders. Frontiers in. Genetics. 2019;**10**:4

[26] Georgieff M, Tran P, Carlson E. Atypical fetal development: Fetal alcohol syndrome, nutritional deprivation, teratogens, and risk for neurodevelopmental disorders and psychopathology. Development and Psychopathology. 2018;**30**(3):1063-1086

[27] Zhou Q, Song L, Chen J, et al. Association of Preconception Paternal Alcohol Consumption with Increased Fetal Birth Defect Risk. JAMA Pediatrics. 2021;**175**(7):742-743

[28] Hagan JF Jr, Balachova T, Bertrand J, Chasnoff I, Dang E, Fernandez-Baca D, et al. Neurobehavioral disorder associated with prenatal alcohol exposure workgroup; American Academy of Pediatrics. Neurobehavioral disorder associated with prenatal alcohol exposure. Pediatrics. 2016;**138**(4):e20151553

[29] Lauren R, Alicia G-G. Genetic causes and modifiers of autism Spectrum disorder. Frontiers in Cellular

Neuroscience. 2019;**13**. Available from: https://www.frontiersin.org/articles/10.3389/fncel.2019.00385/full

[30] Rich SD, Riley LJ. Neurodevelopmental disorder associated with prenatal alcohol exposure: Consumer protection and the Industry's duty to warn. In: Nelson M, Trussler M, editors. Fetal Alcohol Spectrum Disorders in Adults: Ethical and Legal Perspectives. International Library of Ethics, Law, and the New Medicine. Vol. 63. Cham: Springer; 2016

[31] Choate P, Badry D, Bagley K. The alcohol industry and social responsibility: Links to FASD. International Journal of Environmental Research and Public Health. 2022;**19**(13):7744

[32] National Association of Attorneys General. Master Settlement Agreement, 1998. Available from: https://www.naag.org/our-work/naag-center-for-tobacco-and-public-health/the-master-settlement-agreement/

[33] Centers for Disease Control and Prevention, Vital Signs. 2016. Available from: https://www.cdc.gov/vitalsigns/pdf/2016-02-vitalsigns.pdf

Chapter 8

Human Endogenous Retroviruses in Autism Spectrum Disorders: Recent Advances and New Perspectives at the Gene-Environment Interface

Emanuela Balestrieri, Chiara Cipriani, Enrico Garaci, Claudia Matteucci and Paola Sinibaldi-Vallebona

Abstract

Human endogenous retroviruses (HERVs) are genetic elements, derived from their exogenous retroviral counterpart by a process of germline infection and proliferation within the human genome, and their integration as proviruses led to the fixation and the vertical transmission, following Mendelian laws. HERVs currently make up ~8% of the genetic material, and some of them have been cooped for physiological functions. Otherwise, their activation in response to environmental factors has been associated with human pathological conditions. In the setting of neurodevelopmental disorders, HERVs have been proposed as contributing factors involved in Autism Spectrum Disorders (ASD), spanning the bridge between genetic susceptibility, environmental risk factors and immune response. We described a distinct expression profile of some HERV families and cytokines in lymphocytes from autistic children and in their mothers suggesting a close mother-child association in ASD. Moreover, *in vitro* treatment with an antiretroviral drug was able to restore the expression level of HERVs and cytokines providing new insights into the potential role of HERVs as biomarkers of ASD and raising the possibility of using HERVs expression as a therapeutic target for a tailored approach to patient care.

Keywords: human endogenous retroviruses; HERVs, biomarker, mother-child association, gene expression, aetiology, antiretrovirals

1. Introduction

In 1943, the child psychiatrist Leo Kanner described children preferring loneliness with repetitive patterns of behaviour. Similar symptoms were reported by Hans Asperger, an Austrian paediatrician, in 1944 mainly in people of high intelligence [1]. Kanner, first spoke about 'childhood or early-onset schizophrenia', and later he called this condition 'infantile autism', and concerning the aetiology of autism, he attributed autism to a lack of maternal warmth and attachment. Following this hypothesis, Bruno Bettelheim with his book 'The Empty Fortress' popularized the theory of 'refrigerator mother' by stating that 'the infant that misreads the mother's actions or feelings, or correctly assesses her negative feelings, may retreat from her and the world'. This view was widely criticized and nowadays represents an obsolete thought [2]. From this time, many hypotheses and models emerged to explain this complex condition focusing on symptomatology, phenotype and pathogenesis [3, 4]. However, despite many promising hypotheses, the current literature is made up of controversial findings and lacking of definitive proof about the mechanism underlying the complex aethiopathogenesis of Autism Spectrum Disorder (ASD). ASD is currently referred to as a pervasive neurodevelopmental disorder with an impact on emotional and social behaviour that persists throughout life [5]. The clinical presentation is very heterogeneous, and its incidence is continuously increasing [6]. Despite the consolidated evidence that the main contribution to the increase in the incidence of autism comes from the improvement of the diagnostic process, it has also been hypothesized that at the basis of the onset of autism, there is not a single cause but a set of risk factors acting together to produce the phenotype. Decades of studies have indeed shown that autism is a complex pathology influenced by the combination of genetic, environmental and epigenetic factors, mainly acting during prenatal and/or perinatal phases [7–9]. The concordance rate of ASD in monozygotic twins much higher than in dizygotic twins seemed to indicate that genetic factors were more likely to contribute to ASD than environmental factors [10]. More than a thousand ASD-associated genes known to be involved in brain development have been identified to date [11], and many genomic copy number variants have been associated with neurodevelopmental disorders including ASD [12, 13]. Several epidemiological studies indicate that potential risk factors for ASD also include various determinants [14, 15], such as the age of the pregnant woman, advancing paternal age [14, 16, 17] and prematurity [18]. However, an ever increasing important role has been attributed to risk factors related to the early foetal environment, including toxicants, diet, air pollution, smoking or chemicals exposure, which have been suggested to induce a prenatal and/or perinatal brain insult able to contribute to the development of autism in genetically predisposed individuals [19]. These environmental insults share in common the activation of the maternal immune system (MIA), which has therefore been recognized as an additional risk factor for ASD [20]. MIA is an inflammatory response triggered by pathogenic infection and autoimmune diseases in the mother. It is known that several microorganisms, vertically transmitted to the foetus, affect its development resulting in severe complications such as miscarriage and malformations [21]. However, even non-vertically transmitted infections during pregnancy can cause harm to the offspring by producing inflammatory cytokines, which directly damage the foetal brain by crossing the placental and blood-brain barrier [22, 23].

Preclinical studies, using mouse model of MIA induced by prenatal exposure to polyinosinic:polycytidylic acid (Poly I:C), a synthetic double-stranded RNA molecule targeting TLR-3, mimicking viral maternal infection, demonstrated that the exposure to a prenatal insult induced derailed neurodevelopment in offspring. Particularly, in the mothers, the Poly I:C injection leads to the production of interleukin-17 that reaches the foetal brain *via* the placenta inducing cell death and decreasing synaptic density and expression levels of synapse formation-associated proteins and resulting in ASD-like behavioural and morphological brain abnormalities, also described in the pathophysiology of human ASD [24–26]. In line with the hypothesis that maternal immune response could impact on neurodevelopment in the newborn, epidemiological studies have reported that MIA, caused by autoimmune diseases, also increases the risk of ASD [27]. Altogether these studies suggest that MIA-induced inflammation and cytokines can impair placental function and lead to the disruption of its barrier function, resulting in exposure of the foetus to toxic substances. Accumulated evidence also shows an important role of epigenetic factors, such as DNA methylation, histone modification and noncoding RNA in predisposition to disease development. Epigenetic mechanisms regulate chromatin structure and gene expression without altering the DNA sequence. In consideration of this last characteristic, in the past it was believed to have no role in the growth and development of the individual [28] while the study of their interaction with environmental conditions has highlighted their important role in the development of genes related to brain development. In recent years, there have been rapid advances in the understanding of epigenetic mechanisms that ultimately regulate gene activity and expression during development and differentiation or in response to environmental stimuli. Instead, it is now known that the main function of epigenetic factors is to regulate development through cell differentiation processes, tissue specification and maintenance of cell lineages [29]. Therefore, environmental stimuli can alter the epigenome and consequently gene transcription, changing the phenotype [30].

Within this interplay among genetic susceptibility, MIA, epigenetic and environmental factors are placed the human endogenous retroviruses (HERVs), which we proposed as novel contributing factors involved in ASD.

2. Human endogenous retroviruses and their co-evolution with the host

In contrast to the prevailing early twentieth century conception of genetic material as fixed, in the 1940s, the Nobel Prize Barbara McClintock discovered in maize the 'mutable loci' which were capable to move between chromosomes. This pioneering study paved the way for future research into the role of these 'jumping genes' or transposable elements (TEs) in both health and disease conditions [31]. Indeed, it was later discovered that about 46% of the human genome consists of TEs [32]. They consist of repetitive sequences that are able to insert copies of themselves elsewhere in the genome [33]. They are divided, according to their size and functionally related structures, into short interspersed elements (SINEs), long interspersed elements (LINEs), long terminal repetition retrotransposons (LTR) and DNA transposons [34]. The major subset of LTR retrotransposons is represented by HERVs, which together with their derivative sequences comprise at least 8% of the human genome [32, 35].

These elements have their origin in the numerous environmental events that shaped the human genome during evolution, including the occasional infection of germ cells of our ancestors by exogenous retroviruses and the insertion of their RNA genome as proviruses into the cell's chromosomal DNA [36]. Hence, HERVs are transmitted in a Mendelian manner to all subsequent generations (**Figure 1a**). Retroviral proviruses share the canonical structure of retroviruses consisting of an internal region of four essential viral genes (gag, pro, pol and env), flanked at either side by long terminal repeats sequences (the 5′ and 3′ LTRs) that are identical at the time of integration and contain promoter, enhancer and polyadenylation signals that shape the cellular transcriptome (**Figure 1a**) [37].

A non-coding sequence containing a tRNA-specifc primer-binding site (PBS) is usually present between the end of the 5′ LTR and the first codon of the gag gene,

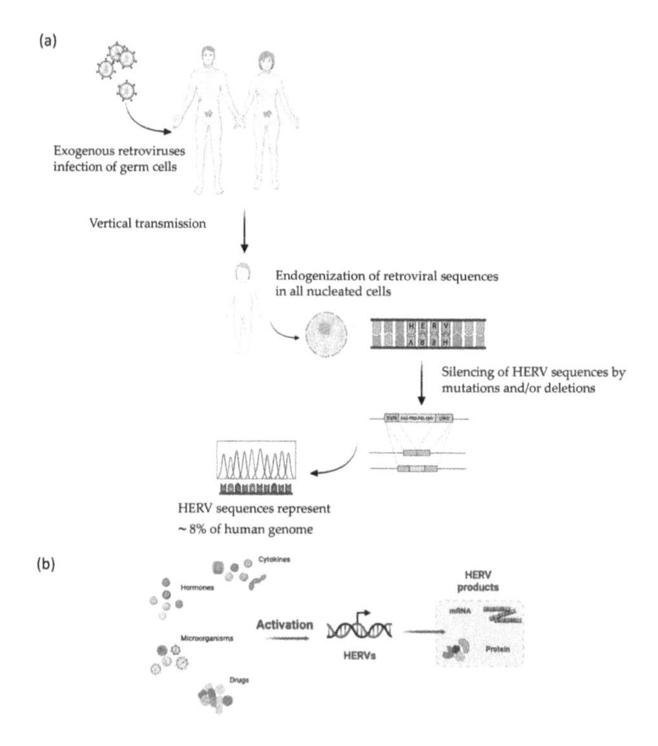

Figure 1.
HERV origin (a) and their activation in response to environmental stimuli (b) (created by BioRender).

and HERVs are classified into families on the basis of the tRNA that binds to the viral primer-binding site to prime reverse transcription.

During human evolution, HERVs invaded the human genome undergoing amplification, retrotransposition and/or reinfection events, and resulting in the presence of multiple copies fixed in the DNA of all nucleated cells [36]. While a majority of these sequences have accumulated mutations and/or deletions and are mostly defective, several HERVs preserve the properties of the ancient viruses and, still being transcriptionally active and competent to produce some retroviral proteins, have been co-opted for physiological functions [36, 38, 39] (**Figure 1a**). In the light of the current knowledge, what Weiss stated in 2016 'If Charles Darwin reappeared today, he might be surprised to learn that humans are descended from viruses as well as from apes' [40] is still current.

3. The role of human endogenous retroviruses in physiological conditions

For a long time, HERVs have been considered as junk DNA with no impact on the host. However, during the last decades, the great efforts of the scientific community highlighted that some 'well preserved' ERV sequences influence different physiological properties being involved in a variety of biological pathways [41, 42]. The most intriguingly example of the co-option of HERVs during the host evolution comes from the well-studied properties of the syncytins, the products of the Envelope (Env) genes of HERV-W-1 and HERV-FRD. Specifically, Syncytin-1, encoded by the HERV-W-1 gene, is the first retroviral protein found to have a defined physiological function mediating the cell-cell fusion as the terminal differentiation of the trophoblast lineage [43]. As emerging from different reports, the decrease of syncytin expression and the consequential fusion deficiency could contribute to placental anomalies including pre-eclampsia disorder [44]. Moreover, other studies suggested that syncytin-1 also possesses non-fusogenic activities, as the regulation of trophoblast proliferation and apoptosis and indicated a widely expression in different cell types such as granulocytes, T lymphocytes, monocytes, glial cell of the brain and cancer cells [45, 46]. In human, syncytin-1 interacts with the type D mammalian retrovirus receptor ASCT-1/ASCT-2 (sodium-dependent neutral amino acid transporter type 1/2) on cell membranes. Syncytin-2, encoded by the HERV-FRD gene, is also expressed in trophoblasts and able of mediating cell fusion by interacting with a different receptor known as MFSD2 (major facilitator superfamily domain containing 2) [47, 48]. Moreover, Syncytin-2 is involved in maternal immune tolerance towards the semi-allogenic foetus [49]. A similar functional domestication emerged for ERV-encoded GAG gene, involved in the memory consolidation in the mammalian brain, including long-term potentiation and depression [50]. Given the abundance of HERVs in the human genome, they represent an important source of genomic variability, also providing potential coding and regulatory elements for the acquisition of new cellular functions [51, 52]. In line, growing evidence has been obtained regarding the general expression of HERVs in normal tissues [53, 54], and in this context, we demonstrated an age-related transcriptional activity of HERV-H, HERV-K and HERV-W in peripheral blood mononuclear cells (PBMCs) from a large cohort of healthy human subjects aged between 1 and 80 years, reinforcing the hypothesis of a physiological correlation between HERV activity and the different stages of life in human [55]. Among the proposed mechanisms by which HERVs could contribute to the human physiology, it is recognized that various sequences, concentrated in the LTRs, are involved in the regulation of the expression of neighbouring genes acting as promoters, enhancers, polyadenylation signals, regulators of chromatin folding and binding sites for transcriptional factors [56, 57]. In the genome, most HERVs reside as solo-LTRs, resulting from homologous recombination between the LTRs of a full-length HERV [58] able to act as alternative tissue-specific promoters to drive the expression of host genes [59–61]. During embryo development, some HERV sequences are also engaged by the host for the regulation of gene expression [62]. In particular, non-coding RNA expressed by the HERV-H group and the recruitment of specific cellular transcriptional factors on HERV-H LTRs seem to be involved in the conservation of stem cell identity [57, 63]. Of note, the HERV-H loci seem to be more preserved in a full-length state than other HERV families, suggesting that the full-length elements rather than solo-LTRs are useful to the host and that the internal regions of HERV-H may be involved in the process of exaptation [64]. Similarly, an ancestral env gene named HEMO [human endogenous MER34 (medium reiteration-frequency-family-34) ORF] has been found highly expressed in embryos, already in the early stages of development and in all subsequent differentiation periods as well as in the placenta and in the blood of pregnant women [65]. Finally, in the regulation of stem cell function, HERV-K ENV was highly expressed in the cell membrane of pluripotent stem cells and signals *via* direct binding to CD98HC, leading to activation of signalling pathways that regulate stem cell function [66]. Moreover, the expression of HERVs has a direct key role for the maintenance of human embryonic stem cells and induced pluripotent stem cells (iPSCs), and their activation could be considered a marker of pluripotency [67].

To conclude, the more profound insight into the mechanisms explaining the roles of HERVs in various biological/physiological contexts will help to clarify the contribution of HERVs in pathological conditions.

4. The activation of human endogenous retroviruses

In addition to their physiological role, HERVs have been also proposed as possible cofactors in the aetiology of several human diseases. Proviruses are known to remain dormant for long periods of time within the host, but they may occasionally be triggered by factors present in the environment. Indeed, one of the peculiar features of HERVs is their intrinsic responsiveness to microenvironmental stress and various stimuli likely *via* epigenetic mechanisms [68, 69]. Epigenetics represents a fine mechanism to control HERV activity to ensure genomic stability and integrity and, on the other side, it represents one of the mechanisms by which HERVs could modulate the gene expression. HERV sequences are epigenetically silenced by DNA methylation and histone modifications in addition to being located in chromosomal regions with heterochromatic chromatin architecture leading to a low transcriptional degree in most cell types [70, 71]. It is known that epigenetics is a driver of the embryonic development, contributing to global remodeling, cell commitment and tissue specification [72] and that ERVs are highly active during early embryogenesis and germline development [62, 73]. Indeed, they are involved in the pre-implantation transcription network although the mechanisms are still unclear [62, 74]. Thus, during a sensitive phase, as the embryogenesis, any environmental insults could have an impact on the development, and epigenetic modifications could directly link the environmental stimuli and the molecular regulatory pathways, explaining some aspects of complex pathologies including HERV activation. A multitude of environmental factors and xenobiotics can activate HERV expression causing DNA rearrangements, HERV reinsertions and HERV copy number variation, resulting in abnormal HERV activity that could, in turn, potentially affect crucial pathway such as inflammation [69, 75, 76]. Microorganisms, cytokines, hormones, vitamins, nutrients and drugs could represent triggers leading to HERV transactivation (**Figure 1b**). Of particular relevance is the role played by the interaction with microbes, including viruses, exogenous retroviruses, intestinal microbiota and protozoan. Among viruses, the herpesviruses, Hepatitis B virus, the human immunodeficiency virus-1 (HIV-1), Influenza A virus and more recently SARS-CoV-2 have been found able to deregulate HERV activity and although so far, an unequivocal pathogenic cause-effect relationship has not been established, their contribution to the development of viral diseases, including virus-associated tumors, has been suggested [77–83]. Moreover, several *in vitro* studies demonstrated that cells express HERVs at high levels in response to stimulation by using lipopolysaccharide or interferon-γ (IFN-γ), cytokines as Interleukine-1β (IL-1β) and tumor necrosis factor-α (TNF-α) or mitogens, such as phytohemagglutinin [84–86]. These observations could be due to the fact that HERVs showed various regulatory sequences that have been linked to the transcriptional modulation systems [87]. More recently, the hormonal regulation of HERVs has been investigated, and specifically, cross talks among the female sex hormones and HERVs in contributing to breast cancer tumorigenesis and proliferation have been elucidated providing useful knowledge for the development of novel cancer therapies. Specifically, the effect of progesterone on HERV-K expression is at least partly mediated by OCT4 known to be involved in embryogenesis and expressed in diverse cancer types as well [88]. These findings were in line with the peculiar expression of HERVs in peripheral leukocytes during the menstrual cycle suggesting a well-coordinated hormonal regulation of HERV activity [89]. Also, drugs are able to modulate HERV expression, both *in vitro* and *in vivo* with different proposed mechanisms, mainly linked to the epigenetic one. In particular, neuroleptics and antidepressants influence HERV activity in human brain cell lines and in post-mortem brain samples of patients with mental disorders in therapy during their lifetime [90].

Thus, HERVs have been found particularly responsive to environmental stimuli that can determine their dysregulation at transcriptional levels and/or encoded protein expression that could influence the onset of complex diseases.

5. The contribution of human endogenous retroviruses in disease development

HERV expression is tightly controlled in normal adult tissues but is reported to be aberrantly expressed in cancer [68], inflammatory and autoimmune diseases [91], aging [92], type 1 diabetes [93] neurological disorders [94] and recently also viral disease [83, 95, 96]. Most of the diseases in which HERVs play a role as cofactor are characterized by a multifactorial aetiology and an inflammatory landscape. As such, HERVs have been proposed as spanning the bridge between environment and genetic background and as shapers of the immune system.

5.1 Human endogenous retroviruses as shapers of the immune system

HERVs can modulate the human immune response by different mechanism. In fact, being integrated as proviruses within the genome and physiologically expressed, HERV antigens can be recognized by the innate immune system as 'self-determinants' but also as potential pathogens. Probably due to their similarity with exogenous viral proteins they are able to activate pathogen recognition receptors (PRRs) by evoking the production of pro-inflammatory mediators (such as IFN, cytokines and chemokines), which in turn can activate and trigger the adaptive immune response [42]. Moreover, the involvement of HERVs in the host antiviral immune system seems to be linked to the Interferon pathway by acting as enhancer elements to directly affect the expression of adjacent interferon-stimulated genes [53, 54, 97]. Since HERVs are an integral part of host immunity, they protect the host from exogenous retroviral infections by PRRs, of which a major class are the Toll-like receptors (TLRs), the first line of defence in detecting a wide variety of pathogens. TLRs' engagements with viral components lead to the activation of MAP kinase and NF-kB resulting in the production of pro-inflammatory cytokines, involved in the infection control. It is also known that HERV RNAs are able to activate the immune system, thus stimulating the production of pro-inflammatory cytokines, which in turn can activate and prime the adaptive immune response [42]. This mechanism could be explained by the presence of transcriptional regulatory elements within retroviral long terminal repeats LTRs [98, 99]. This feedback loop made by HERV upregulation, inflammatory mediators and epigenetic dysregulation could be one way in which HERVs could have pathogenic potential leading to chronic stimulation of the immune system that could sustain the development and/or the progression of several human diseases.

5.2 The role of human endogenous retroviruses in neuroinflammatory and neuropsychiatric disorders

Outdated scientific evidence has reported the possibility of different viruses such as herpesviruses, HIV and Ebola virus to reach the central nervous system (CNS) contributing to the development of diseases. As such, despite the inaccessibility of CNS and the immunological structure that makes it a 'privileged district', the viral replication can occur by exceeding controls and can also happen multiple times during an individual's lifetime increasing the risk of developing neuropathologies [100]. In the last few decades, many researchers demonstrated that the activation of endogenous viral sequences in response to exogenous stimuli, especially viruses, can contribute to a variety of neuroinflammatory and neuropsychiatric disorders, including multiple sclerosis (MS), amyotrophic lateral sclerosis (ALS), schizophrenia (SCZ) and bipolar disorder (BD). The pathways in which retroelements are involved in derailment of the nervous system are diverse: HERVs mainly interact with innate and adaptive immunity [52, 101], LINE activity is linked to neurogenesis, in particular neuronal differentiation and cognitive processes, both in adult brain and in progenitor cells [102, 103], and Alu elements, the most common member of SINEs, are involved in neurogenesis, brain development and cognition pathways [102, 104]. The first paper describing the involvement of HERVs in neurological disorders, especially in MS, dates back to the late 1900s when Perron and colleagues discovered retroviral elements in the leptomeningeal cells of MS patients [105]. From this initial work, several studies succeeded, both *in vitro* and *in vivo*, culminating in the identification of an aetiopathogenetic model in which HERV-W was further revealed to play functional roles in inflammatory processes. Specifically, pro-inflammatory cytokine expression was shown to be induced in both human and murine monocytes upon *in vitro* stimulation with HERV-W recombinant Env protein by a process that required TLR-4 receptor activation [69]. In line with these intriguingly findings, several research groups have contributed to the topic, focusing on different aspects concerning the role of HERVs of the aetiology and/or progression of the disease. MS is a neurodegenerative and neuroinflammatory disease affecting CNS in which it causes multifocal demyelinating lesions leading to physical and cognitive impairments and despite the plethora of studies, definitive proof regarding the aetiology being still lacking. In this setting, HERV-W Env protein has been extensively studied and to date has been recognized as a contributor factor in the MS pathogenesis. As such, the expression level of HERV-W in the brain of MS patients positively correlates with the severity of the clinical signs [106]. Moreover, the env transcripts and proteins of HERV-W are overexpressed in the brain [107] and in peripheral blood and serum of MS patients [108, 109] as a constant imprinting of the disease. Another important aspect characterizing the role of HERVs in MS is the interplay of HERVs with the immune system. Indeed, HERVs can stimulate both the production of pro-inflammatory mediators and innate and adaptive immune cells, which in turn could affect endothelial cells of the blood-brain barrier as well as oligodendroglial precursor and microglial cells [94]. Another pathological condition in which HERV activity has been investigated is ALS, a progressive nervous system disease that affects nerve cells in the brain and spinal cord, causing loss of muscle control. ALS is also characterizing by an imbalance of the immunological mediators with a marked production of inflammatory cytokines. The first demonstration of the involvement of a HERV was the discovery of the activation of HERV-K (subtype HML-2) in the brains of individuals with ALS [110, 111]. Subsequently, the reverse transcriptase activity of

DOI: http://dx.doi.org/10.5772/intechopen.108671

HERV-K was identified in brain, cerebrospinal fluid (CSF) and blood of ALS patients [112, 113], and the expression of HML-2 Env transcripts and protein was found in cortical and anterior horn cells of the spinal cord samples [114]. Although there is consistent evidence linking HML-2 to ALS, very little is known about the mechanisms by which it may cause observed neurotoxicity. Recently, the neurotoxicity of HML-2 Env was clarified in transgenic animals that express the envelope protein developing an ALS-like syndrome. Interestingly, these observations provide the possibility to use HERV-K env-specific antibody in preclinical models to prevent Env toxicity and pave the way for new treatment strategies in sporadic ALS [115]. Schizophrenia, a major neuropsychiatric disorder, is a chronic brain disorder, and when active, symptoms include delusions, hallucinations, trouble with thinking and concentration and lack of motivation [5]. While disease onset typically occurs in late adolescence or early adulthood, several lines of evidence suggest that SCZ results from aberrations occurring in foetal development [116]. Furthermore, growing evidence demonstrates the increased risk of SCZ following early-life exposure to infectious agents or inflammatory stimuli, suggesting the involvement of the immune system in the aetiopathogenesis of the disease [117]. The strongest evidence for an association between HERV and SCZ comes from studies of HERV transcripts in the brain, cerebrospinal fluid and blood samples from affected individuals in which elevated levels of HERV-H, HERV-K and HERV-W were detected [72, 118, 119]. HERV-W Env protein expression in hippocampus was recently shown to alter the N-methyl-d-aspartate receptor-mediated synaptic organization and plasticity leading to defective glutamate synapse maturation, behavioural impairments and psychosis [120]. In addition, the epigenetic status of HERV-K sequences, particularly lower methylation levels in blood samples, has been indicated as marker of the early stages of SCZ [119]. Similarly, HERV-W transcripts and proteins were found to be elevated in the blood, CSF and brains of BD patients [118, 121, 122]. BD is a group of brain disorders that cause extreme fluctuation in a person's mood, energy and ability to function [5]. The precise aetiopathology of BD is unclear, and several reports indicate the involvement of the innate and adaptive immune system including inflammation [123]. Notably, an association between HERV-W Env protein, an increased level of IL-1β and an earlier disease onset was described in BD patients with respect to patients who were negative for HERV-W Env protein, suggesting HERV-W as marker able to define a specific group of patients in bipolar condition [122].

6. Human endogenous retroviruses in neurodevelopmental disorders

The first article pioneering the hypothesis of the possible involvement of HERVs in the aetiopathogenesis of neurodevelopmental disorders was published by us 10 years ago. Specifically, we hypothesized a link between HERV activity and ASD highlighting a distinct expression profile in Italian autistic children in which HERV-H was highly expressed in peripheral lymphocytes, when compared with controls, with higher levels in younger children, supporting the hypothesis that HERV-H overexpression might be regarded as a potential early biomarker of ASD. This view was even more supported by the fact that ASD children with more severe impairments in Communication and Motor Psychoeducational Profile-3 showed the highest expression levels of HERV-H [124]. The analysis of HERV expression profile was then replicated in a cohort of Albanian ASD children who showed HERV-H high expression level in peripheral lymphocytes as already found in Italian ASD children. This allowed us to conclude that HERV-H could be considered as a molecular signature of the disease unrelated to ethnicity [125]. These findings opened a challenging scenario to extend the study to a cohort of attention deficit hyperactivity disorder (ADHD) children in order to verify whether the peculiar HERV expression profile could also be identified in a 'twin disorder' of ASD. Indeed, the two disorders are highly correlated [126], and ADHD often occurs in conjunction with ASD [127]. ADHD children showed the highest expression levels of HERV-H in peripheral lymphocytes correlated with inattention and hyperactivity symptoms, suggesting HERV-H a molecular biomarker also for ADHD [128]. All the evidence emerged from these initial papers was always obtained by studying drug-naïve children considering that, as indicated at the time by other research groups, HERV activity could be strongly influenced by drugs exposure [90]. And it is from all of this that the subsequent work arose, in which the intention was to evaluate HERV-H as a potential biomarker of response to treatment in ADHD patients undergoing methylphenidate (MPH) therapy. As such, the reduction of HERV-H expression levels H in peripheral lymphocytes from ADHD children was found after only 1 week of MPH therapy with a further decrease at 24 weeks of treatments in parallel with improvement in symptoms. These findings suggested HERV-H as a predictive marker of the response to MPH therapy despite the awareness that the absence of a non-responsive patient group is a major limitation of this research preventing definitive conclusions [129]. The validation of early results about HERV expression profile in ASD children and new evidence came from a paper we published in 2019 in which we also included the parents of children in order to investigate the parent-of-origin effects in ASD in terms of HERVs and immune deregulation. ASD children and their mothers shared common expression levels of HERV-H and HEMO and of the cytokines such as TNF-α, IFN-γ and IL-10 in peripheral lymphocytes. Therefore, the abnormal expression of HERVs and cytokines was not an exclusive trait of autistic patients but also of their mothers, suggesting a close mother-child association within the ASD families. Taken together, these findings support the potential use of selected HERVs and cytokines in a set of biomarkers that accounts for the multifaceted nature of the disorder and can complement existing clinical methods [130]. A subgroup of this cohort was also used to conduct a proof of concept study in which lymphocytes from ASD children and their parents were exposed to stimulating factors (Interleukin-2/Phytohaemagglutinin) or drugs, such as the antiepileptic drug valproic acid (VPA) and the antiretroviral drug efavirenz (EFV) with the intent to investigate whether the expression level of HERVs and cytokines could be modulated. Lymphocytes from ASD children and their mothers share intrinsic responsiveness to stimulating factors and VPA in expressing HERVs and cytokines. EFV specifically restored the HERV activity with a concomitant modulation of cytokines, in particular lowering the pro-inflammatory while maintaining high regulatory ones. This evidence provided new insights into the potential role of HERVs as biomarkers of ASD and raising the possibility of using HERV expression as a therapeutic target for a tailored approach to patient care [86].

With the intent of deciphering other factors linked to HERV activity that could contribute to ASD pathogenesis, the expression of epigenetic effectors known to regulate HERV expression and brain functions has been evaluated in ASD children. The authors found a correlation among the overexpression of these elements and several HERVs suggesting their involvement in pathogenetic mechanisms leading to ASD [131]. All the studies above described were conducted using peripheral lymphocytes from ASD cohorts in agreement with the findings of various research studies that there is a shared gene expression profile between whole blood and brain tissues, suggesting that the cautious and thoughtful use of peripheral gene expression may be a useful surrogate for analysis in the brain. Of course, the brain remains the district of choice for studying neurodevelopmental alterations and to circumvent the issue, different preclinical models of ASD have been developed enabling studies on the aetiology, pathogenesis and possible prevention and treatment modalities of ASD. The main categories of models comprise genetic animal models, idiopathic strain, models of infection/inflammation and chemically induced animal models displaying robust and well-replicated social deficits and repetitive behaviours [132]. The idiopathic strain BTBR T+tf/J (BTBR) and the prenatally CD-1 VPA-induced models of ASD have been extensively studied to characterize the expression profile of ERV and immune mediators. As such, whole embryos at about half of gestation, brain and blood tissues at different postnatal ages have been analysed. Both ASD models showed higher expression levels of ERVs beginning from intrauterine life and up to adulthood (**Figure 2**). Moreover, the aberrant expression of some ERV families correlated with expression levels of pro-inflammatory cytokines and TLR-3 and TLR-4 in embryos and brain tissues, supporting the interplay between ERVs and neuroinflammation as contributing factors in the appearance of ASD-like phenotype [133]. Subsequently, we conceived a study to evaluate the multigenerational impact of prenatal VPA exposure, demonstrating transgenerational changes in both behaviour and ERV expression that last, with fading of epigenetic memories across generations, till the third one that lacks a direct exposure

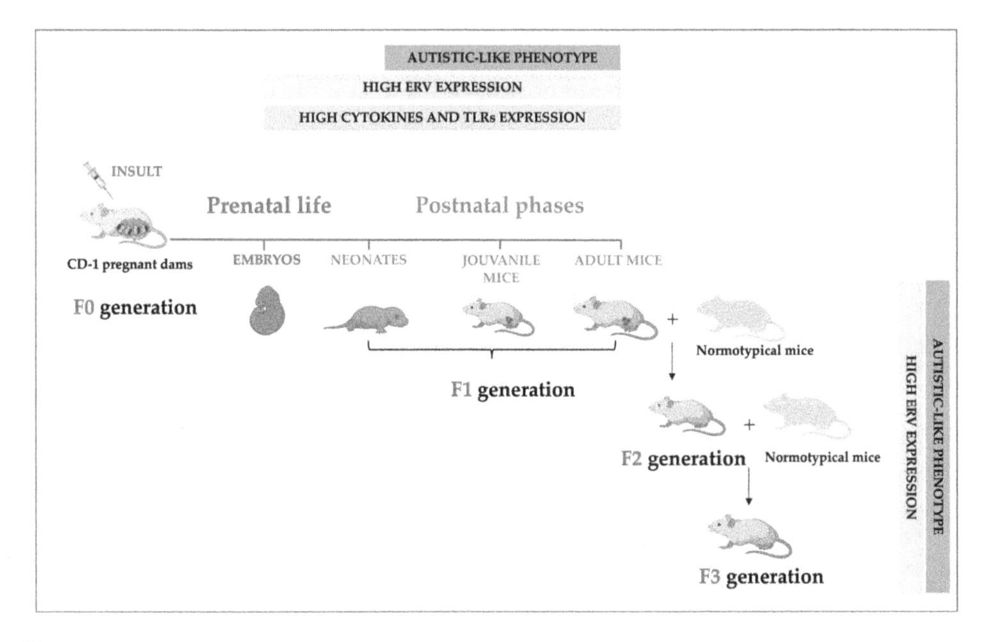

Figure 2.
The abnormal ERV, cytokines and TLRs expression in mice with autistic-like phenotype prenatally exposed to valproic acid (created by BioRender).

to the drug (**Figure 2**). Of note, offspring from maternal lineages showed more marked transcriptional effects compared with paternal lineages both in the second and in third generations suggesting the hypothesis of maternal imprinting as a contributing factor in increasing susceptibility to ASD [134]. Moreover, these findings also suggest ERV blood transcriptional levels as a stable peripheral biomarker, even at early life stages, of derailed brain development [135]. In our last paper, we demonstrated that MIA induced abnormal expression of ERVs and immune mediators in mouse off-spring in a sex-dependent fashion. Specifically, we demonstrated that the prenatal exposure to Poly I:C in C57BL6/J mice induced a tissue-specific expression of several ERVs, ERV-related genes and inflammatory mediators with ERVs as the main carriers of the peculiar profile found in brain areas from Poly I:C mice. In addition, Poly I:C induced larger effects on the expression of some retroviral elements only in pre-frontal cortex from female offspring reinforcing the view on sex bias as a possible risk factor for ASD [136].

Taken together, these findings candidate ERV activation as common feature shared by several risk factors of appearance of ASD and suggest ERVs as main carriers of changes occurring in brain from autistic mice, primarily in female offspring. These papers could represent the starting point to set up a new preclinical experimental design to verify the chance to inhibit ERV activity to rescue ERV activation, immune dysregulation and ASD-like phenotype observed in offspring trying to figure out cause and effect in this complex interplay. Moreover, a deep characterization of the molecular mechanisms by which gender differences could affect the neurodevelopment will help in identifying gender-specific diagnosis and personalized treatment strategies.

7. Human endogenous retroviruses: from aetiological to therapeutic implications in neurological diseases

Given the now well-established knowledge regarding the implication of HERVs in different pathological conditions, new avenues for the development of targeted therapies directed against HERV products have been opened. In this direction, a humanized monoclonal antibody (mAb) directed against HERV-W ENV, called GNbAC1 or temelimab, has been developed. The drug targets a linear non-glycosylated epitope of the surface unit domain of the HERV-W Env, blocking its interaction with the TLR-4 receptor and thus, the release of pro-inflammatory mediators and the inhibition of the myelin repair process. Different *in vitro* and preclinical studies offered promising results that culminated in clinical trials in which temelimab has been proposed as novel drug for MS treatment first to test pharmacokinetics, safety and efficacy providing encouraging results about its neuroprotective and regenerative effects in parallel with antiretroviral effects, which does not impair the immune system [137, 138]. Starting from the observations that also in type 1 diabetes (T1D) patients, HERV-W Env has been detected in blood and pancreatic acinar cells and after different reports concerning the activity of temelimab in *in vivo* and *in vitro* models of T1D [139], this drug was offered to patients as a part of a clinical trial to test the safety and its effect on the autoimmune process. Also in the case, the drug was well tolerated and reduced the events of hypoglycaemia and the levels of anti-insulin autoantibodies after the first period of treatment [139, 140]. More recently, the same research group proposed an anti-HERV-K Env mAb for the treatment of ALS. In addition to the antibody-based immunotherapy targeting HERV ENV, also the use of antiretroviral drugs has been evaluated in different setting, ranging from the *in vitro* studies to clinical trials, opening new prospects for exploring novel treatments of diseases such as MS [141]. The underlying rationale is that patients with HIV treated with antiretroviral drugs have a lower risk of developing MS than non-infected, healthy population thus suggesting that the antiretroviral treatment may reduce the risk of evolving MS also acting on HERV expression [141, 142]. Also in the treatment of patients with ALS the use of antiretroviral drugs has been proposed. As such, a recent clinical trial including a combination of antiretroviral drug has been conducted showing a decrease in HERV-K expression as well as of disease markers when administered to patients. Remarkably, a high percentage of patients were classified as 'responsive' to treatment reinforcing even more the role of HERV-K in the clinical course of the disease [143, 144].

Taken together, these findings provide the background for hypothesizing other therapeutic approaches targeting HERVs in different clinical setting towards a personalized medicine.

8. Conclusions and new future perspectives

The physiological roles of HERVs in pregnancy and embryogenesis, their intrinsic responsiveness to external stimuli and the interaction with the immune

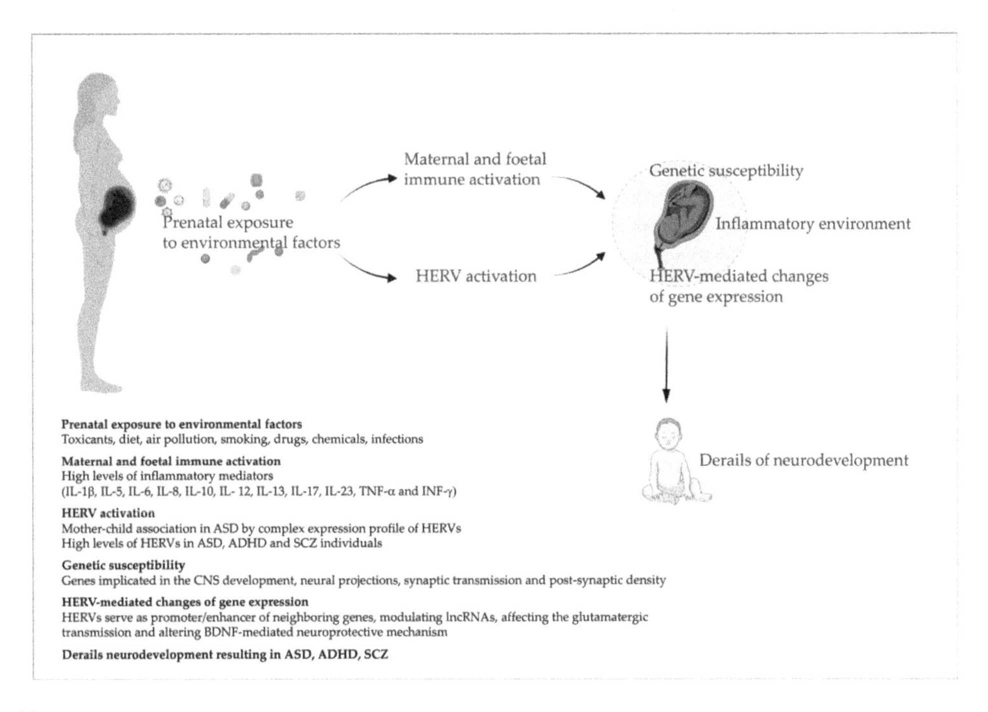

Figure 3.
The potential involvement of human endogenous retroviruses (HERVs) in the interaction among genetic susceptibility, environmental risk factors and immune activation in complex neurodevelopmental disorders (created by BioRender).

system support the hypothesis that their deregulation affects the neurodevelopmental process (**Figure 3**). Nevertheless, it is still debated if HERVs are cofactors or epiphenomenon in neurodevelopmental disorders, and more efforts are needed to investigate the potentially detrimental effect of HERV products in the aetiopathogenic processes. In this complex landscape, the use of animal models could offer countless advantages to deeply investigate the embryonic phase that is certainly crucial for the onset of ASD, and brain district, mostly inaccessible in human studies. Since the brain remains the district of choice for the study of neurodevelopmental alterations, preclinical models of ASD allow to explore and characterize this anatomical district in depth, helping clinical research to make further progress towards the identification of new biomarkers, potentially useful for diagnosis and pharmacological intervention. Moreover, HERVs seem to be a reliable biomarker for ASD, readily detectable in peripheral blood, representing a potential efficient diagnostic tool to complement the current clinical behavioural diagnosis. Furthermore, a biomarker detectable before the onset of symptoms could facilitate early screening and timely initiation of treatment by improving the long-term prognosis of the mental health of affected individuals. Further studies are needed and could represent a new approach to unravel the aethiopathogenesis of ASD, bearing in mind that the retroelements cannot be appropriately understood only through a virologic or genetic approach, since their complex roles in physiology as well in diseases. Both preclinical models and human studies indicate that the abnormal expression of ERVs could represent a molecular signature of neurodevelopmental disorders.

Conflict of interest

The authors declare no conflict of interest

Author details

Emanuela Balestrieri[1*], Chiara Cipriani[1], Enrico Garaci[2,3], Claudia Matteucci[1] and Paola Sinibaldi-Vallebona[1,4]

1 Department of Experimental Medicine, University of Rome Tor Vergata, Rome, Italy

2 University San Raffaele, Rome, Italy

3 IRCCS San Raffaele Pisana, Rome, Italy

4 Institute of Translational Pharmacology, National Research Council, Rome, Italy

*Address all correspondence to: balestrieri@med.uniroma2.it

References

[1] Simon BC. Leo Kanner, Hans Asperger and the discovery of autism. The Lancet. 2015;**386**(10001):1329-1330

[2] Klin A. Autismo e síndrome de Asperger: uma visão geral [Autism and Asperger syndrome: An overview]. Braz J Psychiatry. 2006;**28**(1):S3-S11

[3] Betancur C. Etiological heterogeneity in autism spectrum disorders: More than 100 genetic and genomic disorders and still counting. Brain Research. 2011;**1380**:42-77

[4] Inui T, Kumagaya S, Myowa-Yamakoshi M. Neurodevelopmental Hypothesis about the Etiology of Autism Spectrum Disorders. Frontiers in Human Neuroscience. 2017;**11**:354

[5] American Psychiatric Association [APA]. Neurodevelopmental disorders. In: Diagnostic and Statistical Manual of Mental Disorders. Washington, DC: APA; 2013. pp. 31-86

[6] Maenner MJ, Shaw KA, Bakian AV, et al. Prevalence and characteristics of autism spectrum disorder among children aged 8 years - autism and developmental disabilities monitoring network, 11 Sites, United States, 2018. MMWR Surveillance Summary. 2021;**70**(11):1-16

[7] Abrahams BS, Geschwind DH. Advances in autism genetics: On the threshold of a new neurobiology. Nature Review Genetics. 2008;**9**(5):341-355

[8] Landrigan PJ, Lambertini L, Birnbaum LS. A research strategy to discover the environmental causes of autism and neurodevelopmental disabilities. Environmental Health Perspectives. 2012;**120**(7):a258-a260

[9] Lyall K, Croen L, Daniels J, Fallin MD, Ladd-Acosta C, Lee BK, et al. The changing epidemiology of autism spectrum disorders. Annual Review of Public Health. 2017;**38**:81-102

[10] Bailey A, Le Couteur A, Gottesman I, Bolton P, Simonoff E, Yuzda E, et al. Autism as a strongly genetic disorder: Evidence from a British twin study. Psychological Medicine. 1995;**25**(1):63-77

[11] Yoon SH, Choi J, Lee WJ, Do JT. Genetic and epigenetic etiology underlying autism spectrum disorder. Journal of Clinical Medicine. 2020;**9**(4):966

[12] Chawner SJRA, Doherty JL, Anney RJL, et al. A genetics-first approach to dissecting the heterogeneity of autism: Phenotypic comparison of autism risk copy number variants. American Journal of Psychiatry. 2021;**178**(1):77

[13] Douard E, Zeribi A, Schramm C, Tamer P, Loum MA, Nowak S, et al. Effect sizes of deletions and duplications on autism risk across the genome. The American Journal of Psychiatry. 2021;**178**(1):87-98

[14] Durkin MS, Maenner MJ, Newschaffer CJ, Lee LC, Cunniff CM, Daniels JL, et al. Advanced parental age and the risk of autism spectrum disorder. American Journal of Epidemiology. 2008;**168**(11):1268-1276

[15] Atladóttir HO, Thorsen P, Østergaard L, Schendel DE, Lemcke S, Abdallah M, et al. Maternal infection requiring hospitalization during pregnancy and autism spectrum disorders. Journal of Autism

and Developmental Disorders. 2010;**40**(12):1423-1430

[16] Croen LA, Najjar DV, Fireman B, Grether JK. Maternal and paternal age and risk of autism spectrum disorders. Archives of Pediatrics & Adolescent Medicine. 2007;**161**(4):334-340

[17] Sandin S, Hultman CM, Kolevzon A, Gross R, MacCabe JH, Reichenberg A. Advancing maternal age is associated with increasing risk for autism: A review and meta-analysis. Journal of American Academy Child Adolescence Psychiatry. 2012;**51**(5):477-486

[18] Allen L, Leon-Attia O, Shaham M, Shefer S, Gabis LV. Autism risk linked to prematurity is more accentuated in girls. PLoS One. 2020;**15**(8):e0236994

[19] Doi M, Usui N, Shimada S. Prenatal environment and neurodevelopmental disorders. Frontiers in Endocrinology. 2022;**12**:860110

[20] Estes ML, McAllister AK. Maternal immune activation: Implications for neuropsychiatric disorders. Science. 2016;**353**(6301):772-777

[21] Meyer U. Neurodevelopmental resilience and susceptibility to maternal immune activation. Trends in Neurosciences. 2019;**42**(11):793-806

[22] Knuesel I, Chicha L, Britschgi M, Schobel SA, Bodmer M, Hellings JA, et al. Maternal immune activation and abnormal brain development across CNS disorders. Nature Reviews. Neurology. 2014;**10**(11):643-660

[23] Massarali A, Adhya D, Srivastava DP, Baron-Cohen S, Kotter MR. Virus-induced maternal immune activation as an environmental factor in the etiology of autism and schizophrenia. Frontiers in Neuroscience. 2022;**16**:834058

[24] Choi GB, Yim YS, Wong H, Kim S, Kim H, Kim SV, et al. The maternal interleukin-17a pathway in mice promotes autism-like phenotypes in offspring. Science. 2016;**351**(6276):933-939

[25] Shin Yim Y, Park A, Berrios J, Lafourcade M, Pascual LM, Soares N, et al. Reversing behavioural abnormalities in mice exposed to maternal inflammation. Nature. 2017;**549**(7673):482-487

[26] Pendyala G, Chou S, Jung Y, Coiro P, Spartz E, Padmashri R, et al. Maternal immune activation causes behavioral impairments and altered cerebellar cytokine and synaptic protein expression. Neuropsychopharmacology. 2017;**42**(7):1435-1446

[27] Jain S, Baer RJ, McCulloch CE, Rogers E, Rand L, Jelliffe-Pawlowski L, et al. Association of maternal immune activation during pregnancy and neurologic outcomes in offspring. Journal of Pediatrics. 2021;**238**:87-93

[28] Goldberg AD, Allis CD, Bernstein E. Epigenetics: A landscape takes shape. Cell. 2007;**128**(4):635-638

[29] LaSalle JM, Powell WT, Yasui DH. Epigenetic layers and players underlying neurodevelopment. Trends in Neurosciences. 2013;**36**(8):460-470

[30] Toraño EG, García MG, Fernández-Morera JL, Niño-García P, Fernández AF. The impact of external factors on the epigenome: In utero and over lifetime. BioMed Research International. 2016;**2016**:2568635

[31] Mcclintock B. The origin and behavior of mutable loci in maize. Proceedings of the National Academy of Sciences of the United States of America. 1950;**36**(6):344-355

[32] Lander ES, Linton LM, Birren B, Nusbaum C, Zody MC, et al. International Human Genome Sequencing Consortium. Initial sequencing and analysis of the human genome. Nature. 2001;**409**(6822):860-921

[33] Lanciano S, Cristofari G. Measuring and interpreting transposable element expression. Nature Reviews. Genetics. 2020;**21**(12):721-736

[34] Deininger PL, Moran JV, Batzer MA, Kazazian HH Jr. Mobile elements and mammalian genome evolution. Current Opinion in Genetics & Development. 2003;**13**(6):651-658

[35] Medstrand P, van de Lagemaat LN, Dunn CA, Landry JR, Svenback D, Mager DL. Impact of transposable elements on the evolution of mammalian gene regulation. Cytogenetic and Genome Research. 2005;**110**(1-4):342-352

[36] Bannert N, Kurth R. The evolutionary dynamics of human endogenous retroviral families. Annual Review of Genomics and Human Genetics. 2006;**7**:149-173

[37] Coffin JM, Hughes SH, Varmus HE. The interactions of retroviruses and their hosts. In: Coffin JM, Hughes SH, Varmus HE, editors. Retroviruses. Cold Spring Harbor (NY): Cold Spring Harbor Laboratory Press; 1997. pp. 335-341

[38] Löwer R, Löwer J, Kurth R. The viruses in all of us: Characteristics and biological significance of human endogenous retrovirus sequences. Proceedings of the National Academy of Sciences of the United States of America. 1996;**93**(11):5177-5184

[39] Bannert N, Kurth R. Retroelements and the human genome: New perspectives on an old relation. Proceedings of the National Academy of Sciences of the United States of America. 2004;**101**(2):14572-14579

[40] Weiss RA. Human endogenous retroviruses: Friend or foe? APMIS. 2016;**124**(1-2):4-10

[41] Greenwood AD, Ishida Y, O'Brien SP, Roca AL, Eiden MV. Transmission, evolution, and endogenization: Lessons learned from recent retroviral invasions. Microbiology and Molecular Biology Reviews. 2017;**82**(1):e00044-e00017

[42] Grandi N, Tramontano E. Human endogenous retroviruses are ancient acquired elements still shaping innate immune responses. Frontiers in Immunology. 2018;**9**:2039

[43] Blond JL, Lavillette D, Cheynet V, Bouton O, Oriol G, Chapel-Fernandes S, et al. An envelope glycoprotein of the human endogenous retrovirus HERV-W is expressed in the human placenta and fuses cells expressing the type D mammalian retrovirus receptor. Journal of Virology. 2000;**74**(7):3321-3329

[44] Cui L, Wang H, Lu X, Wang R, Zheng R, Li Y, et al. Effects of individually silenced N-glycosylation sites and non-synonymous single-nucleotide polymorphisms on the fusogenic function of human syncytin-2. Cell Adhesion & Migration. 2016;**10**(1-2):39-55

[45] Huang Q, Li J, Wang F, Oliver MT, Tipton T, Gao Y, et al. Syncytin-1 modulates placental trophoblast cell proliferation by promoting G1/S transition. Cellular Signalling. 2013;**25**(4):1027-1035

[46] Huang Q, Chen H, Wang F, Brost BC, Li J, Gao Y, et al. Reduced syncytin-1 expression in choriocarcinoma BeWo

cells activates the calpain1-AIF-mediated apoptosis, implication for preeclampsia. Cellular and Molecular Life Sciences. 2014;**71**(16):3151-3164

[47] Marin M, Lavillette D, Kelly SM, Kabat D. N-linked glycosylation and sequence changes in a critical negative control region of the ASCT1 and ASCT2 neutral amino acid transporters determine their retroviral receptor functions. Journal of Virology. 2003;**77**(5):2936-2945

[48] Cheynet V, Oriol G, Mallet F. Identification of the hASCT2-binding domain of the Env ERVWE1/syncytin-1 fusogenic glycoprotein. Retrovirology. 2006;**3**:41

[49] Lokossou AG, Toudic C, Nguyen PT, Elisseeff X, Vargas A, Rassart É, et al. Endogenous retrovirus-encoded Syncytin-2 contributes to exosome-mediated immunosuppression of T cells. Biology of Reproduction. 2020;**102**(1):185-198

[50] Pastuzyn ED, Day CE, Kearns RB, Kyrke-Smith M, Taibi AV, McCormick J, et al. The neuronal gene arc encodes a repurposed retrotransposon gag protein that mediates intercellular RNA transfer. Cell. 2018;**172**(1-2):275-288

[51] Jern P, Coffin JM. Effects of retroviruses on host genome function. Annual Review of Genetics. 2008;**42**:709-732

[52] Chuong EB, Elde NC, Feschotte C. Regulatory activities of transposable elements: From conflicts to benefits. Nature Reviews. Genetics. 2017;**18**(2):71-86

[53] Ehlhardt S, Seifert M, Schneider J, Ojak A, Zang KD, Mehraein Y. Human endogenous retrovirus HERV-K(HML-2) Rec expression and transcriptional activities in normal and rheumatoid arthritis synovia. The Journal of Rheumatology. 2006;**33**(1):16-23

[54] Schmitt K, Heyne K, Roemer K, Meese E, Mayer J. HERV-K(HML-2) rec and np9 transcripts not restricted to disease but present in many normal human tissues. Mobile DNA. 2015;**6**:4

[55] Balestrieri E, Pica F, Matteucci C, Zenobi R, Sorrentino R, Argaw-Denboba A, et al. Transcriptional activity of human endogenous retroviruses in human peripheral blood mononuclear cells. BioMed Research International. 2015;**2015**:164529

[56] Buzdin A, Kovalskaya-Alexandrova E, Gogvadze E, Sverdlov E. At least 50% of human-specific HERV-K (HML-2) long terminal repeats serve in vivo as active promoters for host nonrepetitive DNA transcription. Journal of Virology. 2006;**80**(21):10752-10762

[57] Wang J, Xie G, Singh M, Ghanbarian AT, Raskó T, Szvetnik A, et al. Primate-specific endogenous retrovirus-driven transcription defines naive-like stem cells. Nature. 2014;**516**(7531):405-409

[58] Hughes JF, Coffin JM. Human endogenous retrovirus K solo-LTR formation and insertional polymorphisms: Implications for human and viral evolution. Proceedings of the National Academy of Sciences of the United States of America. 2004;**101**(6):1668-1672

[59] Ting CN, Rosenberg MP, Snow CM, Samuelson LC, Meisler MH. Endogenous retroviral sequences are required for tissue-specific expression of a human salivary amylase gene. Genes & Development. 1992;**6**(8):1457-1465

[60] Bièche I, Laurent A, Laurendeau I, Duret L, Giovangrandi Y, Frendo JL, et al.

Placenta-specific INSL4 expression is mediated by a human endogenous retrovirus element. Biology of Reproduction. 2003;**68**(4):1422-1429

[61] Dunn CA, Medstrand P, Mager DL. An endogenous retroviral long terminal repeat is the dominant promoter for human beta1,3-galactosyltransferase 5 in the colon. Proceedings of the National Academy of Sciences of the United States of America. 2003;**100**(22):12841-12846

[62] Grow EJ, Flynn RA, Chavez SL, Bayless NL, Wossidlo M, Wesche DJ, et al. Intrinsic retroviral reactivation in human preimplantation embryos and pluripotent cells. Nature. 2015;**522**(7555):221-225

[63] Glinsky GV. Transposable elements and DNA methylation create in embryonic stem cells human-specific regulatory sequences associated with distal enhancers and noncoding RNAs. Genome Biology and Evolution. 2015;**7**(6):1432-1454

[64] Gemmell P, Hein J, Katzourakis A. Phylogenetic analysis reveals that ERVs "Die Young" but HERV-H is unusually conserved. PLoS Computational Biology. 2016;**12**(6):e1004964

[65] Heidmann O, Béguin A, Paternina J, Berthier R, Deloger M, Bawa O, et al. HEMO, an ancestral endogenous retroviral envelope protein shed in the blood of pregnant women and expressed in pluripotent stem cells and tumors. Proceedings of the National Academy of Sciences of the United States of America. 2017;**114**(32):E6642-E6651

[66] Wang T, Medynets M, Johnson KR, Doucet-O'Hare TT, DiSanza B, Li W, et al. Regulation of stem cell function and neuronal differentiation by HERV-K via mTOR pathway. Proceedings of the National Academy of Sciences of the United States of America. 2020;**117**(30):17842-17853

[67] Göke J, Ng HH. CTRL+INSERT: Retrotransposons and their contribution to regulation and innovation of the transcriptome. EMBO Reports. 2016;**17**(8):1131-1144

[68] Matteucci C, Balestrieri E, Argaw-Denboba A, Sinibaldi-Vallebona P. Human endogenous retroviruses role in cancer cell stemness. Seminars in Cancer Biology. 2018;**53**:17-30

[69] Perron H, Lang A. The human endogenous retrovirus link between genes and environment in multiple sclerosis and in multifactorial diseases associating neuroinflammation. Clinical Reviews in Allergy and Immunology. 2010;**39**(1):51-61

[70] Schulz WA, Steinhoff C, Florl AR. Methylation of endogenous human retroelements in health and disease. Current Topics in Microbiology and Immunology. 2006;**310**:211-250

[71] Turelli P, Castro-Diaz N, Marzetta F, Kapopoulou A, Raclot C, Duc J, et al. Interplay of TRIM28 and DNA methylation in controlling human endogenous retroelements. Genome Research. 2014;**24**(8):1260-1270

[72] Li F, Sabunciyan S, Yolken RH, Lee D, Kim S, Karlsson H. Transcription of human endogenous retroviruses in human brain by RNA-seq analysis. PLoS One. 2019;**14**(1):e0207353

[73] Göke J, Lu X, Chan YS, Ng HH, Ly LH, Sachs F, et al. Dynamic transcription of distinct classes of endogenous retroviral elements marks specific populations of early human embryonic cells. Cell Stem Cell. 2015;**16**(2):135-141

[74] Fu B, Ma H, Liu D. Endogenous retroviruses function as gene expression regulatory elements during mammalian pre-implantation embryo development. International Journal of Molecular Sciences. 2019;**20**(3):790

[75] Perron H, Dougier-Reynaud HL, Lomparski C, Popa I, Firouzi R, Bertrand JB, et al. Human endogenous retrovirus protein activates innate immunity and promotes experimental allergic encephalomyelitis in mice. PLoS One. 2013;**8**(12):e80128

[76] Zhang M, Liang JQ, Zheng S. Expressional activation and functional roles of human endogenous retroviruses in cancers. Reviews in Medical Virology. 2019;**29**(2):e2025

[77] Chen J, Foroozesh M, Qin Z. Transactivation of human endogenous retroviruses by tumor viruses and their functions in virus-associated malignancies. Oncogene. 2019;**8**(1):6

[78] Ruprecht K, Obojes K, Wengel V, Gronen F, Kim KS, Perron H, et al. Regulation of human endogenous retrovirus W protein expression by herpes simplex virus type 1: Implications for multiple sclerosis. Journal of Neurovirology. 2006;**12**(1):65-71

[79] Leung A, Trac C, Kato H, Costello KR, Chen Z, Natarajan R, et al. LTRs activated by Epstein-Barr virus-induced transformation of B cells alter the transcriptome. Genome Research. 2018;**28**(12):1791-1798

[80] Charvet B, Reynaud JM, Gourru-Lesimple G, Perron H, Marche PN, Horvat B. Induction of proinflammatory multiple sclerosis-associated retrovirus envelope protein by human herpesvirus-6A and CD46 receptor engagement. Frontiers in Immunology. 2018;**9**:2803

[81] Young GR, Terry SN, Manganaro L, Cuesta-Dominguez A, Deikus G, Bernal-Rubio D, et al. HIV-1 infection of primary CD4+ T cells regulates the expression of specific human endogenous retrovirus HERV-K (HML-2) elements. Journal of Virology. 2017;**92**(1):e01507-e01517

[82] Li F, Nellåker C, Sabunciyan S, Yolken RH, Jones-Brando L, Johansson AS, et al. Transcriptional derepression of the ERVWE1 locus following influenza A virus infection. Journal of Virology. 2014;**88**(8):4328-4337

[83] Balestrieri E, Minutolo A, Petrone V, Fanelli M, Iannetta M, Malagnino V, et al. Evidence of the pathogenic HERV-W envelope expression in T lymphocytes in association with the respiratory outcome of COVID-19 patients. eBioMedicine. 2021;**66**:103341

[84] Johnston JB, Silva C, Holden J, Warren KG, Clark AW, Power C. Monocyte activation and differentiation augment human endogenous retrovirus expression: Implications for inflammatory brain diseases. Annals of Neurology. 2001;**50**(4):434-442

[85] Mommert M, Tabone O, Oriol G, Cerrato E, Guichard A, Naville M, et al. LTR-retrotransposon transcriptome modulation in response to endotoxin-induced stress in PBMCs. BMC Genomics. 2018;**19**(1):522

[86] Cipriani C, Giudice M, Petrone V, Fanelli M, et al. Modulation of human endogenous retroviruses and cytokines expression in peripheral blood mononuclear cells from autistic children and their parents. Retrovirology. 2022. DOI: 10.1186/s12977-022-00603-6

[87] Ito J, Sugimoto R, Nakaoka H, Yamada S, Kimura T, Hayano T, et al. Systematic identification and characterization of

regulatory elements derived from human endogenous retroviruses. PLoS Genetics. 2017;**13**(7):e1006883

[88] Nguyen TD, Davis J, Eugenio RA, Liu Y. Female sex hormones activate human endogenous retrovirus Type K through the OCT4 transcription factor in T47D breast cancer cells. AIDS Research and Human Retroviruses. 2019;**35**(3):348-356

[89] Mueller O, Moore DW, Giovannucci J, Etter AR, Peterson EM, Mudge A, et al. Expression of human endogenous retroviruses in peripheral leukocytes during the menstrual cycle suggests coordinated hormonal regulation. AIDS Research and Human Retroviruses. 2018;**34**(11):909-911

[90] Diem O, Schäffner M, Seifarth W, Leib-Mösch C. Influence of antipsychotic drugs on human endogenous retrovirus (HERV) transcription in brain cells. PLoS One. 2012;**7**(1):e30054

[91] Greenig M. HERVs, immunity, and autoimmunity: Understanding the connection. PeerJ. 2019;**7**:e6711

[92] Gorbunova V, Seluanov A, Mita P, McKerrow W, Fenyö D, Boeke JD, et al. The role of retrotransposable elements in ageing and age-associated diseases. Nature. 2021;**596**(7870):43-53

[93] Levet S, Charvet B, Bertin A, Deschaumes A, Perron H, Hober D. Human endogenous retroviruses and type 1 diabetes. Current Diabetes Reports. 2019;**19**(12):141

[94] Küry P, Nath A, Créange A, Dolei A, Marche P, Gold J, et al. Human endogenous retroviruses in neurological diseases. Trends in Molecular Medicine. 2018;**24**(4):379-394

[95] Römer C. Viruses and endogenous retroviruses as roots for neuroinflammation and neurodegenerative diseases. Frontiers in Neuroscience. 2021;**15**:648629

[96] van der Kuyl AC. HIV infection and HERV expression: A review. Retrovirology. 2012;**9**:6

[97] Wang M, Wang L, Liu H, Chen J, Liu D. Transcriptome analyses implicate endogenous retroviruses involved in the host antiviral immune system through the interferon pathway. Virologica Sinica. 2021;**36**(6):1315-1326

[98] Manghera M, Douville RN. Endogenous retrovirus-K promoter: A landing strip for inflammatory transcription factors? Retrovirology. 2013;**10**:16

[99] Hurst TP, Magiorkinis G. Activation of the innate immune response by endogenous retroviruses. The Journal of General Virology. 2015;**96**(Pt 6):1207-1218

[100] Louveau A, Harris TH, Kipnis J. Revisiting the mechanisms of CNS immune privilege. Trends in Immunology. 2015;**36**(10):569-577

[101] Chuong EB, Elde NC, Feschotte C. Regulatory evolution of innate immunity through co-option of endogenous retroviruses. Science. 2016;**351**(6277):1083-1087

[102] Baillie JK, Barnett MW, Upton KR, Gerhardt DJ, Richmond TA, De Sapio F, et al. Somatic retrotransposition alters the genetic landscape of the human brain. Nature. 2011;**479**(7374):534-537

[103] Coufal NG, Garcia-Perez JL, Peng GE, Yeo GW, Mu Y, Lovci MT, et al. L1 retrotransposition in human neural progenitor cells. Nature. 2009;**460**(7259):1127-1131

[104] Mehler MF, Mattick JS. Noncoding RNAs and RNA editing in brain development, functional diversification, and neurological disease. Physiological Reviews. 2007;**87**(3):799-823

[105] Perron H, Geny C, Laurent A, Mouriquand C, Pellat J, Perret J, et al. Leptomeningeal cell line from multiple sclerosis with reverse transcriptase activity and viral particles. Research in Virology. 1989;**140**(6):551-561

[106] Sotgiu S, Mameli G, Serra C, Zarbo IR, Arru G, Dolei A. Multiple sclerosis-associated retrovirus and progressive disability of multiple sclerosis. Multiple Sclerosis. 2010;**16**(10):1248-1251

[107] Perron H, Garson JA, Bedin F, Beseme F, Paranhos-Baccala G, Komurian-Pradel F, et al. Molecular identification of a novel retrovirus repeatedly isolated from patients with multiple sclerosis. The Collaborative Research Group on Multiple Sclerosis. Proceedings of the National Academy of Sciences of the United States of America. 1997;**94**(14):7583-7588

[108] Garson JA, Tuke PW, Giraud P, Paranhos-Baccala G, Perron H. Detection of virion-associated MSRV-RNA in serum of patients with multiple sclerosis. Lancet. 1998;**351**(9095):33

[109] Perron H, Germi R, Bernard C, et al. Human endogenous retrovirus type W envelope expression in blood and brain cells provides new insights into multiple sclerosis disease. Multi Sclerosis. 2012;**18**(12):1721

[110] Viola MV, Frazier M, White L, Brody J, Spiegelman S. RNA-instructed DNA polymerase activity in a cytoplasmic particulate fraction in brains from Guamanian patients. The Journal of Experimental Medicine. 1975;**142**(2):483-494

[111] Li Y, Chen Y, Zhang N, Fan D. Human endogenous retrovirus K (HERV-K) env in neuronal extracellular vesicles: A new biomarker of motor neuron disease. Amyotroph Lateral Scler Frontotemporal Degener. 2022;**23**(1-2):100-107

[112] Alfahad T, Nath A. Retroviruses and amyotrophic lateral sclerosis. Antiviral Research. 2013;**99**(2):180-187

[113] Douville R, Liu J, Rothstein J, Nath A. Identification of active loci of a human endogenous retrovirus in neurons of patients with amyotrophic lateral sclerosis. Annals of Neurology. 2011;**69**(1):141-151

[114] Li W, Lee MH, Henderson L, Tyagi R, Bachani M, Steiner J, et al. Human endogenous retrovirus-K contributes to motor neuron disease. Science Translational Medicine. 2015;**7**(307):307ra153

[115] Steiner JP, Bachani M, Malik N, DeMarino C, Li W, Sampson K, et al. Human endogenous retrovirus K envelope in spinal fluid of amyotrophic lateral sclerosis is toxic. Annals of Neurology. 2022;**92**(4):545-561

[116] Cannon TD, van Erp TG, Bearden CE, Loewy R, Thompson P, Toga AW, et al. Early and late neurodevelopmental influences in the prodrome to schizophrenia: Contributions of genes, environment, and their interactions. Schizophrenia Bulletin. 2003;**29**(4):653-669

[117] Brown AS, Meyer U. Maternal immune activation and neuropsychiatric illness: A translational research perspective. The American Journal of Psychiatry. 2018;**175**(11):1073-1083

[118] Perron H, Hamdani N, Faucard R, Lajnef M, Jamain S, Daban-Huard C, et al. Molecular characteristics of Human Endogenous Retrovirus type-W in schizophrenia and bipolar disorder. Translational Psychiatry. 2012;**2**(12):e201

[119] Mak M, Samochowiec J, Frydecka D, Pełka-Wysiecka J, Szmida E, Karpiński P, et al. First-episode schizophrenia is associated with a reduction of HERV-K methylation in peripheral blood. Psychiatry Research. 2019;**271**:459-463

[120] Johansson EM, Bouchet D, Tamouza R, Ellul P, Morr AS, Avignone E, et al. Human endogenous retroviral protein triggers deficit in glutamate synapse maturation and behaviors associated with psychosis. Science Advances. 2020;**6**:eabc0708

[121] Li W, Lin L, Malhotra R, Yang L, Acharya R, Poss M. A computational framework to assess genome-wide distribution of polymorphic human endogenous retrovirus-K In human populations. PLoS Computational Biology. 2019;**15**(3):e1006564

[122] Tamouza R, Meyer U, Foiselle M, Richard JR, Wu CL, Boukouaci W, et al. Identification of inflammatory subgroups of schizophrenia and bipolar disorder patients with HERV-W ENV antigenemia by unsupervised cluster analysis. Translational Psychiatry. 2021;**11**(1):377

[123] Harrison PJ, Geddes JR, Tunbridge EM. The emerging neurobiology of bipolar disorder. Focus (Am Psychiatr Publ). 2019;**17**(3):284-293

[124] Balestrieri E, Arpino C, Matteucci C, Sorrentino R, Pica F, Alessandrelli R, et al. HERVs expression in autism spectrum disorders. PLoS One. 2012;**7**(11):e48831

[125] Balestrieri E, Cipriani C, Matteucci C, Capodicasa N, Pilika A, Korca I, et al. Transcriptional activity of human endogenous retrovirus in Albanian children with autism spectrum disorders. The New Microbiologica. 2016;**39**(3):228-231

[126] Cross-Disorder Group of the Psychiatric Genomics Consortium. Cross-disorder group of the psychiatric genomics consortium. genomic relationships, novel loci, and pleiotropic mechanisms across eight psychiatric disorders. Cell. 2019;**179**(7):1469-1482

[127] Mellahn OJ, Knott R, Tiego J, Kallady K, Williams K, Bellgrove MA, et al. Understanding the diversity of pharmacotherapeutic management of ADHD with co-occurring autism: An Australian Cross-Sectional Survey. Frontiers in Psychiatry. 2022;**13**:914668

[128] Balestrieri E, Pitzianti M, Matteucci C, D'Agati E, Sorrentino R, Baratta A, et al. Human endogenous retroviruses and ADHD. The World Journal of Biological Psychiatry. 2014;**15**(6):499-504

[129] Cipriani C, Pitzianti MB, Matteucci C, D'Agati E, Miele MT, Rapaccini V, et al. The decrease in human endogenous retrovirus-H activity runs in parallel with improvement in ADHD symptoms in patients undergoing methylphenidate therapy. International Journal of Molecular Sciences. 2018;**19**(11):3286

[130] Balestrieri E, Cipriani C, Matteucci C, Benvenuto A, Coniglio A, Argaw-Denboba A, et al. Children with autism spectrum disorder and their mothers share abnormal expression of selected endogenous retroviruses families and cytokines. Frontiers in Immunology. 2019;**10**:2244

[131] Tovo PA, Davico C, Marcotulli D, Vitiello B, Daprà V, Calvi C, et al. Enhanced expression of human endogenous retroviruses, TRIM28 and SETDB1 in autism spectrum disorder. International Journal of Molecular Sciences. 2022;**23**(11):5964

[132] Ornoy A, Weinstein-Fudim L, Ergaz Z. Prevention or amelioration of autism-like symptoms in animal models: Will it bring us closer to treating human ASD? International Journal of Molecular Sciences. 2019;**20**(5):1074

[133] Cipriani C, Ricceri L, Matteucci C, De Felice A, Tartaglione AM, Argaw-Denboba A, et al. High expression of Endogenous Retroviruses from intrauterine life to adulthood in two mouse models of Autism Spectrum Disorders. Scientific Reports. 2018;**8**(1):629

[134] Tartaglione AM, Cipriani C, Chiarotti F, Perrone B, Balestrieri E, Matteucci C, et al. Early behavioral alterations and increased expression of endogenous retroviruses are inherited across generations in mice prenatally exposed to valproic acid. Molecular Neurobiology. 2019;**56**(5): 3736-3750

[135] Balestrieri E, Matteucci C, Cipriani C, Grelli S, Ricceri L, Calamandrei G, et al. Endogenous retroviruses activity as a molecular signature of neurodevelopmental disorders. International Journal of Molecular Sciences. 2019;**20**(23):6050

[136] Cipriani C, Tartaglione AM, Giudice M, D'Avorio E, Petrone V, Toschi N, et al. Differential expression of endogenous retroviruses and inflammatory mediators in female and male offspring in a mouse model of maternal immune activation. International Journal of Molecular Sciences. 2022;**23**:13930

[137] Curtin F, Perron H, Kromminga A, Porchet H, Lang AB. Preclinical and early clinical development of GNbAC1, a humanized IgG4 monoclonal antibody targeting endogenous retroviral MSRV-Env protein. MAbs. 2015;**7**(1):265-275

[138] Curtin F, Vidal V, Bernard C, Kromminga A, Lang AB, Porchet H. Serum pharmacokinetics and cerebrospinal fluid concentration analysis of the new IgG4 monoclonal antibody GNbAC1 to treat multiple sclerosis: A Phase 1 study. MAbs. 2016;**8**(5):854-860

[139] Curtin F, Bernard C, Levet S, Perron H, Porchet H, Médina J, et al. Simpson R; RAINBOW-T1D investigators. A new therapeutic approach for type 1 diabetes: Rationale for GNbAC1, an anti-HERV-W-Env monoclonal antibody. Diabetes, Obesity & Metabolism. 2018;**20**(9):2075-2084

[140] Curtin F, Champion B, Davoren P, Duke S, Ekinci EI, Gilfillan C, et al. A safety and pharmacodynamics study of temelimab, an antipathogenic human endogenous retrovirus type W envelope monoclonal antibody, in patients with type 1 diabetes. Diabetes, Obesity & Metabolism. 2020;**22**(7):1111-1121

[141] Morandi E, Tanasescu R, Tarlinton RE, Constantin-Teodosiu D, Gran B. Do antiretroviral drugs protect from multiple sclerosis by inhibiting expression of MS-associated retrovirus? Frontiers in Immunology. 2019;**9**:3092

[142] Gold J, Goldacre R, Maruszak H, Giovannoni G, Yeates D, Goldacre M. HIV and lower risk of multiple sclerosis: Beginning to unravel a mystery using a record-linked database study. Journal of Neurology, Neurosurgery, and Psychiatry. 2015;**86**(1):9-12

[143] Gold J, Rowe DB, Kiernan MC, Vucic S, Mathers S, van Eijk RPA, et al. Safety and tolerability of Triumeq in amyotrophic lateral sclerosis: The Lighthouse trial. Amyotrophic Lateral Sclerosis Frontotemporal Degeneration. 2019;**20**(7-8):595-604

[144] Garcia-Montojo M, Fathi S, Norato G, Smith BR, Rowe DB, Kiernan MC, et al. Inhibition of HERV-K (HML-2) in amyotrophic lateral sclerosis patients on antiretroviral therapy. Journal of the Neurological Sciences. 2021;**423**:117358

Chapter 9

Positron Emission Tomography in the Neuroimaging of Autism Spectrum Disorder

Zhiqiang Tan, Weijian Ye, Hao Xu and Lu Wang

Abstract

Autism spectrum disorder (ASD) is a pervasive developmental disease characterized by persistent impairment, repetitive and stereotypical behaviors in social interaction, as well as restricted interests and activities. The etiology of ASD is not clear yet, which results in difficulties in clinical diagnosis and treatment, and also brings heavy burden to patients and society. Positron emission tomography (PET) is a frequently used molecular imaging technology in quantitative, dynamic and in vivo research for therapeutic efficacy evaluation, pathophysiological mechanism investigation, thereby promoting development of ASD therapeutic drugs. More and more imaging studies have been reported on ASD recently, and the physiological changes featured by PET have been disclosed. This chapter reviews the specific radioligands for PET imaging of critical biomarkers involved in ASD. Herein, we discuss cerebral blood perfusion, cerebral glucose metabolism, and neurotransmitter system (transporters, precursors and receptors), as well as some other novel targets, including arginine vasopressin receptor targets and neuroinflammation related targets. The status of application and future prospect of the PET technology in research of ASD were discussed. This chapter provides a detailed and comprehensive literature review on ASD PET probe development, thereby can help readers intuitively and conveniently understand the status quo of research on ASD PET, and develop new research directions in this field.

Keywords: autism spectrum disorder, ASD, neuroimaging, positron emission tomography, PET, radioligands

1. Introduction

Autism spectrum disorder (ASD) is a pervasive developmental disorder characterized by persistently impaired interpersonal communication and social interactions, significantly limited activities and interests, as well as repetitive, stereotyped and limited behaviors. The fifth edition of the Diagnostic and Statistical Manual of Mental Disorders (DSM-5) published in 2013 revolutionized the ASD diagnostic criteria [1], and identified four previously defined pervasive developmental disorders that are now referred to as ASD: pervasive developmental disorder not otherwise specified (PDD-NOS), autistic disorder, childhood disintegrative syndrome (also known as Heller Syndrome), and asperger syndrome (AS). The diagnostic criteria were reduced to two items: social dysfunction, and stereotypical and repetitive behavior. The previous diagnostic criteria including and non-verbal and verbal communication disorders are ascribed to social disorders. These changes have impacted the diagnosis and therapy of a variety of pervasive developmental disorder subtypes, and influenced the comparability and consistency of imaging studies. Each document cited will be marked with "ASD/AS/AutismPDD" according to diagnostic criteria to avoid unnecessary confusion.

The understanding of etiology of idiopathic ASD is still not sufficient, and the current evidence indicates that ASD might be driven by affected synaptic function, cortical networks as well as brain maturations induced by environmental and genetic factor interactions. Obstetric complications and early childhood environmental influences may play critical roles in ASD development [2, 3]. Moreover, children who experience obstetric complications are also more likely to exhibit genetic causation of the disease [4]. The latest large gene study has identified 102 risk genes associated with ASD in human [5]. Most risk genes are closely correlated with neurodevelopment and neurophysiology and are expressed in early stage of brain development, especially in inhibitory and excitatory neurons, consistent with ASD-associated excitation/inhibition imbalances.

Currently, ASD diagnosis is mainly based on clinical evaluation and medical history of patients as well as medical history of patients' families. Autism Diagnostic Interview Revised (ADI-R), a structured interview for patients' family members [6], and the Autism Diagnostic Observation Schedule (ADOS), a play-based interview for children and their families or high-functioning children, adolescents, or adults [7] are two collection tools for medical history data, which are considered gold standard for clinical ASD diagnosis. ASD patients' clinical evaluation mainly includes neurological and physical examinations [8], as well as neuroimaging. Though no specific biomarkers can be used for ASD diagnose thus far, neuroimaging techniques have exhibited potentials for explaining signs and symptoms in ASD [9], and have been applied in elucidation of pathophysiologic mechanisms underlying ASD-related abnormalities in neurotransmitter system, blood perfusion, and brain glucose metabolism in the past decades. Therefore, neuroimaging techniques will act as important tools in ASD diagnosis, therapeutics and efficacy evaluation.

2. Positron emission tomography

Positron emission tomography (PET) detects processes associated with the metabolism and distribution of positron emitting radionuclide-labeled probes *in vivo*. The commonly used radionuclides include ^{11}C ($T_{1/2} \sim 20.4$ min), ^{18}F ($T_{1/2} \sim 109.8$ min), ^{13}N ($T_{1/2} \sim 10.0$ min) and ^{15}O ($T_{1/2} \sim 2.0$ min). It should be noted that radionuclides with short half-lives, such as ^{11}C ($T_{1/2} \sim 20.4$ min) and ^{15}O ($T_{1/2} \sim 2.0$ min), can only be used with onsite cyclotrons at tertiary medical centers. With the probe distribution in the body, nuclear decay occurs, emitting positrons, which collide with electrons surrounding to generate two gamma photons (511 keV each) in a 180° reverse manner. The gamma photon signals detected are then processed by computer software to generate three-dimensional images [10]. Compared to magnetic resonance imaging (MRI) and single photon emission computed tomography (SPECT), PET has significant advantages in spatial resolution, sensitivity, and time efficiency, and therefore is much more advantageous quantification of substantial parameters including protein synthesis rate, enzyme activity and receptor density, glucose metabolic rate, and gene expression.

Based on radioactive probe, PET imaging technology has dramatic advantages in detection a variety of receptors, transporters, metabolites, enzymes, as well as drugs. With microdose, PET tracers can be applied in preclinical and early clinical studies to investigate in vivo drug physiological performance, pharmacodynamics and pharmacokinetics, target occupancy, providing critical information for clinical trials [11]. PET probe can be used for both clinical diagnose and evaluation. More than 1000 PET probes have been developed and applied in numerous fields including labeling of metabolic analogs or substrates including fatty acids, amino acids, and glucose, the [12], labeling specific proteins, such as transporters or receptors [13, 14], as well as labeling in signal transduction, immunological features, hypoxia, angiogenesis, apoptosis and genes [15, 16]. PET probes as effective neuroimaging tools have high binding specificity and affinity, good brain penetration ability, and a good distribution volume and metabolic stability. **Table 1** lists the main ASD research targets and the corresponding PET probes.

3. PET molecular imaging in ASD

The development of PET has provided noninvasive and dynamic technical support for the study of ASD *in vivo* [17]. Though the pathology and etiology of ASD remain unclear, during the past decades, PET has been widely applied in many fields of ASD research, and substantial valuable information and evidence has been obtained [18–26].

The neuroimaging studies on ASD have been reviewed in several articles with different focuses [25–28]. Some focused on the state of ASD imaging research [26, 27]. Others focused on the application of specific neuroimaging techniques [28]. With the development of ASD PET probes, the newly research results need to be updated. In this review, we discuss neurotransmitter system (receptors, precursors, and transporters), cerebral blood perfusion, cerebral glucose metabolism, as well as some new research targets including arginine vasopressin receptor targets and neuroinflammation related targets. The current application and future prospect of PET technology in ASD research were discussed through summarizing both clear ASD pathophysiological mechanism and unclear research conclusions. This review provides a detailed comprehensive literature review on ASD PET probe development, thereby can help readers intuitively and conveniently understand the status quo of research on ASD PET more, and develop new research directions in this field.

3.1 Cerebral glucose metabolism

Glucose is the main energy source of brain cells, therefore, glucose metabolism can reflect brain function changes. [^{18}F]fluorodeoxyglucose ([^{18}F]FDG) is glucose analog, and can be taken up by brain cells, however, [^{18}F]FDG cannot be used in glycolysis due to the absence of oxygen at site 2, therefore, [^{18}F]FDG can be used to reflect glucose uptake and distribution in brain cells [29]. [^{18}F]FDG is therefore very valuable in ASD PET research due to its excellent imaging characteristics, including a long half-life, short scanning time, mature preparation process, and relatively simple scanning process [25].

Brain glucose metabolism has been most frequently studied in ASD PET. Most studies have focused on changes in brain glucose metabolism in ASD patients. However, no consistent conclusion has been drawn FDG metabolism changes in ASD

Target	PET probe	Chemical formula	Clinical application
Glucose	[^{18}F]FDG	$C_6H_{11}{}^{18}FO_5$	Y
CBF	[^{15}O]H2O	$H_2{}^{15}O$	Y
	[^{15}O]CO2	$CO^{15}O$	Y
	[^{11}C]butanol	$C_2{}^{11}CH_8O$	Y
5-HT precursor	[^{11}C]AMT	$C_{11}{}^{11}CH_{14}N_2O_2$	Y
5-HTT	[^{11}C](+)McN5652	$C_{18}{}^{11}CH_{21}NS$	Y
	[^{11}C]DASB	$C_{15}{}^{11}CH_{17}N_3S$	Y
	[^{11}C]MADAM	$C_{15}{}^{11}CH_{20}N_2S$	Y
	[^{18}F]FMeNER-d2	$C_{18}H_{18}D_2{}^{18}FNO_3$	Y
	[^{11}C]ADAM	$C_{14}{}^{11}CH_{17}IN_2S$	N
	[^{11}C]DAPA	$C_{14}{}^{11}CH_{17}BrN_2S$	N
	[^{11}C]AFM	$C_{15}{}^{11}CH_{19}FN_2S$	N
5-HT_{2A}R	[^{18}F]setoperone	$C_{21}H_{24}{}^{18}FN_3O_2S$	Y
	[^{11}C]MDL100907	$C_{22}H_{18}{}^{18}FNO_3$	Y
	[^{18}F]altanserin	$C_{22}H_{22}{}^{18}FN_3O_2S$	N
5-HT_{1A}R	[^{18}F]MPPF	$C_{25}H_{27}{}^{18}FN_4O_2$	Y
	[^{18}F]F13714	$C_{21}H_{25}ClF^{18}FN_4O$	N
OXT OXTR	[^{11}C]PF-3274167	$C_{18}{}^{11}CH_{19}ClFN_5O_3$	N
	[^{11}C]EMPA	$C_{22}{}^{11}CH_{26}N_4O_4S$	N
DA precursor	[^{18}F]FDOPA	$C_9H_{10}{}^{18}FNO_4$	Y
DAT	[^{11}C]WIN35,428	$C_{15}{}^{11}CH_{20}FNO^2$	Y
	[^{11}C]methylphenidate [^{11}C]cocaine	$C_{14}H_{19}NO_2$ $C_{17}H_{21}NO_4$	N N
	[^{18}F]FE-PE2I	$C_{20}H_{25}{}^{18}FINO_2$	N
D_2R	[^{11}C]NMS	$C_{23}{}^{11}CH_{28}FN_3O_2$	Y
	[^{11}C]raclopride	$C_{14}{}^{11}CH_{20}Cl_2N_2O_3$	Y
D_2R, D_3R	[^{18}F]fallypride	$C_{20}H_{29}{}^{18}FN_2O_3$	N
	[^{11}C]-(+)-PHNO	$C_{14}{}^{11}CH_{21}NO_2$	N
D_1R	[^{11}C]NNC112	$C_{18}{}^{11}CH_{18}ClNO_2$	N
	[^{11}C]SCH23390	$C_{16}{}^{11}CH_{18}ClNO$	Y
GABA $GABA_B$R	[^{18}F]1b	$C_{16}H_{16}Cl^{18}FN_2O_3$	N
$GABA_A$R	[^{18}F]FMZ	$C_{15}H_{14}{}^{18}FN_3O_3$	Y
	[^{11}C]Ro15–4513	$C_{14}{}^{11}CH_{14}N_6O_3$	Y
AChE receptor	[^{18}F]FA	$C_9H_{11}{}^{18}FN_2O$	N
precursor	[^{11}C]MP4A	$C_7{}^{11}CH_{15}NO_2$	Y
Leucine	[^{11}C]leucine	$C_5{}^{11}CH_{13}NO_2$	Y

Target	PET probe	Chemical formula	Clinical application
Glutamate			
mGLuR5	[^{18}F]FPEB	$C_{14}H_7{}^{18}FN_2$	Y
	[^{11}C]ABP-688	$C_{14}{}^{11}CH_{16}N_2O$	N
mGLuR1	[^{11}C]ITMM	$C_{18}{}^{11}CH_{18}N_5O_2S$	N
mGLuR7	[^{11}C]MMPIP	$C_{18}{}^{11}CH_{15}N_3O_3$	N
TSPO	[^{11}C]PK11195	$C_{20}{}^{11}CH_{21}ClN_2O$	Y
	[^{11}C]DPA713	$C_{20}{}^{11}CH_{28}N_4O_2$	N
	[^{18}F]FEPPA	$C_{22}H_{21}{}^{18}FN_2O_3$	N
	[^{11}C]PBR28	$C_{20}{}^{11}CH_{20}N_2O_3$	Y
	[^{11}C]ER176	$C_{19}{}^{11}CH_{20}ClN_3O$	N
	[^{18}F]GE180	$C_{20}H_{27}{}^{18}FN_2O_2$	N
	[^{18}F]FEPPA	$C_{22}H_{21}{}^{18}FN_2O_3$	N
P2X7R	[^{11}C]A-740003	$C_{25}{}^{11}CH_{30}N_6O_3$	N
	[^{11}C]JNJ-717	$C_{18}{}^{11}CH_{17}Cl_2N_5O_2$	N
	[^{18}F]JNJ64413739	$C_{18}H_{14}F_3{}^{18}FN_6O$	N
	[^{11}C]SMW139	$C_{18}{}^{11}CH_{21}ClF_3NO_2$	N
MAO-B	[^{11}C]SL25.1188	$C_{15}{}^{11}CH_{17}F_3N_2O_5$	N
COX-1	[^{11}C]PS13	$C_{17}{}^{11}CH_{16}F_3N_3O_3$	N
COX-2	[^{11}C]MC1	$C_{16}{}^{11}CH_{17}N_3O_3S_2$	N
CSF1R	[^{11}C]CPPC	$C_{21}{}^{11}CH_{27}N_5O_2$	N
AVP V1aR	[^{18}F]SRX246 [^{11}C]SRX246 [^{11}C](1S,5R)-1 [^{11}C]PF-184563	$C_{42}H_{48}{}^{18}FN_5O_5$ $C_{42}{}^{11}CH_{51}N_5O_5$ $C_{25}{}^{11}CH_{30}N_2O_2$ $C_{20}{}^{11}CH_{23}ClN_6$	N N N N

Abbreviations: Application, Whether applied in ASD research; CBF, Cerebral Blood Flow; 5-HT, 5-Hydroxytryptamine/Serotonin, 5-HT; 5-HTT, 5-Hydroxytryptamine Transporter/Serotonin Transporter; 5-HT$_{2A}$R, Serotonin 2A Receptor; 5-HT$_{1A}$R, Serotonin 1A Receptor; OXT, Oxytocin; OXTR, Oxytocin Receptor; DA, Dopamine; DAT, Dopamine Transporter; D$_1$R, Dopamine D1 Receptor; D$_2$R, Dopamine D$_2$ Receptor; D$_3$R, Dopamine D$_3$ Receptor; GABA, γ-Aminobutyric Acid; GABA$_A$R, γ-Aminobutyric Acid Type A Receptor; GABA$_B$R, γ-Aminobutyric Acid Type B Receptor; AChE, Acetylcholinesterase; mGLuR1, metabotropic Glutamate Receptor 1; mGLuR5, metabotropic Glutamate Receptor 5; mGLuR7, metabotropic Glutamate Receptor 7; TSPO, 18 kDa Translocator Protein; P2X7R, Purinergic P2X7 Receptor; MAO-B, monoamine oxidase B; COX-1, Cyclooxygenase 1; COX-2, Cyclooxygenase 2; CSF1R, Colony Stimulating Factor 1 Receptor; AVP, Arginine Vasopressin; V1Ar, Vasopressin 1a Receptor; Y, Yes; N, No.

Table 1.
Summary of ASD research targets and their corresponding PET probes.

patients. As early as 1985, Rumsey et al., performed a brain [^{18}F]FDG PET study and found that the cerebral glucose metabolism in ASD patients was more diffuse compared with that in controls [30]. However, most of the following [^{18}F]FDG PET studies found a reduced brain glucose metabolism in ASD patients than controls except for specific brain regions [31–38]. Chugani et al. observed reduced glucose metabolism in cerebellum, frontal cortex, anterior cingulate gyrus, right temporal cortex, and bilateral medial temporal regions in four autistic children with wine spotting [39]. The glucose metabolism asymmetry in frontal temporal lobe was different from the symptom in typical autism children. More studies showed that ASD patients exhibited either increased or decreased glucose metabolism in different regions of brain [40–45]. In addition, earlier studies also reported no significant difference in cerebral glucose metabolism between the autism and control subjects [46–48]. No consensus has been drawn on glucose metabolism change in different specific brain regions in ASD patients, however, some common findings included decreased glucose metabolism in temporal lobe as well as abnormal glucose metabolism in the highly connected areas including the adjacent limbic cortex, parietal lobe, and frontal lobe, which is consistent with the anatomical connectivity between the associative and supratemporal cortexes [49–51] and is supported by findings on the brain functional network for glucose metabolism [52–54].

[^{18}F] FDG PET is applied in both study of glucose metabolism changes in specific brain regions of ASD patients and ASD treatment evaluation via neuroimaging. An [^{18}F]FDG PET study performed on fluoxetine treated ASD patients found that the glucose metabolic rate in the right frontal lobe, especially in the orbitofrontal cortex and anterior cingulate gyrus, was remarkably increased after treatment. Moreover, they found the patients with higher glucose metabolic rates in the anterior cingulate and medial frontal lobe before treatment exhibited a more significant response to fluoxetine, indicating that response to fluoxetine is closely correlated with baseline cingulate metabolism [55]. However, the cerebral glucose metabolism in ASD patients after treatment does not consistently exhibit an increasing glucose metabolism. Another [^{18}F]FDG PET study conducted on a 14 years old ASD patient showed that after two years of treatment with nucleus accumbens (NAc) deep brain stimulation (DBS), the patient's clinical symptoms were significantly improved with brain [^{18}F] FDG PET results showing that the glucose metabolism in the occipital, frontal, and prefrontal cortexes was dramatically reduced after treatment [56]. Another [^{18}F] FDG PET study was conducted on a 6 years old ASD patient to assess the efficacy of ketogenic diet (KD) treatment, a commonly used therapy for refractory epilepsy. Glucose metabolism bilateral local reduction was observed in the cerebellum, proximal meso-temporal lobe, and basal ganglia region in patient, and after a 12-month KD treatment, glucose metabolism was markedly decreased throughout the entire cerebral cortex [57], with the main brain cell energy changing from glucose to ketone bodies as the underlying mechanism [58, 59]. The findings taken together suggest that ASD therapy can alter the cerebral glucose metabolism state and improve patients' clinical symptoms. The [^{18}F]FDG PET application in glucose metabolism assessment can help screen subjects for further efficient clinical therapy, as well as evaluate treatment efficacy. It is worth noting that the effects of ASD therapeutic drugs targeting dopamine, 5-hydroxytryptamine, gamma-aminobutyric acid, as well as other neurotransmitter systems on brain glucose metabolism need further study.

3.2 Cerebral blood flow

The [^{15}O]CO_2 steady-state inhalation technique has been widely used in the early stages of PET imaging to study cerebral perfusion, but its reliability is insufficient. Imaging with probes that have a small relative molecular weight and are uncharged and fat-soluble (mainly [^{15}O]H_2O) are now more preferable. These probes can go through the blood–brain barrier, so the probe amount in brain cells is positively related to regional cerebral blood flow (rCBF), which is directly correlated with local brain function. Therefore, cerebral perfusion imaging can reflect the local brain function to a certain extent. To calculate rCBF, the dynamic intracranial distribution of probe in human body is recorded, and blood samples are collected continuously to assess the input function of carotid artery. With image processing, the radiation concentration-time curves are obtained for calculation of the rCBF values for different brain regions [60].

In early experiments, cerebral perfusion imaging was performed on 6 ASD patients and 8 normal controls after nasal inhalation of $[^{15}O]CO_2$ and no difference in rCBF was found [47]. These negative results may be due to the influence of $[^{15}O]CO_2$ absorption on cerebral perfusion imaging quality or limitations of early low-resolution PET cameras. High-resolution PET combined with statistical parameter mapping was able to find some local abnormalities that the low-resolution PET failed to detect [61]. In subsequent experiments, $[^{15}O]H_2O$ was administrated to ASD patients via intravenous injection for cerebral perfusion imaging. The cerebral perfusion imaging was performed with patients carrying out various tasks or social functions such as listening, speaking, thinking, emotional processing, etc., and based on the voxel statistical parameters, the image data analysis was performed to compare perfusion in distinct brain regions between ASD patients and controls [62–64]. The different activation regions for different tasks shown by cerebral perfusion imaging were correlated with behavioral function control areas in brain. Due to the influence of factors, such as IQ and age on ASD patients' ability to perform tasks, the results from different studies were not comparable. However, continuous studies revealed general rules for rCBF and brain function changes in ASD patients. When $[^{15}O]H_2O$ PET was used to study the differences in rCBF in four ASD patients and five controls during a verbal task [63], it was found that the left frontal region 46 and right dentate nucleus were activated more during motor speech function while less during hearing, speech, and expressive language in ASD patients compared with controls. During speech expression, the thalamus exhibited similar intergroup differences with those in region 46. In 1999, $[^{15}O]H_2O$ PET was used to explore differences in rCBF between five highly functioning adult ASD patients and five typical developing controls during a verbal task [65]. The results showed that the patients' hearing was closely related to left hemisphere dominance reversal, and cerebellar and bilateral superior temporal gyrus rCBF decreased in ASD patients, indicative of reduced involvement of cerebellar in language expression and non-verbal auditory perception. These results are consistent with a previous report that dentate-thalamo-cortical pathway was affected by dys-serotonin synthesis in ASD boy patients, indicating the dentate-thalamo-cortical pathway atypical functional specialization, in line with brain regional-specific biochemical disorder in autism development [66]. Three studies using $[^{15}O]H_2O$ to explore changes of rCBF in ASD patients during a language task observed decreased rCBF in the left temporal lobe area of patients' brain and the resulted abnormal function of the temporal lobe, consistent with the glucose metabolism pattern changes in brains of ASD patients [61, 67, 68].

For task-state cerebral perfusion imaging, functional magnetic resonance such as arterial spin labeling (ASL) sequence has unique advantages [69]. Comparative studies or joint imaging with PET and fMRI will have a wider application in the future.

3.3 5-hydroxytryptamine system

5-hydroxytryptamine (5-HT)/serotonin, is a well-known inhibitory neurotransmitter, which regulates synaptogenesis and neuronal migration in brain development [70]. The abnormalities of the 5-HT system in autism were first reported in 1961 [71]. In a whole blood test study, 5-HT was found to be significantly increased in 23 children with autism and severe mental disability, and slightly increased in 7 children without autism but had severe mental disability. In contrast, normal level of 5-HT was tested in 12 children with mild mental retardation and four non-autistic and non-mentally handicapped children. Enhanced 5-HT levels in whole blood in ASD patients was further confirmed in follow-up studies; moreover, enhanced whole blood 5-HT levels were also detected in their immediate family members [21]. In addition, 5-HT antagonists can lead to improvement in ASD symptoms [72–74]. 5-HT has been most frequently tested in ASD studies, due to the close relationship between the 5-HT system and ASD. Based on the current ASD-related 5-HT PET imaging studies, the 5-HT system abnormalities in ASD patients mainly include decreased 5-HT transporters in brain, abnormal functions of brain 5-HT receptors, increased whole blood 5-HT levels, and disorder of 5-HT synthesis in brain.

3.3.1 5-HT precursor

Tryptophan hydroxylase is a precursor of 5-HT and α-methyl-L-tryptophan can specifically bind to tryptophan hydroxylase. Therefore, radio-labeled [^{11}C]AMT has been widely used as a specific probe to measure 5-HT synthesis [75, 76]. Unilateral changes in 5-HT synthesis in the dentate-thalamo-cortical pathway in ASD patients were analyzed with [^{11}C]AMT PET [66]. In all the 7 boys with autism tested but not in a girl with autism, 5-HT synthesis asymmetry was observed in cerebellar dentate nucleus, frontal cortex, and thalamus. Decreased 5-HT synthesis was observed in thalamus and left frontal cortex in 5 boys, while in thalamus and right frontal cortex in the other two boys. While increased 5-HT synthesis was detected in the contralateral dentate nucleus of all the 7 boys. Chugani et al. used [^{11}C]AMT PET to test 5-HT synthesis in 30 children with autism, 8 non-autistic siblings of the patients, and 16 non-autistic children with epilepsy [77]. They found in a non-autistic child before 5 years old, 5-HT synthesis was more than twice that of an adult and then dropped to adult levels after 5 years. However, during the childhood of ASD patients, the whole-brain 5-HT synthesis reduced, but between 2 and 15 years old, it gradually increased, and reached a level 1.5 times that of the normal adult level with no gender difference. Age-dependent differences were observed in 5-HT synthesis between the epileptic and autism groups, as well as between the autism and sibling groups. Chandana et al. used [^{11}C]AMT PET to study the relationship between language and handedness functions and serotonin synthesis local and global abnormalities in children with autism [78]. Abnormal 5-HT synthesis in multiple cortex including non-lateralization, left and right cortex was observed by analysis in 117 children with autism. A more severe language impairment was observed in ASD children with reduced AMT binding in the left cortex, while a higher autism prevalence was found in ambidextrous and left-handed ASD children with reduced AMT binding in the right cortex. The local or global serotonin system abnormal asymmetrical development may both cause faulty neural circuitry.

3.3.2 5-HT transporter

5-hydroxytryptamine transporter (5-HTT), also named serotonin transporter (SERT) can transfer 5-HT to 5-hydroxytryptamergic neurons. Dysregulation of 5-HTT and 5-HT system happens simultaneously in ASD patients, but the association between 5-HTT and ASD remains unclear. The current PET probes for 5-HTT study include [^{11}C]DASB, [^{11}C](+)McN5652, [^{11}C]MADAM, and [^{18}F]Fmener-D2.

[^{11}C](+)McN5652 is the first probe used for 5-HTT imaging [79]. Nakamura et al. used [^{11}C](+)McN5652 PET in study of 5-HTT in ASD patients, and found that the whole brain 5-HTT level in ASD patients was lower than controls [80]. [^{11}C]DASB is more widely used probe than [^{11}C](+)McN5652 due to its high reliability and repeatability resulted from its reversible high-affinity binding with 5-HTT [81]. However, different studies on 5-HTT in ASD patients using [^{11}C]DASB reported different results. Girgis et al. did not find significant difference in 5-HTT between ASD and control groups [82]. Andersson et al., found significantly lower levels of 5-HTT in brain stem, gray matter, as well as nine gray matter subregions in ASD patients compared with controls [83], consistent with previous report that in ASD patients, 5-HTT level is decreased [84]. The different conclusions from different studies might be due to the heterogeneous study subjects, or different imaging for different ASD subtypes. The development of new probes for 5-HTT study (such as [^{11}C]AFM, [^{11}C]ADAM, and [^{11}C]DAPA) will promote elucidation of the association between 5-HTT and ASD, and significantly improve our understanding of the ASD pathophysiological mechanisms [85, 86].

3.3.3 5-HT receptor

Totally 14 subtypes of 5-HT receptor (5-HTR) have been found until now. 5-HT can stimulate different subtypes of 5-HTR, thereby exerting different physiological effects. The relationship between 5-HTR content changes and ASD remains unclear. Among 5-HTR subtypes, only 5-HT_{1A}R and 5-HT_{2A}R have been used in studies of ASD PET. [^{18}F]F13714 and [^{18}F]MPPF are 5-HT_{1A}R targeting probes, and [^{18}F]Altanserin, [^{11}C]MDL100907, and [^{18}F]Setoperone are 5-HT_{2A}R targeting probes.

[^{18}F]Setoperone has a high specificity for 5-HT_{2A}R [87]. Beversdorf et al., used [^{18}F]Setoperone PET and found much less [^{18}F]Setoperone binding in the thalamus of ASD patients compared with control group, however, no significant difference was observed in other regions [88]. Goldberg et al. used [^{18}F]Setoperone PET and found a significant lower cortical 5-HT_{2A}R binding potential (BP_{ND}) and also a lower cortical 5-HT_{2A}R density in the parents of the ASD children when compared with the control group. A negative correlation was also observed between the platelet 5-HT levels and the cortical 5-HT_{2A}R BP_{ND} in the parents of the ASD children [89]. These results were consistent with reduced 5-HT_{2A}R expression and function observed in ASD patients, and also further elucidated the pathophysiological mechanism of elevated 5-HT level in ASD patients' peripheral blood. Another study using probe [^{11}C]MDL100907 observed no significant difference in regional [^{11}C]MDL100907 BP_{ND} between adult patients with AS and controls [82].

A PET study using [^{18}F]MPPF, a 5-HT_{1A}R-specific probe was carried out on adult ASD patients and controls to study the correlations between gray matter volume (GMV), social personality, and 5-HT_{1A}R binding potential [90], and found a regional negative relationship between 5-HT_{1A}R BP_{ND} and GMV, while 5-HT_{1A}R density was similar between ASD patients and controls. However, the correlations observed in control group between GMV, 5-HT_{1A}R, and social personality scores in the striatum were not observed in the ASD group, suggesting in the striatum of ASD patients, there is a 5-HT system disturbance correlated with the changes of 5-HT_{1A}R density.

With the development of probe, PET probes targeting other 5-HTR subtypes will be widely applied in ASD research, which can significantly improve elucidation of the ASD pathogenesis [25].

3.4 Oxytocin

Oxytocin (OXT) is a neuropeptide that plays an important role in the regulation of social behavior in mammals by interacting with oxytocin receptor (OTR). Previous studies have found abnormal OXT levels in patients with autism [91]. Numerous studies have demonstrated significantly improved social behavior in ASD patients resulted from intranasal OXT treatment. Guastella et al. reported a significantly improved ASD patient performance in an eye-mind task after administration of OXT via intranasal inhalation [92]. FMRI studies showed that after OXT treatment, several brain regions exhibited enhanced responses to stimuli in ASD patients [93, 94].

Unfortunately, PET probes targeting OTR satisfactorily have yet to be successfully developed. The probes [^{11}C]EMPA [95] and [^{11}C]PF-3274167 [96] have not been widely applied because their physical and chemical properties are not unsatisfactory. 5-HT and OXT are integrated both in structure and function, mediating emotion-based behavior. The amygdala is the key area for 5-HT regulation by OXT. OXT can inhibit the activity of amygdala and reduce anxiety; in contrast, dysregulation of 5-HT and high activity of amygdala are correlated with enhanced anxiety. Substantial studies have been performed to investigate 5-HT system changes after treatment with OXT and further explore the functions and related mechanisms of OXT in ASD. Using [^{18}F]MPPF PET, Mottolese et al. detected changes of 5-HT_{1A}R in the brain after OXT treatment, and found that OXT enhanced [^{18}F]MPPF BP_{ND} in the dorsal raphe nucleus (the core region for 5-HT synthesis), orbitofrontal cortex, insula, and amygdala/hippocampus complex [97]. Using [^{18}F]MPPF PET, Lefevre et al. did not find significant difference in the 5-HT_{1A}R distribution and content between ASD patients and controls [98]. However, they found OXT dramatically enhanced [^{18}F] MPPF BP_{ND} in some regions of brain in control group, but not in ASD group. Using [^{11}C]DASB PET, Hirosawa et al. observed significantly increased [^{11}C]DASB BP_{ND} in the left inferior and left middle frontal gyrus in ASD patients after treatment with OXT. However, no close relationship was found between [^{11}C]DASB BP_{ND} and symptom changes in clinic [99]. Taken together, these studies revealed the inhibitory effect of OXT on 5-HT signaling, and the relationship between serotonergic system changes and prosociality after treatment with OXT. The relationship between OXT and ASD needs further studies.

3.5 Dopamine system

Dopamine (DA) is a neurotransmitter of catecholamine, and it is involved in various central nervous system functions, including social motivation and social reward. A correlation between DA transporter and receptor-associated gene mutations and ASD clinical symptoms has been reported by numerous studies [100–102]. Some DA system-targeting psychotherapeutic medicines have exhibited good efficacy in improving ASD clinical symptoms, suggesting the critical roles of DA system in mediating behaviors of ASD patients. Many PET studies have been conducted on DA system, however, no consensus has been drawn on changes of DA transporters, receptors and precursor in the brains of ASD patients.

3.5.1 DA precursor

Dopa, the precursor of DA, can be absorbed, metabolized, and stored by dopaminergic endings, and [^{18}F]FDOPA imaging can be used to analyze DA synthesis in brain. Using [^{18}F]FDOPA PET, Ernst et al. analyzed the brain DA synthesis difference between 14 ASD children and controls [103], and they found a 39% reduction in DA ratio in anterior medial prefrontal cortex/occipital cortex of ASD children compared with controls. Another study found increased [^{18}F]FDOPA inflow value (Ki) in the striatum and frontal cortex of ASD patients compared with control group [104]. However, other similar studies did not detect significant difference in dopamine production by striatum between ASD patients and controls [105, 106]. The inconsistent results of these studies might be due to the heterogeneity of the study subjects.

3.5.2 DA transporter

A study using [^{11}C]McN-5652 to detect 5-HTT and using [^{11}C]WIN-35,428 to measure DAT observed a remarkably higher DAT binding in the orbital prefrontal cortex of ASD patients when compared with controls. Moreover, in the orbitofrontal cortex of ASD patients, the DAT binding was inversely correlated with 5-HTT binding [80].

3.5.3 DA receptor

Fernell et al. conducted a PET study using [^{11}C]NMS on ASD children treated with R-BH4 (a tyrosine hydroxylase cofactor in the serotonin and catecholamine biosynthesis pathways), and found a 10% reduction of dopamine receptor 2 (D_2R) from pre-treatment abnormally high levels to after treatment normal levels in the caudate and putamen of ASD children compared with controls with improvement in ASD symptoms [107]. Fujino et al. used [^{11}C]SCH23390 PET to explore the differences in dopamine receptor 1 (D_1R) between ASD patients and controls, and they found the D_1R binding in the anterior cingulate cortex, striatum, and temporal cortex was positively correlated with emotional perception scores, while negatively correlated with ASD detail attention scores [108]. However, no significant differences were observed in the anterior cingulate cortex, striatum, and temporal cortex. Another study using [^{11}C]raclopride PET found decreased D_2R/D_3R binding in left caudate nucleus and bilateral putamen in ASD group compared with the control group [109].

3.6 Amino acid neurotransmitters

Protein synthesis is critical and necessary for a series of processes in the brain, including long-term memory, synaptic plasticity, and experience-dependent development. Atypical synapse protein synthesis is very important in ASD due to the close correlation between ASD and single-gene mutations, such as in neuroprotein 1, shank 3, and glial 3/4 [110]. The basic protein components are amino acids, therefore, quantitative analysis of amino acids and their receptors can help reveal abnormal protein synthesis in ASD.

3.6.1 Gamma-aminobutyric acid

Gamma-aminobutyric acid (GABA) is a key inhibitory neurotransmitter, which plays a crucial role in regulation of development and synaptic pruning. GABA dysfunction can induce imbalance in excitation/inhibition of the nervous system, which is closely correlated with ASD [111]. Previous human genetics studies found numerous mutations in the $GABA_A$ receptor gene as well as genes related to GABA synthesis in ASD patients [112, 113]. Autoradiography studies revealed reduced $GABA_A$ in the hippocampus and anterior cingulate cortex of ASD patients [114, 115]. Studies on rodent ASD models of found a prolonged neuronal excitation caused by early GABA inhibition, which may be an underlying ASD induction mechanism [116]. A substantial evidence indicates that GABA changes might relate to ASD, however, current PET studies on GABA are very few.

PET has been widely used to explore the roles of GABA in ASD pathogenesis. A study performed by Mendez et al. using [^{11}C]RO15–4513 PET found markedly decreased $GABA_A$ $\alpha5$ subtype levels in the bilateral amygdala and NAc in the brains of ASD patients compared with controls [117]. These results provide support for further study of GABA system abnormalities in ASD patients. However, another study using [^{18}F]FMZ or [^{11}C]RO15–4513 did not find differences in either $GABA_A$ receptors or $GABA_A$ $\alpha5$ subtype in any region of the brain between ASD and control groups [118]. Fung et al. measured GABA concentrations using ^{1}H-MRS and total $GABA_A$ receptor densities using [^{18}F]FMZ PET. [^{18}F]FMZ PET showed no significant difference in $GABA_A$ receptor density in the left dorsolateral prefrontal cortex (DLPFC) and bilateral thalamus between the ASD and control groups However, ^{1}H-MRS detection revealed a significantly higher GABA/Water ratio in the left DLPFC of ASD patients compared to the control group [119].

3.6.2 Glutamate

Due to the imbalance in brain excitation/inhibition in ASD patients, glutamate is also a focus of ASD neuroimaging research [120]. A series of glutamate receptor specific probes including [^{11}C]ITMM, [^{11}C]MMPIP, and [^{18}F]FPEB have been reported, which can specifically bind to metabolic glutamate receptor 1 ($mGluR_1$), metabolic glutamate receptor 7 ($mGluR_7$), and metabolic glutamate receptor 5 ($mGluR_5$), respectively [121–124]. However, only [^{18}F]FPEB has been widely applied in clinical ASD PET research.

The correlation between glutamate system imbalance and ASD has been demonstrated by animal model studies using [^{18}F]FPEB PET. of a Shank3 complete knockout mouse model (Shank3B−/−) showed that of A significantly increased mGluR5 BP_{ND} was observed in the thalamus, striatum, amygdala, and hippocampus in Shank3B−/− mice compared with normal mice as shown in [^{18}F]FPEB PET imaging [125]. Using [^{18}F]FPEB PET, Fatemi et al. found a remarkably higher [^{18}F]FPEB BP_{ND} in the cerebellum and posterior central gyri of ASD patients [126]. A negative relationship between [^{18}F]FPEB BP_{ND} and age was observed in the cerebellum, but not in the posterior central gyrus. A positive relationship was observed between precuneus [^{18}F]FPEB BP_{ND} and sleepiness scale score on the Abnormal Behavior Checklist (ABC), while a negative relationship was observed between cerebellar [^{18}F]FPEB BP_{ND} and ABC hyperactivity subscale, ABC inappropriate speech subscale, and ABC total score. These results showed altered mGluR5 binding in key regions of ASD patient brains, indicative of abnormal glutamate signaling in these areas, which might influence ASD symptoms. Brašićet al., used [^{18}F]FPEB PET to study the mGluR5 distribution in brain of patients with fragile X syndrome (FXS), TD and idiopathic autism spectrum disorder (IASD) [127], and they observed a significantly increased mGluR5 expression in the cortical regions of IASD patients when compared with TD patients, while they observed a significantly decreased mGluR5 expression in all regions of FXS patients when compared with TD patients.

Currently, some mGluR7 and mGluR1 probes are also under investigation. Future imaging studies will elucidate more pathophysiological mechanisms of glutamate in ASD.

3.6.3 Leucine

Leucine impacts neuron protein synthesis and plays a critical role in dendritic spines regulation, therefore functions in neuropsychiatric diseases [128]. Shandal et al. investigated the leucine involvement in protein synthesis using [^{11}C]Leucine PET [129], and found increased protein synthesis in the temporal lobe language region of stunted children with PDD. Consistently, previous studies showed abnormal protein synthesis in the language region and abnormalities in the temporal lobe region of children with PDD and developmental delay. However, another study reported no significant differences in cerebral protein synthesis between patients with Fragile X syndrome and controls using [^{11}C] Leucine PET for measurement [130]. In contrast, another study using robust radiolabeled assay found decreased protein synthesis in peripheral blood mononuclear cells (PMCS) and platelets of patients with Fragile X syndrome when compared with controls [131]. Taken together, these studies suggest that more research is needed to demonstrate the correlation between leucine abnormality and ASD.

3.6.4 Acetylcholine

A series of studies showed that inhibition of acetylcholinesterase (AChE) attenuated inattention, aggression, and overall ASD symptoms in both ASD patients and ASD animal models [132–134], indicative of the critical roles of the cholinergic system in ASD etiology. However, only one PET study was reported. A lack of cholinergic innervation was observed in the fusiform gyri of ASD patients when using the acetylcholine analog [^{11}C]MP4A to detect the activity of acetylcholinesterase [135]. Additional targeted PET studies in the future will help clarify the role of cholinergic dysfunction in the pathogenesis of ASD.

3.7 Neuroinflammation

Immune-mediated mechanisms are considered to be among the pathophysiological factors leading to ASD [136]. Inflammation including microglial activation and related changes of microglial pathology has been found in central nervous system of ASD patients, and many psychotropic agents have exhibited direct effect on microglia [137]. However, the correlation between microglia and ASD remains unclear.

Microglia play critical roles in development of immunity and central nervous system. The translocator protein (TSPO) is an important neuroinflammation imaging biomarker, which is overexpressed in activated microglia. A series of TSPO probes have been developed including [^{11}C]PK11195, the first generation, [^{18}F]FEPPA, [^{11}C]PBR28 and [^{11}C]DPA713, the second generation and [^{11}C]ER176 and [^{18}F]GE180, the third generation [138, 139]. Suzuki et al. investigated microglia activation differences between ASD patients and controls using [^{11}C]PK11195 [140], and they found increased [^{11}C]PK11195 binding in prefrontal cortex, fusiform gyrus, midbrain, cerebellum and cingulate cortex in ASD patients compared with controls. Another study using [^{11}C]PBR28 reported a lower regional TSPO expression in bilateral precuneus/posterior cingulate gyrus, bilateral temporal gyrus, bilateral insular cortex, superior limbic gyrus, and angular gyrus of brain in ASD patients than in controls [141]. These two studies reported inconsistent results, possibly due to the heterogeneity of ASD patients or the influence of TSPO gene polymorphism. The applications of more TSPO probes have been reported [142–145]. Future imaging studies will help us understand the relationship between neuroinflammation and ASD.

A series of novel neuroinflammation targets and corresponding probes have been developed including cyclooxygenase (COX)-1 and its specific probe [^{11}C]PS13, monoamine oxidase B (MAO-B) and its specific probe [^{11}C]SL25.1188, colony-stimulating factor 1 receptor (CSF1R) and its specific probe [^{11}C]CPPC, and purinergic P2X7 receptor (P2X7R) and its specific probes [^{11}C]JNJ-54173717 (JNJ-717), [^{18}F]JNJ-64413739, and [^{11}C]SMW139, as well as cyclooxygenase (COX)-2 and its specific probe [^{11}C]MC1. These probes have been successfully applied in neuroimaging to explore the potential functions of these targets in neuroinflammation, as well as the potential relationships with ASD [24].

3.8 Arginine vasopressin

Arginine vasopressin (AVP) plays a series of physiological roles in mammals including increasing blood pressure, regulating social behavior, releasing adrenal corticosteroid, as well as antidiuretic activity [146, 147]. Since early animal studies have found that AVP plays critical roles in regulating biosocial behaviors, including parentage, mating, aggression and sociability, an increasing number of studies have focused on the correlation between AVP and ASD [148–150]. Regarding the differences in AVP contents between ASD patients and controls, although no consistent conclusion has been drawn, AVP related signaling pathways have been demonstrated to be promising and studies on them could help ASD diagnosis and treatment [151–154]. V1a receptor antagonists have been shown to be able to regulate AVP functions, thereby improving the ASD symptoms. A novel V1a receptor antagonist of Balovaptan can improve the Vineland-II Adaptive Behavior Scale (including social interaction, daily living skills, and secondary endpoints of communication) in ASD adults [155], but not in ASD children and adolescents [156]. The V1a receptor has become a new focus of ASD research, and a series of V1a receptor probes including [^{11}C]SRX246, [^{18}F]SRX246 [157], [^{11}C](1S,5R)-1 [158], and [^{11}C]PF-184563 [159] have been developed recently. These PET probes have exhibited their values in in autoradiography and animal studies, however, they have not been applied in human studies yet. The development of PET probes that can be widely used inhuman ASD studies will help elucidate the relationship between AVP and ASD.

4. Conclusion

ASD is a disease induced by both environmental and heredity factors, and its major cause and induction process still remain unclear. Early and clear diagnosis of ASD is conducive to improving ASD symptoms in patients, thereby affecting treatment efficacy. PET can be applied to quantitatively and dynamically evaluate cerebral glucose metabolism, task and resting states, neurotransmitter system biomarkers, and cerebral blood flow perfusion, explore ASD pathophysiology, and promote ASD therapeutic drug development, as well as in ASD diagnosis and treatment. The identification of ASD biomarkers and PET probes is critical in ASD diagnosis, and drug development and evaluation. Numerous ASD associated biomarkers have been identified in cerebral blood perfusion, glucose metabolism, neuroinflammation, and neurotransmitter systems. However, due to the differences in ASD subtypes, experimental design (e.g., imaging conditions, anesthesia/sleep/awake, and/or task-state/resting-state), and subjects (e.g., gender, IQ and age), contradictory conclusions may be drawn from different studies [160]. There a limitation in the current ASD studies.

The PET imaging studies showed that there might be differences in the pathophysiological mechanisms for different ASD subtypes and therefore different results may be observed and different conclusions may be drawn for different ASD subtypes. Therefore, more attention should be paid on this in future ASD PET studies to explore the possible differences in the pathophysiological mechanisms of different ASD subtypes, and selection of experimental subjects and design of experiments should be determined and performed based on these differences to provide more valuable references for clinical diagnosis and treatment of ASD [161].

In this chapter, several ASD related targets, including cerebral blood perfusion, cerebral glucose metabolism, neuroinflammation, arginine vasopressin receptor, neurotransmitter system, as well as the corresponding probes and their applications in ASD imaging studies and the experimental results are summarized. PET studies using different probes can obtain similar results, while PET studies using the same probe can also produce different results due to the heterogeneity of ASD patients and the influence of TSPO gene polymorphism [162]. Therefore, although identify new biomarkers and develop novel PET probes are very helpful for ASD study, evaluation the application value of each probe in the existing system is difficult. Therefore, it is crucial to seek and investigate the associations between a probe, a biomarker, and a specific ASD subtype at molecular level [163], which is the most valuable exploration direction in future ASD studies.

PET molecular imaging is very helpful for ASD diagnosis and treatment, however, there are still some limitations and difficulties in execution. First, patients are required to lie on a machine for PET/MR and PET/CT scanning, and protection from radiation is required during the imaging process, so high coordination of patients is very important. Second, ASD patients often have a large age span and significant differences in IQ, so professional technicians need to train some patients to make them get familiar with drug injection, task process or even anesthesia operation and adapt to scanning environment. Therefore, the joint efforts of patients, doctors, technicians, nurses, researchers, as well as other specialists in neuropsychiatry, rehabilitation, and nuclear medicine to promote continuous advancements in ASD research, diagnosis and treatment.

Acknowledgements

We would like to thank the support of K.C. Wong Education Foundation (China). This work was financially supported by the National Natural Science Foundation of China (No. 82071974 and No. 82102107), and the Science and Technology Program of Guangzhou, China (202206010106).

Conflicts of interest

The authors declare no conflicts of interest.

Author details

Zhiqiang Tan, Weijian Ye, Hao Xu and Lu Wang*
Department of Nuclear Medicine and PET/CT-MRI Center, Center of Cyclotron and PET Radiopharmaceuticals, The First Affiliated Hospital of Jinan University, Guangzhou, China

*Address all correspondence to: l_wang1009@jnu.edu.cn

References

[1] Association AP. Diagnostic and Statistical Manual of Mental Disorders (DSM-5). 5th ed. Arlington, VA: Author; 2013

[2] Brasic JR, Holland JA. Reliable classification of case-control studies of autistic disorder and obstetric complications. Journal of Developmental and Physical Disabilities. 2006;**18**(4):355-381

[3] Brasic JR, Holland JA. A qualitative and quantitative review of obstetric complications and autistic disorder. Journal of Developmental and Physical Disabilities. 2007;**19**(4):337-364

[4] Katsanis N. The continuum of causality in human genetic disorders. Genome Biology. 2016;**17**(1):233

[5] Satterstrom FK, Kosmicki JA, Wang J, Breen MS, De Rubeis S, An JY, et al. Large-scale exome sequencing study implicates both developmental and functional changes in the neurobiology of autism. Cell. 2020;**180**(3):568-84.e23

[6] Le Couteur A, Lord C, Rutter M. The Autism Diagnostic Interview-Revised (ADI-R). Los Angeles, CA: Western Psychological Services; 2003

[7] Lord C, Rutter M, DiLavore PC, Risi S, Gotham K, Bishop S. Autism Diagnostic Observation Schedule: ADOS-2. Los Angeles, CA: Western Psychological Services; 2012

[8] Brasić JR, Barnett JY, Kowalik S, Tsaltas MO, Ahmad R. Neurobehavioral assessment of children and adolescents attending a developmental disabilities clinic. Psychological Reports. 2004;**95** (3 Pt 2):1079-1086

[9] Walton E, Turner JA, Ehrlich S. Neuroimaging as a potential biomarker to optimize psychiatric research and treatment. International Review of Psychiatry. 2013;**25**(5):619-631

[10] Volkow ND, Mullani NA, Bendriem B. Positron emission tomography instrumentation: An overview. American Journal of Physiologic Imaging. 1988;**3**(3):142-153

[11] McCluskey SP, Plisson C, Rabiner EA, Howes O. Advances in CNS PET: The state-of-the-art for new imaging targets for pathophysiology and drug development. European Journal of Nuclear Medicine and Molecular Imaging. 2020;**47**(2):451-489

[12] Shiue CY, Welch MJ. Update on PET radiopharmaceuticals: Life beyond fluorodeoxyglucose. Radiologic Clinics of North America. 2004;**42**(6):1033-1053 viii

[13] Smith GS, Koppel J, Goldberg S. Applications of neuroreceptor imaging to psychiatry research. Psychopharmacology Bulletin. 2003;**37**(4):26-65

[14] Gjedde A, Wong DF, Rosa-Neto P, Cumming P. Mapping neuroreceptors at work: On the definition and interpretation of binding potentials after 20 years of progress. International Review of Neurobiology. 2005;**63**:1-20

[15] MacLaren DC, Toyokuni T, Cherry SR, Barrio JR, Phelps ME, Herschman HR, et al. PET imaging of transgene expression. Biological Psychiatry. 2000;**48**(5):337-348

[16] Jain M, Batra SK. Genetically engineered antibody fragments and PET imaging: A new era

of radioimmunodiagnosis. Journal of Nuclear Medicine. 2003;**44**(12):1970-1972

[17] Syed AB, Brasic JR. Nuclear neurotransmitter molecular imaging of autism spectrum disorder. AIMS Molecular Science. 2019;**6**(4):87-106

[18] Schifter T, Hoffman JM, Hatten HP Jr, Hanson MW, Coleman RE, DeLong GR. Neuroimaging in infantile autism. Journal of Child Neurology. 1994;**9**(2):155-161

[19] Rumsey JM, Ernst M. Functional neuroimaging of autistic disorders. Mental Retardation and Developmental Disabilities Research Reviews. 2000;**6**(3):171-179

[20] Chugani DC. Neuroimaging and neurochemistry of autism. Pediatric clinics of North America. 2012;**59**(1): 63-73 x

[21] Hwang BJ, Mohamed MA, Brašić JR. Molecular imaging of autism spectrum disorder. International Review of Psychiatry. 2017;**29**(6):530-554

[22] Wolff JJ, Jacob S, Elison JT. The journey to autism: Insights from neuroimaging studies of infants and toddlers. Development and Psychopathology. 2018;**30**(2):479-495

[23] Girault JB, Piven J. The neurodevelopment of autism from infancy through toddlerhood. Neuroimaging Clinics of North America. 2020;**30**(1):97-114

[24] Meyer JH, Cervenka S, Kim MJ, Kreisl WC, Henter ID, Innis RB. Neuroinflammation in psychiatric disorders: PET imaging and promising new targets. The Lancet Psychiatry. 2020;**7**(12):1064-1074

[25] Zürcher NR, Bhanot A, McDougle CJ, Hooker JM. A systematic review of molecular imaging (PET and SPECT) in autism spectrum disorder: Current state and future research opportunities. Neuroscience and Biobehavioral Reviews. 2015;**52**:56-73

[26] Kowalewska B, Drozdz W, Kowalewski L. Positron emission tomography (PET) and single-photon emission computed tomography (SPECT) in autism research: Literature review. Irish Journal of Psychological Medicine. Sep 2022;**39**(3):272-286

[27] McPartland JC, Lerner MD, Bhat A, Clarkson T, Jack A, Koohsari S, et al. Looking Back at the next 40 years of ASD neuroscience research. Journal of Autism and Developmental Disorders. 2021;**51**(12):4333-4353

[28] Li X, Zhang K, He X, Zhou J, Jin C, Shen L, et al. Structural, functional, and molecular imaging of autism Spectrum disorder. Neuroscience Bulletin. 2021;**37**(7):1051-1071

[29] Fowler JS, Ido T. Initial and subsequent approach for the synthesis of 18FDG. Seminars in Nuclear Medicine. 2002;**32**(1):6-12

[30] Rumsey JM, Duara R, Grady C, Rapoport JL, Margolin RA, Rapoport SI, et al. Brain metabolism in autism. Resting cerebral glucose utilization rates as measured with positron emission tomography. Archives of General Psychiatry. 1985;**42**(5):448-455

[31] Buchsbaum MS, Siegel BV Jr, Wu JC, Hazlett E, Sicotte N, Haier R, et al. Brief report: Attention performance in autism and regional brain metabolic rate assessed by positron emission tomography. Journal of Autism and Developmental Disorders. 1992;**22**(1):115-125

[32] Chugani HT, Da Silva E, Chugani DC. Infantile spasms: III. Prognostic implications of bitemporal hypometabolism on positron emission tomography. Annals of Neurology. 1996;**39**(5):643-649

[33] Haznedar MM, Buchsbaum MS, Metzger M, Solimando A, Spiegel-Cohen J, Hollander E. Anterior cingulate gyrus volume and glucose metabolism in autistic disorder. The American Journal of Psychiatry. 1997;**154**(8):1047-1050

[34] Haznedar MM, Buchsbaum MS, Wei TC, Hof PR, Cartwright C, Bienstock CA, et al. Limbic circuitry in patients with autism spectrum disorders studied with positron emission tomography and magnetic resonance imaging. The American Journal of Psychiatry. 2000;**157**(12):1994-2001

[35] Haznedar MM, Buchsbaum MS, Hazlett EA, LiCalzi EM, Cartwright C, Hollander E. Volumetric analysis and three-dimensional glucose metabolic mapping of the striatum and thalamus in patients with autism spectrum disorders. The American Journal of Psychiatry. 2006;**163**(7):1252-1263

[36] Deriaz N, Willi JP, Orihuela-Flores M, Galli Carminati G, Ratib O. Treatment with levetiracetam in a patient with pervasive developmental disorders, severe intellectual disability, self-injurious behavior, and seizures: A case report. Neurocase. 2012;**18**(5):386-391

[37] Dilber C, Calışkan M, Sönmezoğlu K, Nişli S, Mukaddes NM, Tatlı B, et al. Positron emission tomography findings in children with infantile spasms and autism. Journal of Clinical Neuroscience. 2013;**20**(3):373-376

[38] Manglunia AS, Puranik AD. FDG PET/CT findings in a clinically diagnosed case of childhood autism. Indian Journal of Nuclear Medicine: IJNM. 2016;**31**(2):138-140

[39] Chugani HT, Juhász C, Behen ME, Ondersma R, Muzik O. Autism with facial port-wine stain: A new syndrome? Pediatric Neurology. 2007;**37**(3):192-199

[40] Siegel BV Jr, Asarnow R, Tanguay P, Call JD, Abel L, Ho A, et al. Regional cerebral glucose metabolism and attention in adults with a history of childhood autism. The Journal of Neuropsychiatry and Clinical Neurosciences. 1992;**4**(4):406-414

[41] Asano E, Chugani DC, Muzik O, Behen M, Janisse J, Rothermel R, et al. Autism in tuberous sclerosis complex is related to both cortical and subcortical dysfunction. Neurology. 2001;**57**(7):1269-1277

[42] Hazlett EA, Buchsbaum MS, Hsieh P, Haznedar MM, Platholi J, LiCalzi EM, et al. Regional glucose metabolism within cortical Brodmann areas in healthy individuals and autistic patients. Neuropsychobiology. 2004;**49**(3):115-125

[43] Anil Kumar BN, Malhotra S, Bhattacharya A, Grover S, Batra YK. Regional cerebral glucose metabolism and its Association with phenotype and cognitive functioning in patients with autism. Indian Journal of Psychological Medicine. 2017;**39**(3):262-270

[44] Mitelman SA, Bralet MC, Mehmet Haznedar M, Hollander E, Shihabuddin L, Hazlett EA, et al. Positron emission tomography assessment of cerebral glucose metabolic rates in autism spectrum disorder and schizophrenia. Brain Imaging and Behavior. 2018;**12**(2):532-546

[45] Kadwa RA, Sahu JK, Singhi P, Malhi P, Mittal BR. Prevalence and

characteristics of sensory processing abnormalities and its correlation with FDG-PET findings in children with autism. Indian Journal of Pediatrics. 2019;**86**(11):1036-1042

[46] De Volder A, Bol A, Michel C, Congneau M, Goffinet AM. Brain glucose metabolism in children with the autistic syndrome: Positron tomography analysis. Brain & Development. 1987;**9**(6):581-587

[47] Herold S, Frackowiak RS, Le Couteur A, Rutter M, Howlin P. Cerebral blood flow and metabolism of oxygen and glucose in young autistic adults. Psychological Medicine. 1988;**18**(4):823-831

[48] Heh CW, Smith R, Wu J, Hazlett E, Russell A, Asarnow R, et al. Positron emission tomography of the cerebellum in autism. The American Journal of Psychiatry. 1989;**146**(2):242-245

[49] Seltzer B, Pandya DN. Afferent cortical connections and architectonics of the superior temporal sulcus and surrounding cortex in the rhesus monkey. Brain Research. 1978;**149**(1):1-24

[50] Pandya DN, Yeterian EHJCC. Architecture and connections of cortical association areas. In: Peters A, Jones EG, editors. Association and Auditory Cortices. Cerebral Cortex. Vol. 4. Boston, MA: Springer; 1985

[51] Sitoh YY, Tien RD. The limbic system. An overview of the anatomy and its development. Neuroimaging Clinics of North America. 1997;**7**(1):1-10

[52] Lee H, Chung MK, Kang H, Kim BN, Lee DS. Computing the shape of brain networks using graph filtration and Gromov-Hausdorff metric. Medical Image Computing and Computer-Assisted Intervention: MICCAI International Conference on Medical Image Computing and Computer-Assisted Intervention. Springer, Berlin, Heidelberg, 2011;14(Pt 2):302-309.

[53] Lee H, Lee DS, Kang H, Kim BN, Chung MK. Sparse brain network recovery under compressed sensing. IEEE Transactions on Medical Imaging. 2011;**30**(5):1154-1165

[54] Lee H, Kang H, Chung MK, Kim BN, Lee DS. Persistent brain network homology from the perspective of dendrogram. IEEE Transactions on Medical Imaging. 2012;**31**(12):2267-2277

[55] Buchsbaum MS, Hollander E, Haznedar MM, Tang C, Spiegel-Cohen J, Wei TC, et al. Effect of fluoxetine on regional cerebral metabolism in autistic spectrum disorders: A pilot study. The International Journal of Neuropsychopharmacology. 2001;**4**(2):119-125

[56] Park HR, Kim IH, Kang H, Lee DS, Kim BN, Kim DG, et al. Nucleus accumbens deep brain stimulation for a patient with self-injurious behavior and autism spectrum disorder: Functional and structural changes of the brain: Report of a case and review of literature. Acta Neurochirurgica. 2017;**159**(1):137-143

[57] Żarnowska I, Chrapko B, Gwizda G, Nocuń A, Mitosek-Szewczyk K, Gasior M. Therapeuticuseofcarbohydrate-restricted diets in an autistic child; a case report of clinical and 18FDG PET findings. Metabolic Brain Disease. 2018;**33**(4):1187-1192

[58] Frye RE, Rossignol DA. Treatments for biomedical abnormalities associated with autism spectrum disorder. Frontiers in Pediatrics. 2014;**2**:66

[59] Courchesne-Loyer A, Croteau E, Castellano CA, St-Pierre V,

Hennebelle M, Cunnane SC. Inverse relationship between brain glucose and ketone metabolism in adults during short-term moderate dietary ketosis: A dual tracer quantitative positron emission tomography study. Journal of Cerebral Blood Flow and Metabolism. 2017;**37**(7):2485-2493

[60] Joseph-Mathurin N, Su Y, Blazey TM, Jasielec M, Vlassenko A, Friedrichsen K, et al. Utility of perfusion PET measures to assess neuronal injury in Alzheimer's disease. Alzheimer's & Dementia. 2018;**10**:669-677

[61] Boddaert N, Chabane N, Barthélemy C, Bourgeois M, Poline JB, Brunelle F, et al. Bitemporal lobe dysfonction in infantile autism: Positron emission tomography study. Journal de Radiologie. 2002;**83**(12 Pt 1): 1829-1833

[62] Happé F, Ehlers S, Fletcher P, Frith U, Johansson M, Gillberg C, et al. 'Theory of mind' in the brain. Evidence from a PET scan study of Asperger syndrome. Neuroreport. 1996;**8**(1):197-201

[63] Müller RA, Chugani DC, Behen ME, Rothermel RD, Muzik O, Chakraborty PK, et al. Impairment of dentato-thalamo-cortical pathway in autistic men: Language activation data from positron emission tomography. Neuroscience Letters. 1998;**245**(1):1-4

[64] Hall GB, Szechtman H, Nahmias C. Enhanced salience and emotion recognition in autism: A PET study. The American Journal of Psychiatry. 2003;**160**(8):1439-1441

[65] Müller RA, Behen ME, Rothermel RD, Chugani DC, Muzik O, Mangner TJ, et al. Brain mapping of language and auditory perception in high-functioning autistic adults: A PET study. Journal of Autism and Developmental Disorders. 1999;**29**(1):19-31

[66] Chugani DC, Muzik O, Rothermel R, Behen M, Chakraborty P, Mangner T, et al. Altered serotonin synthesis in the dentatothalamocortical pathway in autistic boys. Annals of Neurology. 1997;**42**(4):666-669

[67] Boddaert N, Belin P, Chabane N, Poline JB, Barthélémy C, Mouren-Simeoni MC, et al. Perception of complex sounds: Abnormal pattern of cortical activation in autism. The American Journal of Psychiatry. 2003;**160**(11):2057-2060

[68] Boddaert N, Chabane N, Belin P, Bourgeois M, Royer V, Barthelemy C, et al. Perception of complex sounds in autism: Abnormal auditory cortical processing in children. The American Journal of Psychiatry. 2004;**161**(11):2117-2120

[69] Saitovitch A, Rechtman E, Lemaitre H, Tacchella J-M, Vinçon-Leite A, Douard E, et al. Superior temporal sulcus hypoperfusion in children with autism spectrum disorder: An arterial spin-labeling magnetic resonance study. BioRxiv. 2019:771584

[70] Yang CJ, Tan HP, Du YJ. The developmental disruptions of serotonin signaling may involved in autism during early brain development. Neuroscience. 2014;**267**:1-10

[71] Schain RJ, Freedman DX. Studies on 5-hydroxyindole metabolism in autistic and other mentally retarded children. The Journal of Pediatrics. 1961;**58**:315-320

[72] McDougle CJ, Naylor ST, Cohen DJ, Volkmar FR, Heninger GR, Price LH. A double-blind, placebo-controlled study of fluvoxamine in adults with autistic

disorder. Archives of General Psychiatry. 1996;**53**(11):1001-1008

[73] Croen LA, Grether JK, Yoshida CK, Odouli R, Hendrick V. Antidepressant use during pregnancy and childhood autism spectrum disorders. Archives of General Psychiatry. 2011;**68**(11):1104-1112

[74] Hollander E, Soorya L, Chaplin W, Anagnostou E, Taylor BP, Ferretti CJ, et al. A double-blind placebo-controlled trial of fluoxetine for repetitive behaviors and global severity in adult autism spectrum disorders. The American Journal of Psychiatry. 2012;**169**(3):292-299

[75] Chakraborty PK, Mangner TJ, Chugani DC, Muzik O, Chugani HT. A high-yield and simplified procedure for the synthesis of alpha-[11C]methyl-L-tryptophan. Nuclear Medicine and Biology. 1996;**23**(8):1005-1008

[76] Chugani DC, Muzik O. Alpha[C-11] methyl-L-tryptophan PET maps brain serotonin synthesis and kynurenine pathway metabolism. Journal of Cerebral Blood Flow and Metabolism. 2000;**20**(1):2-9

[77] Chugani DC, Muzik O, Behen M, Rothermel R, Janisse JJ, Lee J, et al. Developmental changes in brain serotonin synthesis capacity in autistic and nonautistic children. Annals of Neurology. 1999;**45**(3):287-295

[78] Chandana SR, Behen ME, Juhász C, Muzik O, Rothermel RD, Mangner TJ, et al. Significance of abnormalities in developmental trajectory and asymmetry of cortical serotonin synthesis in autism. International Journal of Developmental Neuroscience. 2005;**23**(2-3):171-182

[79] Suehiro M, Scheffel U, Ravert HT, Dannals RF, Wagner HN Jr. [11C](+) McN5652 as a radiotracer for imaging serotonin uptake sites with PET. Life Sciences. 1993;**53**(11):883-892

[80] Nakamura K, Sekine Y, Ouchi Y, Tsujii M, Yoshikawa E, Futatsubashi M, et al. Brain serotonin and dopamine transporter bindings in adults with high-functioning autism. Archives of General Psychiatry. 2010;**67**(1):59-68

[81] Wilson AA, Ginovart N, Hussey D, Meyer J, Houle S. *In vitro* and *in vivo* characterisation of [11C]-DASB: A probe for in vivo measurements of the serotonin transporter by positron emission tomography. Nuclear Medicine and Biology. 2002;**29**(5):509-515

[82] Girgis RR, Slifstein M, Xu X, Frankle WG, Anagnostou E, Wasserman S, et al. The 5-HT(2A) receptor and serotonin transporter in Asperger's disorder: A PET study with [^{11}C]MDL 100907 and [^{11}C]DASB. Psychiatry Research. 2011;**194**(3):230-234

[83] Andersson M, Tangen Ä, Farde L, Bölte S, Halldin C, Borg J, et al. Serotonin transporter availability in adults with autism-a positron emission tomography study. Molecular Psychiatry. May 2021;**26**(5):1647-1658

[84] Lundberg J, Halldin C, Farde L. Measurement of serotonin transporter binding with PET and [11C]MADAM: A test-retest reproducibility study. Synapse. 2006;**60**(3):256-263

[85] Huang Y, Bae S-A, Zhu Z, Guo N, Hwang D-R, Laruelle M. Fluorinated analogues of ADAM as new PET radioligands for the serotonin transporter: Synthesis and pharmacological evaluation. Journal of Labelled Compounds and Radiopharmaceuticals. 2001;**44**(S1):S18-S20

[86] Huang Y, Hwang DR, Narendran R, Sudo Y, Chatterjee R, Bae SA, et al. Comparative evaluation in nonhuman primates of five PET radiotracers for imaging the serotonin transporters: [11C] McN 5652, [11C]ADAM, [11C]DASB, [11C]DAPA, and [11C]AFM. Journal of Cerebral Blood Flow and Metabolism. 2002;**22**(11):1377-1398

[87] Blin J, Sette G, Fiorelli M, Bletry O, Elghozi JL, Crouzel C, et al. A method for the in vivo investigation of the serotonergic 5-HT2 receptors in the human cerebral cortex using positron emission tomography and 18F-labeled setoperone. Journal of Neurochemistry. 1990;**54**(5):1744-1754

[88] Beversdorf DQ, Nordgren RE, Bonab AA, Fischman AJ, Weise SB, Dougherty DD, et al. 5-HT2 receptor distribution shown by [18F] setoperone PET in high-functioning autistic adults. The Journal of Neuropsychiatry and Clinical Neurosciences. 2012;**24**(2):191-197

[89] Goldberg J, Anderson GM, Zwaigenbaum L, Hall GB, Nahmias C, Thompson A, et al. Cortical serotonin type-2 receptor density in parents of children with autism spectrum disorders. Journal of Autism and Developmental Disorders. 2009;**39**(1):97-104

[90] Lefevre A, Richard N, Mottolese R, Leboyer M, Sirigu A. An Association between serotonin 1A receptor, Gray matter volume, and sociability in healthy subjects and in autism Spectrum disorder. Autism Research. 2020;**13**(11):1843-1855

[91] Modahl C, Green L, Fein D, Morris M, Waterhouse L, Feinstein C, et al. Plasma oxytocin levels in autistic children. Biological Psychiatry. 1998;**43**(4):270-277

[92] Guastella AJ, Einfeld SL, Gray KM, Rinehart NJ, Tonge BJ, Lambert TJ, et al. Intranasal oxytocin improves emotion recognition for youth with autism spectrum disorders. Biological Psychiatry. 2010;**67**(7):692-694

[93] Domes G, Heinrichs M, Kumbier E, Grossmann A, Hauenstein K, Herpertz SC. Effects of intranasal oxytocin on the neural basis of face processing in autism spectrum disorder. Biological Psychiatry. 2013;**74**(3):164-171

[94] Gordon I, Vander Wyk BC, Bennett RH, Cordeaux C, Lucas MV, Eilbott JA, et al. Oxytocin enhances brain function in children with autism. Proceedings of the National Academy of Sciences of the United States of America. 2013;**110**(52):20953-20958

[95] Wang C, Moseley CK, Carlin SM, Wilson CM, Neelamegam R, Hooker JM. Radiosynthesis and evaluation of [11C] EMPA as a potential PET tracer for orexin 2 receptors. Bioorganic & Medicinal Chemistry Letters. 2013;**23**(11):3389-3392

[96] Vidal B, Karpenko IA, Liger F, Fieux S, Bouillot C, Billard T, et al. [(11) C]PF-3274167 as a PET radiotracer of oxytocin receptors: Radiosynthesis and evaluation in rat brain. Nuclear Medicine and Biology. 2017;**55**:1-6

[97] Mottolese R, Redouté J, Costes N, Le Bars D, Sirigu A. Switching brain serotonin with oxytocin. Proceedings of the National Academy of Sciences of the United States of America. 2014;**111**(23):8637-8642

[98] Lefevre A, Mottolese R, Redouté J, Costes N, Le Bars D, Geoffray MM, et al. Oxytocin fails to recruit serotonergic neurotransmission in the autistic brain. Cerebral Cortex. 2018;**28**(12):4169-4178

[99] Hirosawa T, Kikuchi M, Ouchi Y, Takahashi T, Yoshimura Y, Kosaka H, et al. A pilot study of serotonergic modulation after long-term administration of oxytocin in autism spectrum disorder. Autism Research. 2017;**10**(5):821-828

[100] Gadow KD, Roohi J, DeVincent CJ, Hatchwell E. Association of ADHD, tics, and anxiety with dopamine transporter (DAT1) genotype in autism spectrum disorder. Journal of Child Psychology and Psychiatry, and Allied Disciplines. 2008;**49**(12):1331-1338

[101] Staal WG, de Krom M, de Jonge MV. Brief report: The dopamine-3-receptor gene (DRD3) is associated with specific repetitive behavior in autism spectrum disorder (ASD). Journal of Autism and Developmental Disorders. 2012;**42**(5):885-888

[102] Hamilton PJ, Campbell NG, Sharma S, Erreger K, Herborg Hansen F, Saunders C, et al. De novo mutation in the dopamine transporter gene associates dopamine dysfunction with autism spectrum disorder. Molecular Psychiatry. 2013;**18**(12):1315-1323

[103] Ernst M, Zametkin AJ, Matochik JA, Pascualvaca D, Cohen RM. Low medial prefrontal dopaminergic activity in autistic children. Lancet. 1997;**350**(9078):638

[104] Nieminen-von Wendt TS, Metsähonkala L, Kulomäki TA, Aalto S, Autti TH, Vanhala R, et al. Increased presynaptic dopamine function in Asperger syndrome. Neuroreport. 2004;**15**(5):757-760

[105] Schalbroeck R, de Geus-Oei LF, Selten JP, Yaqub M, Schrantee A, van Amelsvoort T, et al. Cerebral [(18) F]-FDOPA uptake in autism Spectrum disorder and its Association with autistic traits. Diagnostics. 2021;**11**(12):2404

[106] Schalbroeck R, van Velden FHP, de Geus-Oei LF, Yaqub M, van Amelsvoort T, Booij J, et al. Striatal dopamine synthesis capacity in autism spectrum disorder and its relation with social defeat: An [(18)F]-FDOPA PET/ CT study. Translational Psychiatry. 2021;**11**(1):47

[107] Fernell E, Watanabe Y, Adolfsson I, Tani Y, Bergström M, Hartvig P, et al. Possible effects of tetrahydrobiopterin treatment in six children with autism--clinical and positron emission tomography data: A pilot study. Developmental Medicine and Child Neurology. 1997;**39**(5):313-318

[108] Fujino J, Tei S, Takahata K, Matsuoka K, Tagai K, Sano Y, et al. Binding of dopamine D1 receptor and noradrenaline transporter in individuals with autism Spectrum disorder: A PET study. Cerebral Cortex. 2020;**30**(12):6458-6468

[109] Zürcher NR, Walsh EC, Phillips RD, Cernasov PM, Tseng CJ, Dharanikota A, et al. A simultaneous [(11)C]raclopride positron emission tomography and functional magnetic resonance imaging investigation of striatal dopamine binding in autism. Translational Psychiatry. 2021;**11**(1):33

[110] Kelleher RJ 3rd, Bear MF. The autistic neuron: Troubled translation? Cell. 2008;**135**(3):401-406

[111] Pizzarelli R, Cherubini E. Alterations of GABAergic signaling in autism spectrum disorders. Neural Plasticity. 2011;**2011**:297153

[112] Cook EH Jr, Courchesne RY, Cox NJ, Lord C, Gonen D, Guter SJ, et al. Linkage-disequilibrium mapping of

autistic disorder, with 15q11-13 markers. American Journal of Human Genetics. 1998;**62**(5):1077-1083

[113] Coghlan S, Horder J, Inkster B, Mendez MA, Murphy DG, Nutt DJ. GABA system dysfunction in autism and related disorders: From synapse to symptoms. Neuroscience and Biobehavioral Reviews. 2012;**36**(9):2044-2055

[114] Blatt GJ, Fitzgerald CM, Guptill JT, Booker AB, Kemper TL, Bauman ML. Density and distribution of hippocampal neurotransmitter receptors in autism: An autoradiographic study. Journal of Autism and Developmental Disorders. 2001;**31**(6):537-543

[115] Oblak A, Gibbs TT, Blatt GJ. Decreased GABAA receptors and benzodiazepine binding sites in the anterior cingulate cortex in autism. Autism Research. 2009;**2**(4):205-219

[116] Tyzio R, Nardou R, Ferrari DC, Tsintsadze T, Shahrokhi A, Eftekhari S, et al. Oxytocin-mediated GABA inhibition during delivery attenuates autism pathogenesis in rodent offspring. Science. 2014;**343**(6171):675-679

[117] Mendez MA, Horder J, Myers J, Coghlan S, Stokes P, Erritzoe D, et al. The brain GABA-benzodiazepine receptor alpha-5 subtype in autism spectrum disorder: A pilot [(11)C]Ro15-4513 positron emission tomography study. Neuropharmacology. 2013;**68**:195-201

[118] Horder J, Andersson M, Mendez MA, Singh N, Tangen Ä, Lundberg J, et al. GABA(a) receptor availability is not altered in adults with autism spectrum disorder or in mouse models. Science Translational Medicine. 2018;**10**(461):eaam8434

[119] Fung LK, Flores RE, Gu M, Sun KL, James D, Schuck RK, et al. Thalamic and prefrontal GABA concentrations but not GABA(a) receptor densities are altered in high-functioning adults with autism spectrum disorder. Molecular Psychiatry. 2020;**26**(5):1634-1646

[120] Rubenstein JL, Merzenich MM. Model of autism: Increased ratio of excitation/inhibition in key neural systems. Genes, Brain, and Behavior. 2003;**2**(5):255-267

[121] Barret O, Tamagnan G, Batis J, Jennings D, Zubal G, Russel D, et al. Quantitation of glutamate mGluR5 receptor with 18F-FPEB PET in humans. NeuroImage. 2010;**52**:215

[122] Sullivan JM, Lim K, Labaree D, Lin SF, McCarthy TJ, Seibyl JP, et al. Kinetic analysis of the metabotropic glutamate subtype 5 tracer [(18)F] FPEB in bolus and bolus-plus-constant-infusion studies in humans. Journal of Cerebral Blood Flow and Metabolism. 2013;**33**(4):532-541

[123] Wong DF, Waterhouse R, Kuwabara H, Kim J, Brašić JR, Chamroonrat W, et al. 18F-FPEB, a PET radiopharmaceutical for quantifying metabotropic glutamate 5 receptors: A first-in-human study of radiochemical safety, biokinetics, and radiation dosimetry. Journal of Nuclear Medicine. 2013;**54**(3):388-396

[124] Toyohara J, Sakata M, Oda K, Ishii K, Ito K, Hiura M, et al. Initial human PET studies of metabotropic glutamate receptor type 1 ligand 11C-ITMM. Journal of Nuclear Medicine. 2013;**54**(8):1302-1307

[125] Cai G, Wang M, Wang S, Liu Y, Zhao Y, Zhu Y, et al. Brain mGluR5 in Shank3B(−/−) mice studied with *in vivo* [(18)F]FPEB PET imaging and *ex vivo*

immunoblotting. Frontiers in Psychiatry. 2019;**10**:38

[126] Fatemi SH, Wong DF, Brašić JR, Kuwabara H, Mathur A, Folsom TD, et al. Metabotropic glutamate receptor 5 tracer [(18)F]-FPEB displays increased binding potential in postcentral gyrus and cerebellum of male individuals with autism: A pilot PET study. Cerebellum & Ataxias. 2018;**5**:3

[127] Brašić JR, Nandi A, Russell DS, Jennings D, Barret O, Martin SD, et al. Cerebral expression of metabotropic glutamate receptor subtype 5 in idiopathic autism Spectrum disorder and fragile X syndrome: A pilot study. International Journal of Molecular Sciences. 2021;**22**(6):2863

[128] Shih YT, Hsueh YP. The involvement of endoplasmic reticulum formation and protein synthesis efficiency in VCP- and ATL1-related neurological disorders. Journal of Biomedical Science. 2018;**25**(1):2

[129] Shandal V, Sundaram SK, Chugani DC, Kumar A, Behen ME, Chugani HT. Abnormal brain protein synthesis in language areas of children with pervasive developmental disorder: A L-[1-11C]-leucine PET study. Journal of Child Neurology. 2011;**26**(11):1347-1354

[130] Schmidt KC, Loutaev I, Quezado Z, Sheeler C, Smith CB. Regional rates of brain protein synthesis are unaltered in dexmedetomidine sedated young men with fragile X syndrome: A L-[1-(11) C]leucine PET study. Neurobiology of Disease. 2020;**143**:104978

[131] Dionne O, Lortie A, Gagnon F, Corbin F. Rates of protein synthesis are reduced in peripheral blood mononuclear cells (PBMCs) from fragile X individuals. PLoS One. 2021;**16**(5):e0251367

[132] Hardan AY, Handen BL. A retrospective open trial of adjunctive donepezil in children and adolescents with autistic disorder. Journal of Child and Adolescent Psychopharmacology. 2002;**12**(3):237-241

[133] Nicolson R, Craven-Thuss B, Smith J. A prospective, open-label trial of galantamine in autistic disorder. Journal of Child and Adolescent Psychopharmacology. 2006;**16**(5):621-629

[134] Karvat G, Kimchi T. Acetylcholine elevation relieves cognitive rigidity and social deficiency in a mouse model of autism. Neuropsychopharmacology. 2014;**39**(4):831-840

[135] Suzuki K, Sugihara G, Ouchi Y, Nakamura K, Tsujii M, Futatsubashi M, et al. Reduced acetylcholinesterase activity in the fusiform gyrus in adults with autism spectrum disorders. Archives of General Psychiatry. 2011;**68**(3):306-313

[136] Stigler KA, Sweeten TL, Posey DJ, McDougle CJ. Autism and immune factors: A comprehensive review. Research in Autism Spectrum Disorder. 2009;**3**(4):840-860

[137] Kato TA, Yamauchi Y, Horikawa H, Monji A, Mizoguchi Y, Seki Y, et al. Neurotransmitters, psychotropic drugs and microglia: Clinical implications for psychiatry. Current Medicinal Chemistry. 2013;**20**(3):331-344

[138] Best L, Ghadery C, Pavese N, Tai YF, Strafella AP. New and old TSPO PET Radioligands for imaging brain microglial activation in neurodegenerative disease. Current Neurology and Neuroscience Reports. 2019;**19**(5):24

[139] Werry EL, Bright FM, Piguet O, Ittner LM, Halliday GM, Hodges JR, et al. Recent developments in TSPO PET imaging

as a biomarker of Neuroinflammation in neurodegenerative disorders. International Journal of Molecular Sciences. 2019;**20**(13):3161

[140] Suzuki K, Sugihara G, Ouchi Y, Nakamura K, Futatsubashi M, Takebayashi K, et al. Microglial activation in young adults with autism spectrum disorder. JAMA Psychiatry. 2013;**70**(1):49-58

[141] Zürcher NR, Loggia ML, Mullett JE, Tseng C, Bhanot A, Richey L, et al. [(11)C]PBR28 MR-PET imaging reveals lower regional brain expression of translocator protein (TSPO) in young adult males with autism spectrum disorder. Molecular Psychiatry. 2020;**26**(5):1659-1669

[142] Owen DR, Howell OW, Tang SP, Wells LA, Bennacef I, Bergstrom M, et al. Two binding sites for [3H]PBR28 in human brain: Implications for TSPO PET imaging of neuroinflammation. Journal of Cerebral Blood Flow and Metabolism. 2010;**30**(9):1608-1618

[143] Fujita M, Kobayashi M, Ikawa M, Gunn RN, Rabiner EA, Owen DR, et al. Comparison of four (11)C-labeled PET ligands to quantify translocator protein 18 kDa (TSPO) in human brain: (R)-PK11195, PBR28, DPA-713, and ER176-based on recent publications that measured specific-to-non-displaceable ratios. EJNMMI Research. 2017;**7**(1):84

[144] Hafizi S, Tseng HH, Rao N, Selvanathan T, Kenk M, Bazinet RP, et al. Imaging microglial activation in untreated first-episode psychosis: A PET study with [(18)F]FEPPA. The American Journal of Psychiatry. 2017;**174**(2):118-124

[145] Kobayashi M, Jiang T, Telu S, Zoghbi SS, Gunn RN, Rabiner EA, et al. (11)C-DPA-713 has much greater specific binding to translocator protein 18 kDa (TSPO) in human brain than (11)C-(R)-PK11195. Journal of Cerebral Blood Flow and Metabolism. 2018;**38**(3):393-403

[146] Koob GF, Bloom FE. Behavioral effects of neuropeptides: Endorphins and vasopressin. Annual Review of Physiology. 1982;**44**:571-582

[147] Jard S. Vasopressin receptors. A historical survey. Advances in Experimental Medicine and Biology. 1998;**449**:1-13

[148] Goodson JL, Thompson RR. Nonapeptide mechanisms of social cognition, behavior and species-specific social systems. Current Opinion in Neurobiology. 2010;**20**(6):784-794

[149] Kelly AM, Goodson JL. Hypothalamic oxytocin and vasopressin neurons exert sex-specific effects on pair bonding, gregariousness, and aggression in finches. Proceedings of the National Academy of Sciences of the United States of America. 2014;**111**(16):6069-6074

[150] Caldwell HK. Oxytocin and vasopressin: Powerful regulators of social behavior. The Neuroscientist. 2017;**23**(5):517-528

[151] Miller M, Bales KL, Taylor SL, Yoon J, Hostetler CM, Carter CS, et al. Oxytocin and vasopressin in children and adolescents with autism spectrum disorders: Sex differences and associations with symptoms. Autism Research. 2013;**6**(2):91-102

[152] Shou XJ, Xu XJ, Zeng XZ, Liu Y, Yuan HS, Xing Y, et al. A volumetric and functional connectivity MRI study of brain arginine-vasopressin pathways in autistic children. Neuroscience Bulletin. 2017;**33**(2):130-142

[153] Parker KJ, Garner JP, Oztan O, Tarara ER, Li J, Sclafani V, et al. Arginine vasopressin in cerebrospinal fluid is a marker of sociality in nonhuman primates. Science Translational Medicine. 2018;**10**(439):eaam9100

[154] Wilczyński KM, Zasada I, Siwiec A, Janas-Kozik M. Differences in oxytocin and vasopressin levels in individuals suffering from the autism spectrum disorders vs general population - a systematic review. Neuropsychiatric Disease and Treatment. 2019;**15**:2613-2620

[155] Bolognani F, Rubido MV, Squassante L, Wandel C, Derks M, Murtagh L, et al. A phase 2 clinical trial of a vasopressin V1a receptor antagonist shows improved adaptive behaviors in men with autism spectrum disorder. Science Translational Medicine. 2019;**11**(491):eaat7838

[156] Schnider P, Bissantz C, Bruns A, Dolente C, Goetschi E, Jakob-Roetne R, et al. Discovery of Balovaptan, a vasopressin 1a receptor antagonist for the treatment of autism Spectrum disorder. Journal of Medicinal Chemistry. 2020;**63**(4):1511-1525

[157] Fabio K, Guillon C, Lacey CJ, Lu SF, Heindel ND, Ferris CF, et al. Synthesis and evaluation of potent and selective human V1a receptor antagonists as potential ligands for PET or SPECT imaging. Bioorganic & Medicinal Chemistry. 2012;**20**(3):1337-1345

[158] Naik R, Valentine H, Hall A, Mathews WB, Harris JC, Carter CS, et al. Development of a radio ligand for imaging V1a vasopressin receptors with PET. European Journal of Medicinal Chemistry. 2017;**139**:644-656

[159] Haider A, Xiao Z, Xia X, Chen J, Van RS, Kuang S, et al. Development of a triazolobenzodiazepine-based PET probe for subtype-selective vasopressin 1A receptor imaging. Pharmacological Research. 2021;**173**:105886

[160] Lombardo MV, Lai MC, Baron-Cohen S. Big data approaches to decomposing heterogeneity across the autism spectrum. Molecular Psychiatry. 2019;**24**(10):1435-1450

[161] Hong SJ, Vogelstein JT, Gozzi A, Bernhardt BC, Yeo BTT, Milham MP, et al. Toward neurosubtypes in autism. Biological Psychiatry. 2020;**88**(1):111-128

[162] Owen DR, Yeo AJ, Gunn RN, Song K, Wadsworth G, Lewis A, et al. An 18-kDa translocator protein (TSPO) polymorphism explains differences in binding affinity of the PET radioligand PBR28. Journal of Cerebral Blood Flow and Metabolism. 2012;**32**(1):1-5

[163] McPartland JC, Bernier RA, Jeste SS, Dawson G, Nelson CA, Chawarska K, et al. The autism biomarkers consortium for clinical trials (ABC-CT): Scientific context, study design, and Progress toward biomarker qualification. Frontiers in Integrative Neuroscience. 2020;**14**:16

Chapter 10

May Big Data Analysis Be Used to Diagnose Early Autism?

Terje Solsvik Kristensen

Abstract

In this paper, a technique for early autism identification is presented. Both a multilayered perceptron (MLP) neural network and a support vector machine (SVM) have been used for classification. Detection of early autism is important, since the prognosis to treat autism is then much better. The patterns of both methods to use have been extracted from high-performance liquid chromatography data in urine. The training samples consist of two types, one from normal children and one from children with autism. The classification rate has been estimated for both algorithms to about 80% or better. The algorithm that gave the best result was SVM. The program that we used to do the analysis we have developed in Java. A lot of work remains to improve the results and increase the recognition rate of the data. The parameter values used in both networks and also the configuration of the networks are not yet optimal. This could be solved by using a particle swarm optimization (PSO) method. We have not yet been using a deep learning network, for instance, a TensorFlow network to raise the classification rate of the different algorithms. We have not yet made a classification between different types of autism of the autism spectrum. All this belongs to future work.

Keywords: autism, HPLC spectra, MLP, SVM, PSO, TensorFlow

1. Introduction

Autism is usually diagnosed by a series of behavioral tests and symptoms [1]. Autism effects the information processing in the brain by changing how the nerve cells (neurons) and their synapses are connecting and organizing themselves. What is triggering this process is not yet understood. Globally, about 25 million people is estimated to suffer from autism. Autism is therefore a huge problem to solve. However, at the moment there is no known cure for it.

Suffering from autism may be identified early at an age of 5 months. However, a clear diagnosis is usually not possible before the children are one and half year or three years old. There seems to be a growing evidence that the earlier the behavioral therapies of autism are started, the better the chances are for the children to be able to live relatively normal lives when growing up.

Autism may be linked to metabolic abnormalities, and these metabolic changes may be detectable in the children's urine. By using high-performance liquid chromatography (HPLC) spectral data [2], we have found that children of the autism group and the normal group seem to have distinct chemical fingerprints in their urine.

An early test may soon be a reality to identify children at risk for developing early autism. The urine of children with autism may have a certain chemical signature. This indicates also that there can be certain substances in the urine that may trigger the onset of autism [3, 4].

If we are able to develop a method to identify early autism by a chemical or statistical test rather by observing a full-blown behavior, we can start the treatment earlier. There also exist scientists that are linking autism with the production of toxins that may interfere with the brain development [5]. One compound that may be identified in the urine is N-methyl nicotinamide (NMND) which also has been associated with Parkinson's disease. There are also scientists that are arguing for that autism may be associated with metabolic products of certain bacteria that must be identified [6].

However, this work is on how to use a multi-layered perceptron (MLP) neural network [7, 8] and a support vector machine (SVM) [9], to classify between HPLC samples belonging to normal children and samples belonging to children suffering from autism.

The organization of the chapter is as follows: in Section 2, the data is described, and in Section 3 the feature extraction techniques used have been presented. Section 4 defines a MLP neural network and the algorithm used for training it is defined. In Section 5, the SVM network and training algorithm for such a network is presented and in Section 6 we present the results of both a small-scale experiment and a proof of concept experiment. Section 7 gives the conclusion. In Section 8, we present further work on how we may use more advanced technology to confirm and validate the results achieved in this chapter.

2. The data

The HPLC data was recording by a company Tipogen ltd. at Bergen Hightech Centre, Norway. The company went corrupt some years ago. These of the first experiment was based on 30 samples of urine spectra from both normal and autism children. The aim of this first experiment was to verify a so-called *proof of principle*. First, we want to find out if datamining based on machine learning algorithms could be used to verify autism using HPLC spectra of children [2]. **Figure 1** shows how HPLC spectra look like.

The first axis represents what is called "*retention time*." This represents the peak ID. The second axis represents the intentions or the "*peak area*." The data was delivered in a spread sheet format. One spread sheet for normal children and one spread sheet for children with autism.

3. Feature extraction

The sample length may vary for both control and autism data. This was not easy to handle in an adequate way early in the analysis. An example of a pattern generated from the data is given in **Figure 2**. Each sample has a specific number of peaks. The different numbers of peaks belonging to each sample makes the analysis more complicated and was an important parameter to be estimated in the recognition process.

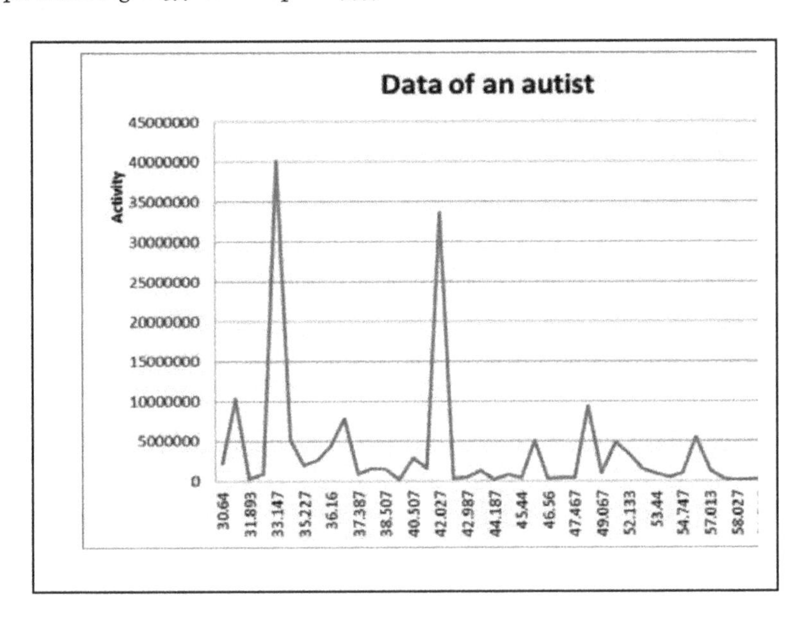

Figure 1.
An example of a HLPC spectrum of a child with autism.

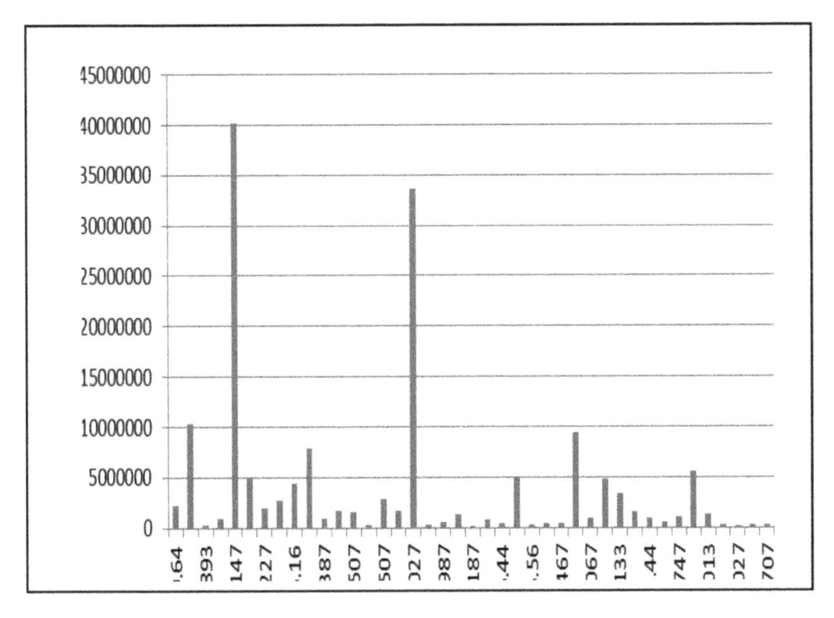

Figure 2.
HPLC peak extraction is generating by the data patterns.

3.1 Pattern diagnostics

To discriminate patterns acquired from healthy individuals and individuals affected from a disease is the most important aspect of a pattern diagnostic technique. Pattern diagnostic is based on the analysis of a huge amount of HPLC data [2] and may be used to find patterns to identify a disease.

Mass spectrometry (MS) data in the blood is an alternative method to be used [10, 11]. This method has been given promising results in detection of early cancer [12] and may also be used to show early autism. Mass spectrometry data consists of a set of m/z values (m is the atomic mass and z is the charge of the ion) and the corresponding relative intensities of all molecules present with that m/z ratio. The MS data of a chemical sample is thus an indication of the actual molecules. The data might therefore be used to predict the presence of a disease condition and distinguish it from a sample taken from a healthy individual.

4. Multi-layered perceptron

A multi-layered perceptron (MLP) network generally contains three or more layers of processing units [7, 8]. The topology of such a network is shown in **Figure 3**. Here, the network is containing three layers of nodes. The first layer defines the input layer. The middle layer or the "hidden" layer consists of "feature detectors"—units that respond to particular features that may appear in the input pattern. Usually, we may have more than one hidden layer. The output layer is the last layer. The activities of the output units are read as output from the network and define different categories of patterns.

4.1 The hidden layers

A MLP network usually have many network layers connected by adjustable weights. This removes the restriction that the network is only able to be able to

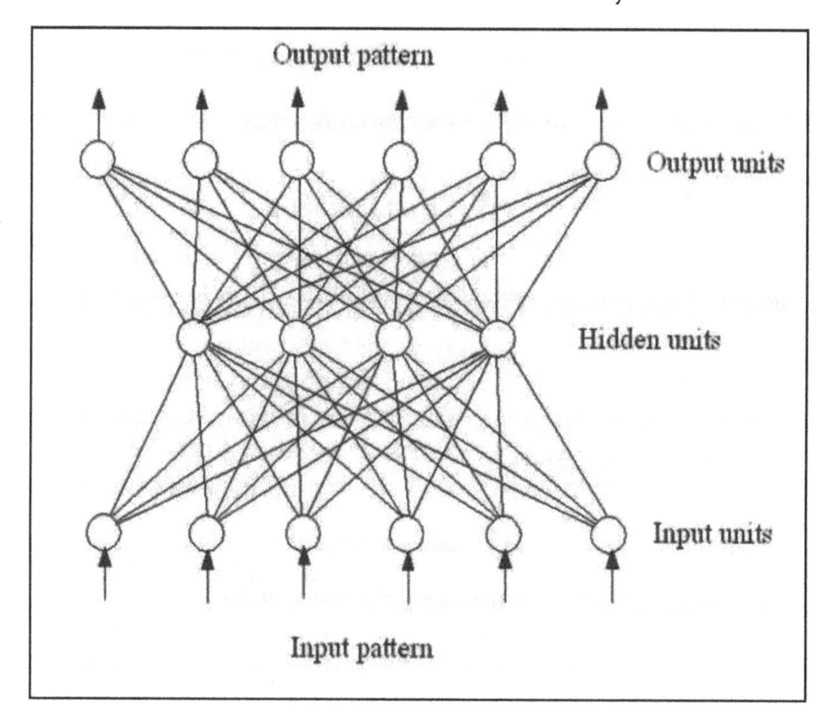

Figure 3.
A MLP network consisting of three layers of nodes.

classify linear separable patterns that the ordinary perceptron network only is able to do. By introducing many hidden layers, more complex patterns can be classified. By inserting a new hidden layer, the network may learn more complex pattern, but at the same time more hidden layers could decrease the rate of performance of the network. Many degrees of freedom may then be introduced that are not really needed. This depends, however, on the actual algorithm being used.

4.2 Training of MLP

A supervised learning algorithm is used to train the MLP network. The network is presented to a set of training examples, where a target vector is given for each training example. The target vector is then compared to the output vector. The weights of the network are adjusted to make the network perform better according to the training examples and targets defined. The training algorithm used in this chapter is the backpropagation algorithm. This is a well-known learning algorithm used for classification [13–15].

Each node in the network is activated in accordance with the input of the node and the node activation function. The difference between the calculated output and the target output is compared. All the weights between the output layer, hidden layers, and the input layer are then adjusted by using this error value. The sigmoidal function $f(x) = 1/(1 + e^{-x})$ is used to compute the output of a node, but other functions may also be used and may even give better performance. The weighted sum $S_j = \sum w_{ji}a_i$ is inserted into the sigmoidal function, and the result of the output value from a unit j is given by:

$$f(S_j) = 1/(1 + e^{-S_j}), \tag{1}$$

The error value of an output unit j is computed by formula:

$$\delta_j = (t_j - a_j)f'(S_j) \tag{2}$$

t_j and a_j are the target and output value for unit j, and f' is the derivative of the function f. The error value calculated for a hidden node is given by:

$$\delta_j = \sum \delta_k \, w_{kj} \left(f''(S_j)\right) \tag{3}$$

From the formula, we see that the error of a processing unit in the hidden layer is computed by the upper layer. Finally, the weights can be adjusted by:

$$\Delta w_{ji} = \alpha \delta_j \, a_i \tag{4}$$

Here, α is the learning rate parameter.

Very often another parameter is also used in the MLP network. It is called the momentum (β). This additional parameter can be very helpful in speeding up the convergence of the algorithm and avoiding local minima [7]. By including momentum in the Eq. (5), the next iteration step can be written as:

$$w_{ji}(t+1) = w_{ji}(t) + \alpha \delta_j \, a_i + \beta \Delta w_{ji} \, (t) \tag{5}$$

Here again α is the learning rate, β is the momentum, and Δw_{ji} is the weight change from the previous processing step.

5. SVM theory

SVM (support vector machine) is a computationally efficient learning algorithm that now is being widely used in pattern recognition and classification problems [8]. The algorithm has been derived from the ideas of statistical learning theory to control the generalization abilities of a learning machine [16, 17]. An optimal hyperplane is learnt that classifies the given pattern that the machine is learning. By use of what we called kernel functions, the input feature space can be transformed into a higher dimensional space where the optimal hyperplane can be learnt. Such an approach gives great flexibility by using one of many learning models by changing the kernel function. A nonlinear mapping $\Phi : R^D \rightarrow F$ where F represents the feature space and k (x, x′) is a Mercer's Kernel [18]. The inner product k(x, x′) of Φ, is defined by:

$$\phi : R^D \rightarrow F \tag{6}$$

$$k(x, x') = \phi^T(x')\ \phi(x) \tag{7}$$

where the dimension D of the input space is much less than the dimension of the feature space F. Mercer's kernels are known mathematical functions (polynomial, sigmoid, etc. ...) and therefore we can calculate the inner product of Φ without actually knowing it. The learning algorithm selects support vectors to build the decision surface in the feature space. Support vectors are patterns (vectors) that are most difficult to categorize and are lying on the margins of the SVM classifier. This mapping is achieved by first solving a *convex* optimization problem and then applying a linear mapping from the feature space to the output space. The advantage of having a convex optimization problem is that the solution is unique. This is in contrast to ANN where we may have many local minima or maxima of the error function. **Figure 4** illustrates visually the concept of SVM.

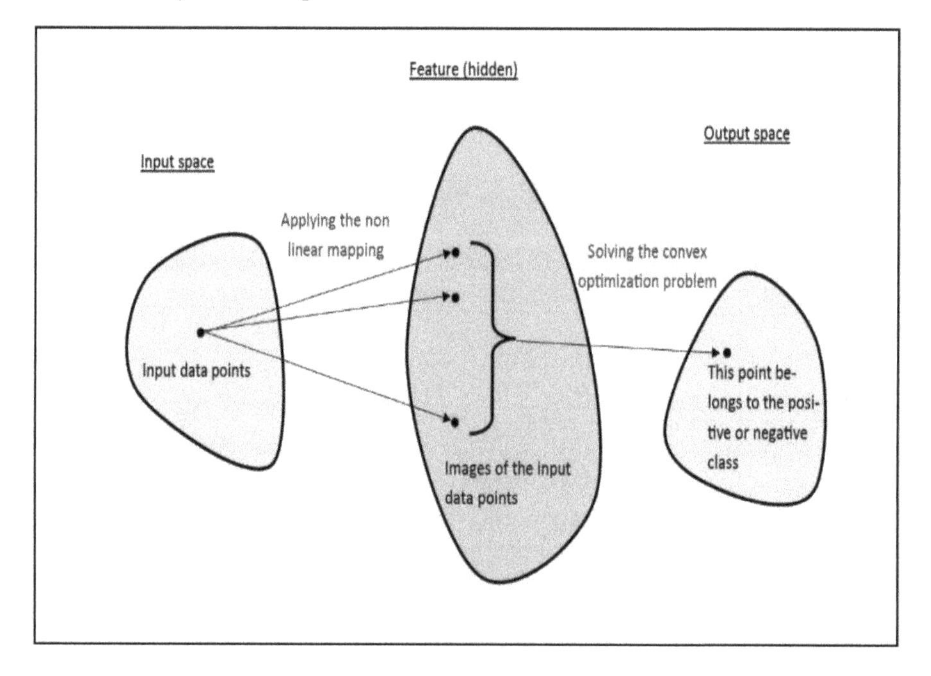

Figure 4.
The mappings of SVM.

Calculating ϕ may be a time-consuming process and often not feasible. However, Mercer's theorem allows us to avoid this computation so there is no need to explicitly describe the nonlinear mapping ϕ neither the image points in the feature space F. This technique is known as the Kernel trick [19].

5.1 The SVM classifier

The concept of the SVM classifier is illustrated in **Figure 5**. **Figure 1** shows the simplest case where the data vectors (marked by 'X' s and 'O' s) can be separated by a hyperplane.

There may exist many separating hyperplanes. The SVM classifier seeks the separating hyperplane that produces the largest separation of margins. In a more general case, where the data points are not linearly separable in the input space, a nonlinear transformation is used to map the data vectors into a high-dimensional space (the feature space) prior to applying the linear maximum margin classifier.

SVM has been initially designed to classify only binary data as in **Figure** 5. A multi-class SVM, however, has been designed by allowing classification of a finite number of classes [18]. This kind of learning assumes a priori knowledge of the data. In the case of autism, we may then have different kinds of autisms (which is also the reality), and the SVM algorithm may then be able to learn to categorize between them.

5.2 The kernel

SVM uses a kernel function where the nonlinear mapping is implicitly embedded. The discriminant function of the SVM classifier can be defined as:

$$f(\mathbf{x}) = \sum_{i=1}^{N} \alpha_i y_i \, K(\mathbf{x_i}, \mathbf{x}) + b \quad (8)$$

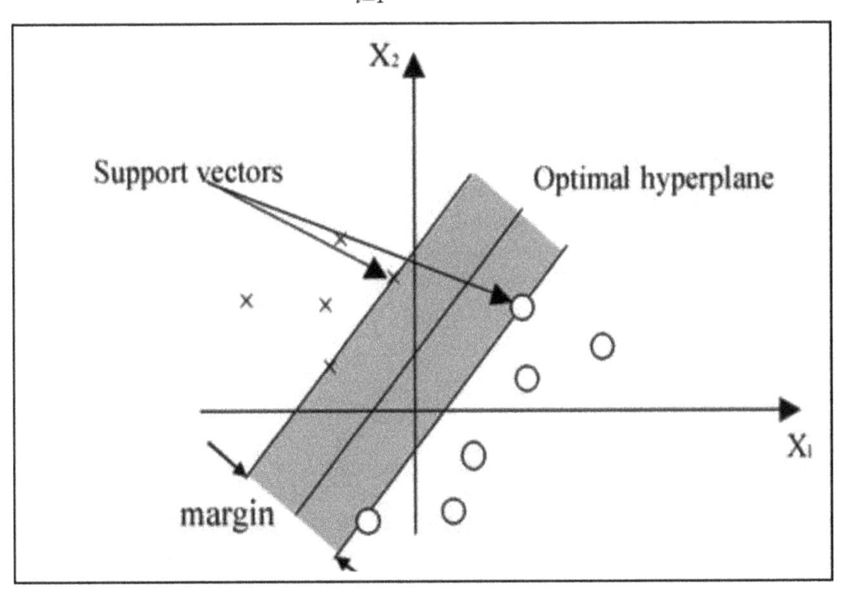

Figure 5.
A SVM classification maximizes the margins between the different classes.

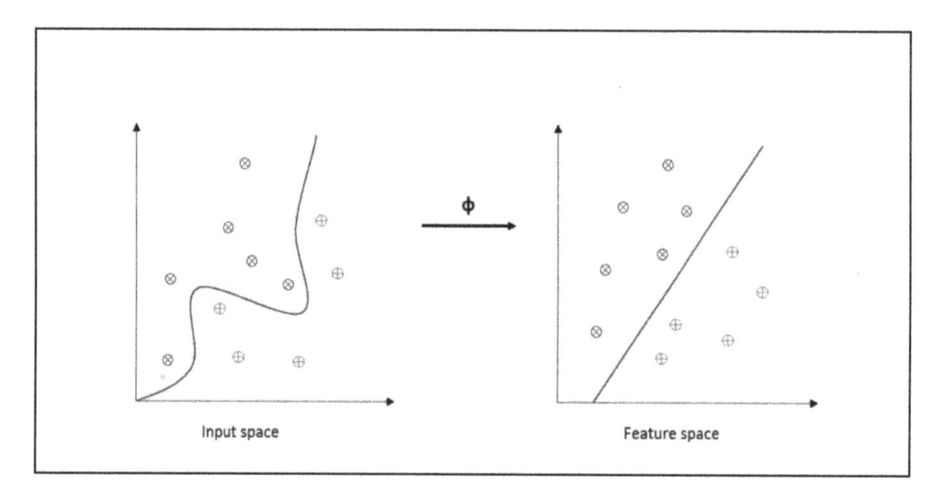

Figure 6.
The cover theorem.

Here, K(−,-) is the kernel function, $\mathbf{x_i}$ are the support vectors determined from the training data, y_i is the class indicator (e.g. +1 and −1 for a two class problem) associated with each $\mathbf{x_i}$, N is the number of supporting vectors determined during training, α is the Lagrange multiplier for each point in the training set, and b (bias) is a scalar representing the perpendicular distance of the hyperplane from the origin.

A problem using SVM soon appears. As the dimension of data increases, the complexity of the problem also increases. This is called the *curse of dimension* [20]. However, this may be overcome using the kernel trick from the Mercer's theorem.

The most commonly used kernel functions are the polynomial kernel given by:

$$K(\mathbf{x_i}, \mathbf{x_j}) = (\mathbf{x_i}^T \mathbf{x_j} + 1)^p, \text{where } p > 0 \text{ is a constant} \tag{9}$$

And the Gaussian radial basis function (RBF) kernel is given by:

$$K(\mathbf{x_i}, \mathbf{x_j}) = \exp.\left(-\|\mathbf{x_i} - \mathbf{x_j}\|^2 / 2\sigma^2\right) \tag{10}$$

Here, $\sigma > 0$ is a constant that defines the kernel width.

The mapping to the output space is based on the Cover theorem [21] illustrated in **Figure 6**. By transforming to a higher-dimensional space, we are able to categorize nonlinear input as linear in the output space using this theorem. This means that what is nonlinear in the input space becomes linear in the output space. In this way, we are able to categorize nonlinear data by use of the SVM algorithm.

6. Experiments and results

A Java program was made to generate the patterns from the original HPLC data. The generation of optimal selection of patterns was very much dependent on computing the right number of peaks from the HPLC spectra.

The training and testing data that we used were written to file to later being read into a Java program. The Java program developed for training uses the package

DOI: http://dx.doi.org/10.5772/intechopen.109537

javANN (java Artificial Neural Network). This program was developed by the company Pattern solutions Ltd. [22] in Norway.

A Java program was then developed to change the format of data, so it could be used in the LIBSVM toolbox [23] and be able to classify between a normal and an autism child. Before the training started, a regularization parameter C (cost) has to be determined. The value of C was determined experimentally. This is not an optimal way to do it. The performance of the SVM classifier was optimal for C values from 100 and up to around 200. The SVM algorithm was tested on the same samples of data (unseen) as the MLP algorithm was, and with a constant C equal 100 or 20n The SVM algorithm also uses another constant ɤ (gamma) that has to be defined or the algorithm may determine it by default.

6.1 MLP and SVM experiments

6.1.1 Small-scale experiments

In the first experiment, 18 samples were used for training and 12 samples were used for testing. These are the samples that the algorithm never has seen before. In the MLP experiments, the number of hidden nodes was selected to 100. The learning rate was set to 0.1 and the momentum to 0.9. The number of iterations was set to 10,000.

The MLP algorithm has been tested on 12 unseen samples. The test data were unknown to the system, but we knew what category they belong to. The performance rate was then easy to calculate. The MLP network was able to correctly classify 11 either as an autist or normal child. The best performance was estimated to 11/12 = 91.7%.

The SVM algorithm best performance was estimated to 83.4% where 10 of 12 samples were classified correctly. One false-positive sample was estimated on the average. This corresponds to where a normal child was classified as an autist. This is a far more serious mistake than a false-negative classification error where an autist is classified as normal.

6.1.2 Large-scale experiments

The second delivery of data consist of 62 samples of autism children and 52 samples of normal children, totally 114 samples. In the second analysis, we wanted to see if a *proof of principle* experiment in the first delivery of data and could be extended to a *proof of concept* experiment. The training set consists now of 71 samples of data and 43 samples of testing data.

The best performance of the SVM algorithm was estimated to 88.4% with a penalty constant C = 100. This implies that 38 of 43 samples were correctly classified. The average performance of using SVM was then estimated to about 85%.

The MLP network gave the best performance estimated to 81.4% with an average value of 78.3%. This implies that 35 of 43 samples were classified correctly. The average number of false-positive cases in both experiments was equal to 2 for both algorithms.

7. Conclusion

Pattern diagnostics represents new ways to detect early diseases. This method may also be used to classify for instance between different DNA sequences [24–26]. In this chapter, we have used it to diagnose early autism. Such an analysis requires only small amount of urine to create the HPLC spectra. Mass spectrometry (MS) data is another method that could be used, we believe. The most important aspect of such an analysis is a very high throughput since both HPLC and MS spectra can be determined in short time. An important aspect of this analysis is that the patterns themselves are independent of the identity of proteins as a discriminator. The classification can then be done before the identity of proteins is determined.

Both a proof of principle and a proof of concept experiment have been carried out, and two quite independent algorithms have been used to analyze the data, Both algorithms have shown consistently results with respect to early identification of autism from their HPLC data.

8. Future work

The values of the parameters used in the algorithms are not optimal. The selection of different parameter values has been carried out by doing experiment. A lot of tuning of the parameter values are needed to be able to adapt the algorithms to the given data. One method for optimization is particle swarm optimization (PSO) [27]. This method can be used to determine optimal values of the different parameters, for both the neural network and SVM. PSO is now used very much in different types of applications.

Another aspect of the MLP neural network used is that we have used a sigmodal activation function. However, there are other types of neurons which can be used to introduce nonlinearities in the computation. *Tanh* neurons use a similar kind of nonlinearity as the sigmodal function, but the output of Tanh range from −1 to 1 compared to the sigmodal function where the output is ranging from 0 to 1. Tanh may in many cases give better performance of the neural network.

A different kind of nonlinearity is used by the *restricted linear unit* (ReLU) neuron. It uses the function $f(x) = \max(o,x)$ and may in many cases give the best performance of the ANN.

8.1 Particle swarm intelligence

Computational swarm intelligence (CSI) may be defined by algorithmic models based on the idea where the design of these algorithms came from the study of bird flocks and ant swarms to simulate their behaviors in computer models. These simulations show great ability to explore a multidimensional space and quickly turned into a quite new domain of algorithmic theory. A swarm can be defined as a group of agents cooperating to achieve some goal.

PSO is based on an intrinsic property of swarms to execute complex tasks by defining a self-organization process [28]. This is a new way to explore the high-dimensional search space to find optimal solutions. Birds are similar to particles that fly through a hyperdimensional space. The social tendency of individuals is used to update the velocity of the particles. Each particle is influenced by the experience of its neighbors and their own knowledge. The norm is that the agents should behave with no centralized structure. The local interactions between the agents often lead to emergency of global behavior [29–32]. The particles in the multidimensional space, the search space, represent all feasible solutions of a given problem. By using a *fitness* function, their positions are updated in the process of finding an optimal or near-optimal solution.

How may this be used to improve the results of recognition of early autism? For a neural network, we could use PSO to find a correct configuration of the network. To determine the correct number of neurons in the hidden layer, we could then find the optimal value of the learning rate and momentum of the network.

For the SVM network, we may use of the PSO algorithm to find optimal values for the gamma and cost parameters. We could for instance also use a global PSO algorithm [31] to find these values. So far we have not done this, but it belongs to our future work.

8.2 Deep learning: backpropagation with TensorFlow

Deep learning is another approach that may be used to achieve better performance of the recognition of early autism. A deep neural network is in its simplicity a neural network with many hidden layers [33]; see **Figure 7**. The more the hidden layers, the deeper the network is. As the neural network gets deeper, the processing power to train the network increases substantially. We may also increase the number of nodes in each hidden layer – often called the width of the network. Multiple frameworks of neural networks exist today. Maybe the most used is the TensorFlow [34] which is an open-source machine learning library developed by Google.

In TensorFlow, numerical computations are processed using data flow graphs (illustrated in **Figure 8**). The data is represented as *Tensors.* A Tensor in TensorFlow may be described as a typed multidimensional array. Nodes in the data flow graph are called ops (short for operations). Each op takes zero or more Tensors as input and performs some computation and outputs zero or more Tensors.

The edges in the graph represent Tensors communicated between the nodes of the graph. **Figure 8** illustrates a TensorFlow data graph.

We could also apply a TensorFlow backpropagation algorithm as in [34]. To create a TensorFlow network, we need to break the networks into Tensors. We also have to

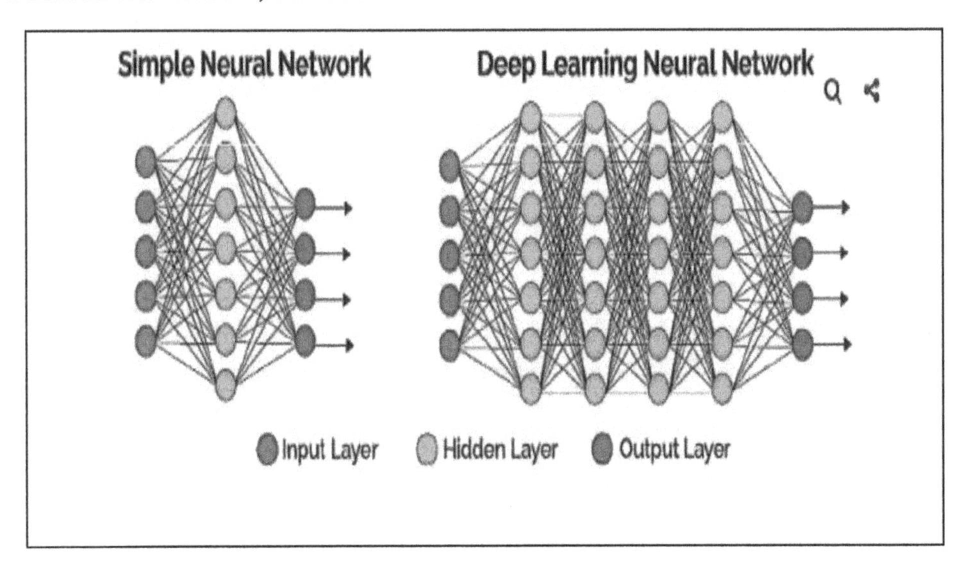

Figure 7.
A simple and deep learning network.

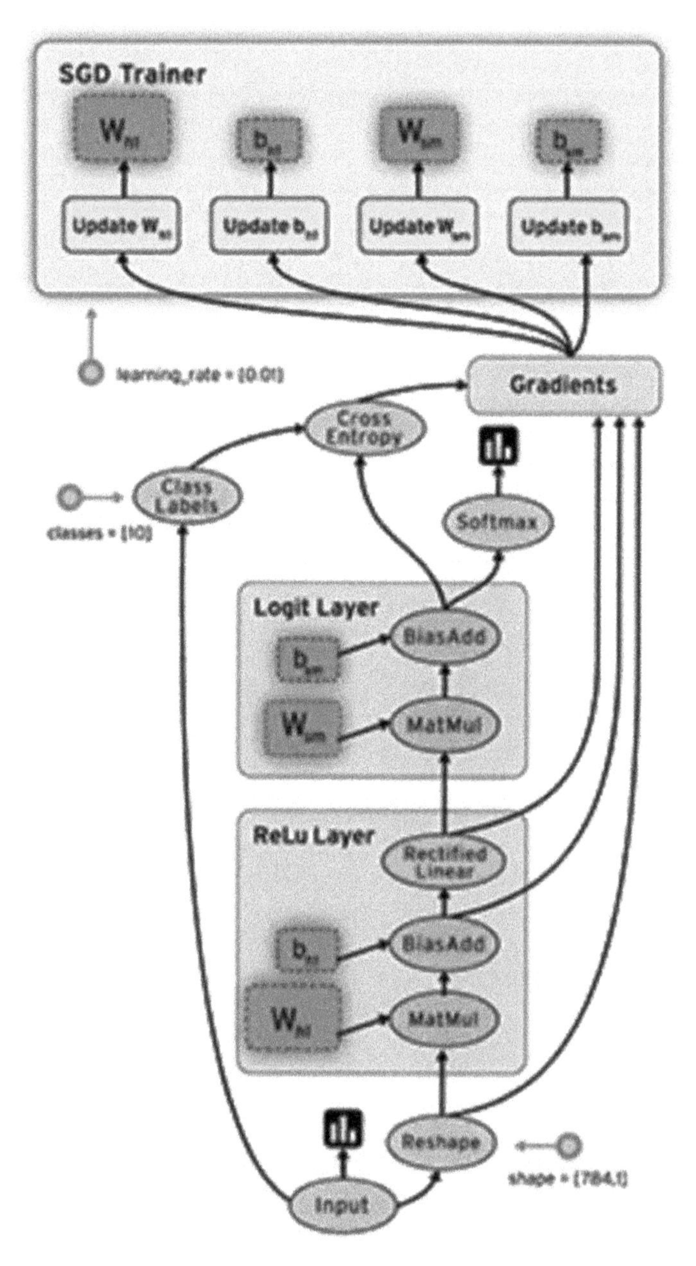

Figure 8.
A TensorFlow Data graph.

define the input data. Then, we need to represent our input as Tensors. We then also need placeholder operations to hold the data.

In the backpropagation algorithm, the cost function is minimized. If we want to see visually what is happening during the learning process, we may introduce a graph and create a TensorFlow session.

To optimize the neural network, different hyperparameters need to be tuned. This may be done by using for instance the PSO method discussed before. These hyperparameters are as follows:

- Number of hidden layers
- Number of nodes in each hidden layer
- Activation function
- Optimization algorithm
- Cost (or error) function
- Learning rate and momentum
- Epochs (iterations)

When using a standard gradient descent algorithm to find the minimum cost function or global error, the weights are updated after each iteration. However, by using a *stochastic* gradient descent algorithm, we may use small batches from the dataset in each iteration.

While standard gradient descent performs a parameter update after each run through the whole training set, a stochastic gradient descent performs a parameter update after each batch. According to LeCun et al. [35], one should use stochastic gradient descent if the training set is large (more than a few hundred samples) and redundant, and the task is classification.

The deeper and wider the network is, the more computational expensive it is to train the network. When using gradient descent, one could use the method "*GradientDescentOptimizer*" in TensorFlow. The algorithm then converges within reasonable time. By introducing a great number of hidden layers and/or a large number of nodes in each hidden layer, we will not necessarily increase the accuracy of the network. However, it may give better performance.

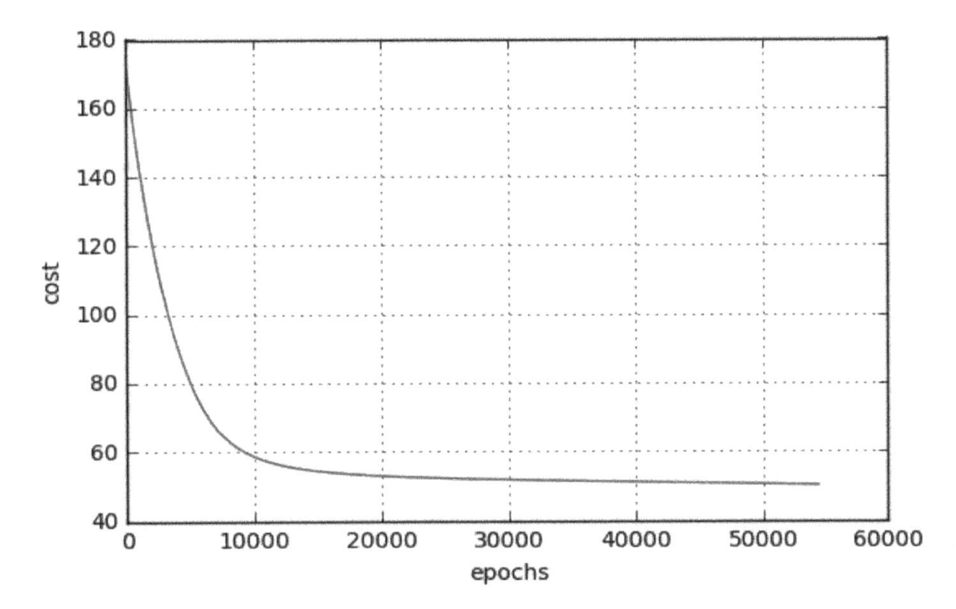

Figure 9.
Gradient descent in a deep learning network.

Figure 9 shows how the cost decreases when using gradient descent of small batches from the dataset in each iteration. An example of a learning curve using a deep learning network with stochastic gradient descent may looks like the one given in **Figure 9**. For the configuration of the network we may, for instance, use up to 10 hidden layers with a number of 10–20 nodes in each layer.

We have not yet used a deep learning network to classify between an autist and a normal child, but this belongs to do in the future. We may also use such a deep learning network for introducing different kinds of autism in the autism spectrum and be able to classify between them, based on their HPLC spectrum data.

Author details

Terje Solsvik Kristensen
Western Norway University of Applied Sciences, Bergen, Norway

*Address all correspondence to: terje.solsvik.kristensen@hvl.no

References

[1] Scientific American. 2012. p. 11

[2] Available from: http://stemedhub.org/resources/714/download/HPLCdata.pdf

[3] Molecular Autism 2013;**4**:14. DOI: 10.1186/2040-2392-4-14

[4] Kristensen T. Classification of early autism based on HPLC Data. In: IFMBE Proceedings of XIII Mediterranean Conference on Medical and Biological Engineering and Computing, Medicon2013. Vol. 41. Sevilla, Spain: Springer; 2013. pp. 774-778

[5] Lilian RH, Farid H, Donald BR. Probabilistic disease classification of expression-dependent proteomic data from mass spectrometry of human serum. Journal of Computational Biology. 2003;**10**:6

[6] New Scientist. 2010. p. 9

[7] Kristensen T. Neural Networks, Fuzzy Logic and Genetic Algorithms. Cappelen Academic Publisher (in Norwegian); 1997

[8] Mitchell TM. Machine Learning. McGraw-Hill Companies; 1997

[9] Burges CJ. Tutorial on support vector machines for pattern recognition. Knowledge Discovery and Data Mining. 1998;**1998**

[10] Aebersold R, Mann M. Mass spectrometry based on proteomics. Nature. 2003;**422**

[11] Lolita AL, Ferrari M, Petricoin E. Clinical proteomics written in blood. Nature. 2003;**425**:905

[12] Petricoin E, Liotta AL. Selditof based serum proteomic pattern diagnostics for early detection of cancer. Current Opinion in Biotechnology. 2004;**15**: 24-30

[13] Haykin S. Neural Networks and Learning Machines. 3rd ed. Pearson; 2009

[14] Kristensen T, Patel R. Classification of eukaryotic and prokaryotic cells by a backpropagation network. In: Proceedings of IEEE International Joint Conference on Neural Networks, (IJCNN 2003); Portland, Oregon, USA. 2003

[15] Kristensen T. Prototypes of ANN Biomedical Pattern Recognition Systems. In: Proceedings of IASTED International Conference on Simulation and Modeling (ASM 2002); Crete, Greece. 2002

[16] Vapnik VN. Statistical Learning Theory. New York: Wiley; 1998

[17] Vapnik VN. An overview of statistical learning theory. IEEE Transactions on Neural Networks. 1999; **1999**

[18] Mercer J. Functions of positive and negative type, and their connection with the theory of integral equations. Transactions of London Philosophical Society. 1909;**1909**:415-446

[19] Huang TM, Kechman V, Kopriva I. Kernel Based Algorithms for Mining Huge Data Sets. Berlin, Heidelberg: Springer-Verlag; 2006

[20] Bellman R. Dynamic Programming. Princeton, USA: Princeton University Press; 1957

[21] Chattamvelli R. Data Mining Algorithms. Oxford, U.K: Alpha Science International Ltd.; 2011

[22] Kristensen T. javANN: Java Artificial Neural Networks. Pattern Solutions AS. 2007. Available from: http://www.patternsolutions.no

[23] Chang CC, Lin CJ. LIBSVM: A library for Support Vector Machines. 2001. Available from: http://www.csie.ntu.edu.tw/cjlin/libsvm

[24] Kristensen T, Guillaume F. Classification of DNA sequences by a MLP and a SVM network. In: Proceedings of International Conference on Bioinformatics and Computational Biology, BIOCOMP'13th July 22-25; Las Vegas. USA: CSCREA Press; 2013

[25] Kristensen T, Guillaume F. Different regimes for classification of DNA sequences. In: IEEE 7th International Conference on Cybernetics and Intelligent Systems & Robotics, Automation and Mechatronics (CIS-RAM 2015). Angkor Wat, Cambodia; 2015

[26] Kristensen T, Guillaume F. Different Regimes for Classification of DNA Sequences. IEEE Press; 2015. pp. 114-119. DOI: 10.1109/ICCIS.7274558

[27] Kristensen T, Guillaume F. PSO in ANN, SVM and Data Clustering. In: Tan Y, editor. Chapter 18. Book: Swarm Intelligence: Volume 1: Principles of current algorithms and methods. London, UK: IET Publisher; 2018

[28] Kohonen T. Self-Organizing Maps: Springer Series in Information Sciences. Vol. 30. Springer-Verlag; 1995

[29] Kennedy J, Eberhart RC. Particle swarm optimization. In: Proceedings of IEEE International conference on Neural Networks. 1995. pp. 1942-1948

[30] Kennedy J, Eberhart RC. A discrete binary version of the particle swarm algorithm. In: Proceedings of the 1997 Conference on Systems, Man, and Cybernetics. Piscataway, N.J: IEEE Service Center; 1997. pp. 4104-4109

[31] Kennedy J, Eberhart RC, Shi Y. Swarm Intelligence. Morgan Kaufmann Academic Press; 2001

[32] Koay C, Srinivasan D. Particle swarm optimization-based approach for generator maintenance scheduling. In: Proceedings of the IEEE Swarm Intelligence Symposium. 2003. pp. 167-173

[33] Nielsen MA. Neural Networks and Deep Learning. Determination Press; 2015

[34] TensorFlow. Available from: https://www.tensorflow.org/2016

[35] LeCun YA, Bottou L, Orr GB, Müller KR. Efficient backpropagation. In: Neural Networks. Berlin Heidelberg: Springer; 1998. pp. 9-48

Section 3

Therapeutic Strategies

Chapter 11

Perspective Chapter: Synaesthesia in Children with Autism – Observations Related to Language Evaluation and Therapy

Krupa Venkatraman and Prathibha Karanth

Abstract

Synaesthesia is a nonpathological sensory perception that happens when a particular sensory stimulus elicits a sensory response in another modality. For example, hearing a word results in the perception of colors. Autism, a neurodevelopmental disorder, is characterized by differences in sensory perception (hyper/hypo). Some research has been done to understand the co-existence of synaesthesia in autism. Although autism and synaesthesia seem to be unrelated, the prevalence of synaesthesia in autism is three times higher than in the general population. This could be attributed to the excessive neuronal connections and activities in both conditions. Based on clinical observations and case studies, this chapter talks about how some of the problems that children with autism spectrum disorder (ASD) have with processing their senses contributes to synaesthetic ability. It also talks about how understanding and using these similarities helped the children develop their language skills.

Keywords: synaesthesia, ideasthesia, sensory processing disorder, savant syndrome, Asperger's syndrome

1. Introduction

Synaesthesia is a perceptual phenomenon that occurs when a specific sensory domain is stimulated, resulting in the involuntary participation of a second sensory pathway. For example, reading a text can cause a color or taste sensation. An inducer is a stimulus that causes synaesthetic sensations, whereas "concurrent" refers to an internally generated synaesthetic sensation [1]. Individuals who experience such synesthetic sensations are referred to as "synaesthetes'. Literature reports an initial claim that such a perception is false or rather a lie. However, consistency in perception has been a hallmark of synaesthetic perception [2]. The onset of synaesthesia could be that children are typically born with a synaesthetic disposition, which may be the result of denser synaptic connectivity in infancy, cortical regions that are less organized to assume domain-specific functions, and an innate propensity to respond synaesthetically [1]. The cortical organization during later development could lead to a reduction in this perception, which could be reflected in adolescence and later adulthood [2].

The perception of synaesthesia is typically bimodal or multimodal. Bimodal perception occurs when stimulation of one sensory modality is felt in another sensory modality [3]. For instance, colored hearing (sounds that cause colors to appear), colored olfaction (when a smell causes one to see colors), or audio motor (when the sounds of various words cause various bodily postures or motions), etc. Multimodal synaesthesia occurs when a sensory stimulus simultaneously activates multiple sensations, such as hearing and seeing. A child might taste the sound's color while hearing it, see it, and feel it tickle his skin.

A weak synaesthetic perception hypothesis state that infants are born unable to discriminate stimuli from multiple modalities and respond to them as a sum of energy perceived across modalities. Infant perception studies as early as 1 month suggest an inability to perceive cross-modal differences between visual and oral stimulation [2]. A stronger hypothesis on synaesthetic perception describes synaesthetic perception as a result of poorly functioning cerebral systems and unorganized functionality of the young brain in infancy [2]. Infants are born with higher synaptic connections, which, as they develop, undergo a process of synaptic deletion to aid in more specialized sensory perception.

2. Autism and synaesthesia

Autism spectrum disorder (ASD) is a neurodevelopmental disorder that typically manifests between 18 and 36 months of age and is characterized by impaired social communication and socialization. Autism is characterized by stereotypical behaviors, and the recent inclusion of atypical sensory processing (auditory, visual, and tactile) has sparked an interest in studying synaesthesia in ASD [4]. Recent DSM-V (Diagnostic and Statistical Manual fifth edition) criteria for ASD include impairments in sensory processing, which are of increasing significance given that 60–96% of children with ASD are likely to have such differences, according to the literature [5]. The inclusion of atypical sensory processing in the DSM-V reiterates the importance of such deviance in perceptual processing due to an underlying neural process. This unusual processing has been observed in visual, auditory, tactile, olfactory, gustatory, and proprioceptive stimuli. The work of Treffert documents the presence of extraordinary skills for music perception in individuals with differences in auditory perception and drawing skills, and hyperlexia (ability to read graphemes without formal teaching) in individuals with visual processing differences, which are key features to be used for intervention [6]. Treffert also argues that these talents are possessed by children with ASD due to sensory processing differences and, although deviant, could be used to facilitate language, socialization, and independence.

Language impairment appears to be the most common characteristic among children with ASD. Language acquisition may be difficult, or even if a language is present, is inefficient for social communication. Due to their capacity to use rote/formulaic language, there is frequently a tendency that expressive language appears to be superior to receptive language [6]. Additionally, they have problems comprehending verbal language and have semantic impairments that make it difficult for them to interpret figurative or allusive language. Some exhibit echolalia, which is a mere repetition of heard utterances. There are instances where verbal stimming and self-talk (repetitive utterances/sounds) are noticed as a part of vocal behavior.

Despite using verbal language for such rote language, they do not show any interest in volitional communication. Some of them with minimal verbal language tend to use these formulaic utterances for need-based communication. Although there is a global understanding of the narrow and bizarrely organized language development such a difference in development signifies a difference in underlying language processing. Even though there are behavioral and neuroscientific explanations for language problems in people with ASD, no research has been done on how sensory differences impact language development or how to see these skills in a positive light.

There are several points of intervention for language impairment in ASD depending on the various classes of explanations that are presented in the research. The majority of the intervention programs for autism are based on operant conditioning techniques like "Applied Behaviour Analysis" (ABA), which focuses on the acquisition of behavior through repeated training. The explanations of the sensory processing issues in ASD are the foundation of sensory-based therapies like "Auditory Integration Therapy." However, given that sensory processing issues of various types and degrees would affect language development in ASD, exploring such parallel perceptual processing in ASD is one way to approach it from a sensory-perceptual standpoint. This in turn would contribute to developing a concrete sensory-perceptual-based strategy for intervention. It is therefore imperative to comprehend the sensory-perceptual processing that underlies language impairment in light of behavioral traits and therapeutic findings.

Although autism and synaesthesia appear to be unrelated, synaesthesia is three times more common in autism than in the general population [7], which could be attributed to excessive neuronal connections and activities in both conditions. A pilot study on the prevalence of synaesthesia in individuals with Asperger's syndrome reports a higher presence of phoneme-grapheme synaesthesia in individuals with Asperger's syndrome compared to the typical population. The genes related to synaesthesia are often similar to those linked to individuals with autism spectrum disorder [4]. Ward et al. [8] studied the atypical sensory processing in individuals with synaesthesia and autism using the Glasgow Sensory Questionnaire. The observations from the study showed that such atypical sensory processing could be a shared feature between these individuals.

Studies evaluating the global perception task reveal a heightened sensitivity of the parvocellular visual pathway in the visual processing of individuals with autism spectrum disorders and synaesthetes [9]. The synaesthetes appear to be able to use their out-of-the-ordinary experiences as mnemonic devices and even exploit them when learning new abstract categories [10].

The concept of savant in autism has been reported for the last 200 years. The literature shows such savant abilities in children with autism could be due to the underlying synaesthetic abilities [11]. Individuals with savant syndrome typically possess extraordinary skills in a specific area, despite having a degree of intellectual impairment. The literature suggests that these exceptional abilities can also be linked to excellent sensory discrimination and synaesthetic ability as a skill. Not only can synaesthesia account for a high cognitive profile, but it can also foster unique abilities, such as the effortless, intuitive, and inductive acquisition of new languages [12].

The cognitive abilities of any individual are highly dependent on the sensory perceptual experiences they gain to develop a sensorimotor contingency. The perceptual abilities due to different sensations cause different actions. The ability of an individual to mirror others' experiences depends on their perception being mapped with others. Therefore, the perceptual differences between individuals with ASD could cause difficulty in developing a theory of mind. The perceptual differences in individuals with ASD, mediated by their synaesthetic abilities, could be the cause of heterogeneity in their cognitive deficits and processing styles [13].

The narrative of Tammet, an individual with Asperger's syndrome (AS) who could memorize pi to 20 thousand decimal places, suggests that he used a different strategy to chunk information for numbers and letters, which was attributed to the combined effect of his condition (AS) with the existing synaesthetic ability [1]. The case is an example of the contribution of synaesthetic ability to exceptional memory for numerals.

Sensory processing dysfunction in individuals with autism spectrum disorder (ASD) emphasizes the need for sensory-based, targeted intervention [14]. These distinctions in sensory processing would also reveal any underlying synaesthetic skill, which, if utilized during language intervention, could assist in eliciting the required verbal response. The synaesthetic experiences of individuals with autism spectrum conditions are commonly misunderstood or overgeneralized as a sensory processing disorder. Synaesthesia is a behavioral phenomenon whose existence and qualities can only be appreciated if the individual expresses them effectively. Given that autism is a social communication disorder, the ability to express these experiences vividly becomes limited, and hence only an inferential comprehension of the client's experience is possible. There are varied opinions related to the impact of synaesthesia on children with ASD and the relevance of this research for cognition, memory, and language in the typical population.

3. Language and synaesthesia

Ramachandran and Hubbard [15] assert that synaesthetic perception could explain the evolution of language and argue that the evolution of proto-language could not happen through mere natural selection. The claim is explained by three important observations. First observation is based on visual description experiments that denote visual representation for phonemes (synaesthesia between object appearance and sound contour). The second explanation posits a nonarbitrary connection between the motor movements for speech and the corresponding auditory phonemic representation mapped in the brain, thereby enabling the verbal output for the auditory sequence of phonemes for objects by sensory-motor synaesthesia (synaesthesia between sound contour and vocalization). The third explanation is a bootstrapping mechanism that happens with a motor-motor-based mapping called synkinesis, which insists on the coexistence of two motor movements with a single word. Therefore, synaesthesia has been viewed as one of the constraints in the evolution of proto-language.

Language seems to have an important role in synesthetic perception as the majority of the synaesthetic inducers are linguistic. For example, letters, digits, words, and especially words in a series [16]. Synaesthetic ability often seems to impact perception, language, memory, cognition, creativity, and imagery [8]. The literature [17, 18] posits synaesthesia as a tool to evaluate the structures of language. The psycholinguistic studies on morphological processing and visual word recognition reiterate the use of synaesthesia to understand language processing. These results are restricted to color-word associations and do not detail the processing mechanism [19]. The accounts of cross-modal sensory association in language processing have been described and argued about for years; one such description by Jacobson mentioned by Reichard et al. [20] explains that children tend to naturally process sounds and words by associating them with colors. They not only assign colors to letters, and numbers but also to words, phrases, and sentences for processing the linguistic unit easily and utilise it as a mnemonic device to recall.

Individuals with synaesthesia often process words in line with their perception, in addition to semantic or verbal encoding. For example, an individual with grapheme-phoneme synaesthesia could code a word as a pattern of colors. In free verbal recall, Radvansky et al. [21] found that synaesthetes were less influenced by semantic factors than controls, implying that they may rely more on perceptual encoding.

Watson et al. [10] assert that children's synaesthetic abilities can be exploited to accomplish various literacy learning tasks. They also claim that when toddlers develop the capacity to classify colors between the ages of 4 and 7, they tend to use this ability to master letters and words. The multisensory processing of stimuli facilitates superior word and letter recognition. The synaesthetic parallel that a child has established with a familiar inducer could be used to symbolize a different component of the inducer that the child is striving to learn. The research says that synaesthesia could complement verbal cognition, which is less abstract and has more information.

Despite synaesthesia being a sensory-perceptual phenomenon, it does have a role in cognitive processing and is frequently assumed to aid high-level semantic mechanisms. The belief that synaesthesia involves sensory-to-sensory connection has been modified, and researchers have incorporated semantic mediation into this process. This recent semantically mediated cross-modal correspondence is equivalent to ideasthesia. Ideathesia suggests that synaesthetes are not born with these sensory associations but acquire them through a conscious process of associating meaning with a stimulus. It is also argued that these associations occur when synaesthetes have trouble assigning meaning to stimuli during the learning process, a phenomenon is known as "semantic vacuum" [22]. According to the theory of ideasthesia, children are exposed to abstract concepts such as letters, numbers, and days of the week, from which they construct entire semantic networks, and they use synaesthesia to enhance the semantic association process. The tendency of autistic children to acquire abstract concepts rather than meaningful words for verbal communication skills may be related to these semantic association difficulties. It could be possible for them to utilize their synaesthetic ability to overcome this obstacle.

The synaesthetic abilities of autistic children, whether innate or acquired as a result of an initial semantic vacuum, can be utilized to help their language development. Therefore, the clinician's knowledge of synaesthesia is crucial for identifying the experience, understanding the child's perceptions, and regulating it so that language skills can be facilitated. This compelled us to investigate synesthetic skills in children with ASD and their potential applications in language intervention. During the intervention, we made behavioral and incidental observations that urged us to connect synaesthetic skills to these children's behaviours. During language intervention, it was explicit that children with ASD have adapted their ways to compensate for their sensory issues.

Given that children with ASD may have atypical processing of any sensory stimuli, the use of language intervention materials influenced by typical development must be validated. The superior sensory processing skills often associated with coexisting synaesthesia could be of significant help in language intervention. In the following sections, four case studies explain how such synaesthetic skills can help children with ASD in language intervention.

4. Case studies

4.1 Case 1

Master B presented with receptive and expressive language disorder and ASD when he was 3 years old. After years of therapy, he remained nonverbal and was not benefitting from alternative communication strategies because he lacked the acceptance and attention skills necessary to use them. At the age of nine, his speech and language skills were reevaluated with the intention of beginning language intervention with a new therapist. Despite his inability to speak on his own, he had a distinct speech pattern that allowed him to sing songs with more than three words per line and appropriate lyrics. He used random words at will but never responded to the communication. When an attempt was made to engage him in writing with support, albeit illegibly, his parents and clinician were surprised to observe him holding a pen and signaling the clinician to hold his wrist for support. He was writing while watching a YouTube video on his phone, which appeared to be audio motor synaesthesia [23–25]. He writes as he hears Mr. Bean's theme song, which is played at the end of each episode. He wrote about his wants and dislikes, along with his thoughts on current events. The writings were cross-checked with real-time events in his day-to-day life, and it assisted him in transitioning from the frame of being noncommunicative and nonresponsive to verbal communication to being a communicator with support through an altered modality, i.e., writing. Ramachandran et al. assert that a sensorimotor type of synaesthesia, specifically a motor response to auditory stimuli, could have contributed to the evolution of language as a system. There could be a mapping of motor (oral) response to an auditory stimulus, but in this case, he used a tone with no lyrics, just high-pitched instrumental music that helped him write with support (motor response). Although their argument explains sensorimotor synaesthesia in terms of typical language evolution, the similarity in stimulus (auditory) and response (motor movements) makes us consider that it could also explain such atypical behavior too.

4.2 Case 2

Master C presented with receptive and expressive language disorder and ASD when he was 2 years old. The parent report and clinical observations revealed that he never engaged in meaningful voluntary communication and never spoke more than a few words on his own. The child had a greater proclivity for rote language, better memory for alphabets and numbers, and delayed echolalia for longer phrases like Bible verses, but he did not attempt meaningful voluntary communication. Whenever he was excited, he typically had a verbal response with the word "Truck." The child's alphabet recall was exceptional, and he showed a heightened interest in drawing (self and clinician). The pre-printed materials used during language therapy, such as flashcards and real objects, were of no great interest to the child, but simple line drawings of trucks did elicit a time-locked response, i.e., as and when the clinician would draw a truck and model him, he would say "Truck" in response to the model. The word "truck" was used as a verbal response inducer to elicit additional verbal responses. Using a line drawing of a truck and my target vocabulary, we created simple mental maps to assist him in expanding his vocabulary. If the target word was an 'apple', for example, a line drawing of an apple would be drawn above the truck, and the child would be modeled to name it. He was able to produce a verbal response with little practice. He eventually began to adapt to this mode of intervention, and this happened quickly. He then began responding to a line drawing of the target vocabulary to be established without the drawing of the truck every time. He now labels pictures. He began responding to the therapist and initiating communication on his own.

4.3 Case 3

Miss D presented with receptive and expressive language disorder and ASD when she was 2 years old. The sensory integration profile of the child revealed a hyposensitivity to auditory and visual stimuli. Although language intervention began immediately after the diagnosis, the child was nonverbal until the age of four and had no voluntary communication. Following a protocol change, language therapy focused on utilizing her visual seeking while also identifying her ability to make sounds for orthographic forms in English (grapheme-phoneme synaesthesia). A letter-inspired sounds or words, which she expressed as soon as she saw the letter. This was an incidental finding when the clinician tried to use phonic sounds to aid her vocalization. The clinician would write alphabets in the child's hand and say the phonics sounds and then attach words to them, e.g., the alphabet "A" would be written in her hand or on a white sheet followed by the clinician's model of the sound 'a-a-a' and then a word like "apple" would be added at the end of the model for that alphabet. She responded to the text with sounds and was able to recall the words. As she could recall the words used as a target vocabulary, incidentally, we observed that the mere presentation of text could elicit a verbal response (Hyperlexia). She read the words without mispronunciation, although she was unaware of their meanings. We then exploited this reading ability by pairing pictures with text to expand her vocabulary. The synaesthetic ability was not only used to elicit a verbal response, but it was also used to elicit sentences, conversational speech, and narration. Although it could be argued that the phenomenon of 'hyperlexia' led to language production, the 'hyperlexia' itself could be interpreted as being due to grapheme-phoneme synaesthesia [26, 27].

4.4 Case 4

Master X presented with receptive and expressive language disorder and ASD at the age of two and had self-initiated rote language, primarily communicating with numbers and alphabets. It was not reciprocatively voluntary communication, he used the numbers at his will. He often seemed to express himself through numbers. This behavior of heightened number sensing is more common in children with ASD [28]. For example, the parent-reported an incident that happened 1 day as he was playing with his cousin running along a railway track that was drawn in the shape of the number 8. The next time he wanted to play the track game, he would simply call out "eight" several times. The parents were puzzled until they recognized what shape the number 8 he wanted to have. They attempted to address his request by providing him with puzzles with an 8 shape and eight objects of play that he used, not knowing whether he was asking for the number or count of 8 or a sticker 8. The potential of numbers to act as a verbal response inducer was exploited with this child, and the target word was placed with the numbers. The child responded to the secondary association for the primary inducer number and said something when the primary inducer number was paired with the target vocabulary. The clinician capitalized on this behavior and started getting a verbal response to the clinician's writing of numerals on his hand or paper. The clinician paired the number with a target word. The clinician initially wrote the numbers one by one and modeled them for the child to recall and get an immediate response. The numbers were then paired with simple line drawings of the target word, e.g., apple will be depicted as 1 (apple as a line drawing) to get the desired response. The child was able to respond to the words paired with the numerals.

5. Conclusion

Although the synaesthetic perception is considered a sensory experience, it has ramifications for language learning and processing. Synaesthesia has been linked to changes in perception, language, memory, and creativity. The claims of Ramachandran and Hubbard, on the contribution of synaesthesia in the evolution of language, inspire the speech-language pathologist to explore its impact on atypical language development. Differences in sensory perception may be one of the causes of the onset of rote language in children with ASD. The most common feature in the cases mentioned above is the use of rote language. The presentation of rote language varies across individuals, with one having superior verbal recall for numerals, the other for letters, and so on. The ability to recall these mnemonic-ordered verbal expressions can be exploited in language intervention. Although there are various presentations, the basic proclivity for rote language suggests that it should be used to learn a functional language [29]. The observations described here as case examples are inferential and incidental. Despite an early diagnosis and intervention, the children remained unresponsive to stimuli or methods used for language intervention until the intervention was facilitated by their perceptual processing skills, as demonstrated by these case studies. Complete profiling of the synaesthetic skills in children with ASD is important to understand the underlying perception that could be exploited to facilitate language. Children's heterogeneity and inter-subject variability must not interfere with the understanding of the existing synaesthesia. The perceptual skills of children with ASD are sparsely recorded and documented in language evaluations. The sensory processing differences cannot be bypassed while addressing the language impairment in these children. These sensory differences have implications for understanding phenomena such as synaesthesia, which could be exploited for language learning during the intervention. The narrative accounts of individuals on the spectrum give an understanding of how they perceive the world differently. The difference in perception is often explicit in their verbal and non-verbal behaviours. When these verbal and nonverbal behaviors are observed, analyzed cautiously, and related to their specific activities of interest, the underlying synaesthetic skills can be understood and utilized. There is a research gap in mapping the existing sensory profile in children with ASD to the synaesthesia types due to the heterogeneity in the presentation of both conditions. However, as a saying by Carl Jung goes, "In all chaos, there is a cosmos, in all disorder, there is a secret order." The order behind these two heterogeneous scenarios must be explored to develop protocols for language intervention for children with ASD.

Author details

Krupa Venkatraman[1*] and Prathibha Karanth[2]

1 Sri Ramachandra Faculty of Audiology and Speech-Language Pathology, Sri Ramachandra Institute of Higher Education and Research (Deemed to be University), Chennai, India

2 The Com DEALL Trust, Bengaluru, India

*Address all correspondence to: krupa.v@sriramachandra.edu.in

References

[1] Ward J. Synesthesia. Annual Review of Psychology. 2013;**64**:49-75. DOI: 10.1146/annurev-psych-113011-143840

[2] Cytowic RE. Synesthesia. Epub ahead of print. 1 Jan 2002. DOI: 10.1604/9780585436791

[3] Baron-Cohen S, Burt L, Smith-Laittan F, Harrison J, Bolton P. Synaesthesia: Prevalence and familiality. Perception. 1996;**25**:1073-1079. DOI: 10.1068/p251073

[4] Neufeld J, Roy M, Zapf A, Sinke C, Emrich HM, Prox-Vagedes V, et al. Is synesthesia more common in patients with Asperger syndrome? Frontiers in Human Neuroscience. 2013;**7**:1-12. DOI: 10.3389/fnhum.2013.00847

[5] Schauder KB, Bennetto L. Toward an interdisciplinary understanding of sensory dysfunction in autism spectrum disorder: An integration of the neural and symptom literatures. 2016;**10**:1-18. DOI: 10.3389/fnins.2016.00268

[6] Boucher J. Language development in autism. International Congress Series. 2003;**1254**:247-253. DOI: 10.1016/s0531-5131(03)00976-2

[7] Baron-Cohen S, Johnson D, Asher J, Wheelwright S, Fisher SE, Gregersen PK, et al. Is synaesthesia more common in autism?. Molecular autism. Dec 2013;**4**(1):1-6

[8] Ward J, Hoadley C, Hughes JEA, Smith P, Allison C, Baron-cohen S, et al. Atypical sensory sensitivity as a shared feature between synaesthesia and autism. Nature Publishing Group. 7 Mar 2017;**7**(1):1-9. DOI: 10.1038/srep41155

[9] Burghoorn F, Dingemanse M, van Lier R, van Leeuwen TM. The relation between autistic traits, the degree of synaesthesia, and local/global visual perception. Journal of Autism and Developmental Disorders. 2020;**50**:12-29. DOI: 10.1007/s10803-019-04222-7

[10] Watson MR, Akins KA, Spiker C, Crawford L, Enns JT, Winawer J, et al. Synesthesia and learning: A critical review and novel theory. 2014;**8**:1-15. DOI: 10.3389/fnhum.2014.00098

[11] Spiller MJ, Jansari A. In: Simner J, Hubbard EM, editors. Synesthesia and Savant. Oxford Handbook of Synesthesia. Online edn. Oxford Academic; 2013. DOI: 10.1093/oxfordhb/9780199603329.013.0036 [Accessed 6 Nov 2022]

[12] Riedel A, Maier S, Wenzler K, Feige B, Tebartz van Elst L, Bölte S, et al. A case of co-occurring synesthesia, autism, prodigious talent and strong structural brain connectivity. BMC psychiatry. Dec 2020;**20**(1):1

[13] Mroczko-Wasowicz A, Werning M. Synesthesia, sensory-motor contingency, and semantic emulation: How swimming style-color synesthesia challenges the traditional view of synesthesia. Frontiers in Psychology. 22 Aug 2012;**3**:279. DOI: 10.3389/fpsyg.2012.00279

[14] Galea V. Brief report: Further evidence of sensory subtypes in Autism. Yearbook of Sports Medicine. 2012;**2012**:382-384. DOI: 10.1016/j.yspm.2012.03.017

[15] Ramachandran VS, Hubbard EM. Synaesthesia-a window into perception, thought and language. Journal of consciousness studies. 1 Dec 2001;**8**(12):3-4

[16] Simner J, Harrold J, Creed H, Monro L, Foulkes L. Early detection of markers for synaesthesia in childhood populations. Brain. 1 Jan 2009;**132**(1):57-64

[17] van Leeuwen TM, Singer W, Nikolić D. The merit of synesthesia for consciousness research. Frontiers in Psychology. 2015;**6**:1-9. DOI: 10.3389/fpsyg.2015.01850

[18] Watson MR, Chromý J, Crawford L, Eagleman DM, Enns JT, Akins KA. The prevalence of synaesthesia depends on early language learning. Consciousness and Cognition. 2017;**48**:212-231. DOI: 10.1016/j.concog.2016.12.004

[19] Mankin JL. Deepening understanding of language through synaesthesia: A call to reform and expand. Philosophical Transactions of the Royal Society B: Biological Sciences. 9 Dec 2019;**374**(1787):20180350

[20] Reichard GA, Jakobson R, Werth E. Language and Synesthesia. Word. 1 Jan 1949;**5**(2):224-233

[21] Radvansky GA, Gibson BS, McNerney MW. Synesthesia and memory: Color congruency, von restorff, and false memory effects. Journal of Experimental Psychology. Learning, Memory, and Cognition 2011;37:219-229. doi:10.1037/a0021329

[22] van Leeuwen TM, Wilsson L, Norrman HN, Dingemanse M, Bölte S, Neufeld J. Perceptual processing links autism and synesthesia: A co-twin control study. cortex. 1 Dec 2021;**145**:236-249

[23] Karanth P. From aphasia and allied disorders to autism spectrum disorders-A mutualistic symbiotic relationship. (A five decade long journey in neuro-communication disorders). Annals of Indian Academy of Neurology. Sep 2020;**23**(Suppl 2):S63. Available from: https://www.ncbi.nlm.nih.gov/pmc/articles/PMC7731685/

[24] Isaccs. Visual perception in autism. 2016. Available from: https://www.autism.org.uk/advice-and-guidance/professional-practice/visual-perception (2022, accessed November 6, 2022). Ref: https://www.autism.org.uk/advice-and-guidance/professional-practice/visual-perception

[25] Bogdashina OB. Synaesthesia in autism. Autism and Developmental Disorders. 2016;**14**:21-31. DOI: 10.17759/autdd.2016140302

[26] Bouvet L, Barbier J, Cason N, Bakchine S. Approach for their differential diagnosis To cite this version: R P Foeer Review On 2018

[27] Ostrolenk A, Forgeot d'Arc B, Jelenic P, Samson F, Mottron L. Hyperlexia: Systematic review, neurocognitive modelling, and outcome. Neuroscience and Biobehavioral Reviews. 2017;**79**:134-149. DOI: 10.1016/j.neubiorev.2017.04.029

[28] Hiniker A, Rosenberg-Lee M, Menon V. Distinctive role of symbolic number sense in mediating the mathematical abilities of children with autism. Journal of Autism and Developmental Disorders. 2016;**46**:1268-1281. DOI: 10.1007/s10803-015-2666-4

[29] Treffert DA. The savant syndrome: An extraordinary condition. A synopsis: Past, present, future. Philosophical Transactions of the Royal Society B: Biological Sciences. 2009;**364**:1351-1357. DOI: 10.1098/rstb.2008.0326

Chapter 12

Cognitive Behavioral Treatment of Anxiety in Children and Adolescents with ASD

Alan Lincoln, Shamiron Bales, Angela Woolard and Felicia Pryor

Abstract

Children and adolescents with a neurodevelopmental disorder experience vulnerabilities and coping deficits that contribute to the likelihood of developing co-occurring anxiety disorders. The development of anxiety disorders, including social anxiety disorder, is very often reported in children and adolescents with autism spectrum disorder (ASD). Cognitive behavior therapy (CBT) has strong evidentiary support both in combination with medication and as a stand-alone treatment for anxiety disorders in general and more specifically for phobic-type anxiety in children, adolescents, and adults. Moreover, specific manualized CBT is an evidentiarily sound method for treating anxiety in children and adolescents with ASD.

Keywords: ASD, autism, autism spectrum disorder, anxiety, social anxiety, cognitive behavior therapy, computer facilitated CBT, CBT, cCBT

1. Introduction

Individuals with autism spectrum disorders (ASD) have increased vulnerability to the development of other co-occurring neuropsychiatric disorders, including both neurodevelopmental disorders such as attention deficit disorder (ADD), intellectual disability, developmental coordination disorder, and learning disability, as well as other neuropsychiatric and medical disorders such as Gilles de la Tourette's disorder, epilepsy, depressive disorders, and anxiety disorders. We use the term co-occurring instead of comorbid, where the latter term suggests some common etiological relationship with ASD. Such potential for comorbidity does seem probable for some of the disorders that do co-occur such as Tourette's syndrome or ADD, presumably due to abnormalities of systems used in the regulation of dopamine, but to date, all that is really known remains hypothetical about such relationships. It is also reasonable to conclude that when a child begins to develop ASD, for which there is overwhelming evidence of neuropathologic, neuropathophysiologic, and substantial genetic influence on etiology, the evident symptoms used to diagnose the disorder are well preceded by the atypical development of the brain. It is also reasonable to conclude that such differences in brain development lead to secondary consequences on various

IntechOpen

brain functions early in development involving attention, perception, the ability to construct social-communication schemes, and the exercise of effective executive control for goal-oriented behavior. The dysfunction of these secondary consequences then leads to vulnerability in basic learning, the development and ability to engage in reciprocal social relationships, the cognitive flexibility to develop effective adaptations to internal and external stress, increased conflict with the environment, and more unsuccessful efforts to receive positive rewards. Additive vulnerabilities increase the potential for a substantial degree of anxiety in children and adolescents with ASD [1–4]. Specifically, it has been reported that nearly 40% of children and adolescents with a diagnosis of ASD meet clinical criteria for at least one co-morbid anxiety disorder [5], and those with high-functioning ASD experience more anxiety than those with ASD and accompanying intellectual impairment [6, 7].

While it is beyond the scope of this chapter to review the various vulnerabilities or relationship among vulnerabilities of persons with ASD to the potential development of anxiety disorders, there is recent evidence that different patterns of functional connectivity may be associated with persons who have ASD with and without co-occurring anxiety [8]. In a resting state functional magnetic resonance study comparing matched samples of persons with ASD with and without anxiety to non-ASD controls, they reported different patterns of functional connectivity in brain regions previously identified in persons with anxiety disorders [9, 10]. Findings suggest comorbid anxiety in ASD may be associated with disrupted emotion monitoring processes supported by amygdala-dorsal anterior cingulate cortex/medial prefrontal cortical pathways [8] Such findings would be favorable to the idea of a comorbid versus co-occurring relationship between the association of ASD and anxiety. Notwithstanding such evidence of comorbidity, a finding that could eventually lead to interventions related to core etiology, this chapter will focus on current evidence-based behavioral interventions for children and particularly children with ASD.

However, it is also worth discussing the nature of anxiety vis-à-vis the development of anxiety disorders. Anxiety disorders are defined in various ways, but generally through consensus opinion involving experts. These experts agree on various symptoms necessary to meet the criteria for some specific anxiety disorder (e.g., social anxiety disorder, generalized anxiety disorder, separation anxiety disorder, etc.) and once some consensus is reached by a professional association those symptoms along with some other considerations such as the duration of symptoms becomes the diagnosis, at least for some period of time until a new revision is made. Alternative methods employ such criteria in developing questionnaires which, when developed properly, generally have better reliability and validity than the original symptom-based classification. Thus, different types of anxiety can be assessed using psychometric measurements. This is generally required if one was to conduct research about anxiety or assess and measure anxiety in some formal way over time.

However, anxiety can also be considered a dimensional symptom that cuts across many types of psychological conditions that lead to human suffering. People experience anxiety to situational stress, threat, trauma, and uncertainty. Anxiety can be triggered by various medications, substances, medical conditions, and even the onset of other psychiatric symptoms such as hallucinations or delusions. So, the unwanted conditions that lead to anxiety are experienced by most humans from time to time throughout their lifespan. However, it is clear that we evolved as a species to have the potential to experience anxiety not as an evolutionary goal to increase our vulnerability to anxiety disorders but to enhance the potential that we could survive long enough to get our genes in the gene pool. Most psychologists and psychiatrists would, in fact, argue that some anxiety is not only beneficial for survival but that in the right doses can improve motivation and serve as a signal or discriminant stimulus to evoke an adaptive coping response when a person is under such stress or threat. Consequently, our goal in the behavioral treatment of anxiety disorders is to help the individual normalize and better tolerate their response to anxiety, and in particular, to learn more effective coping strategies that lessen the overreliance on avoidant coping and increase the potential for more problem-solving coping and interpersonal problem-solving coping.

2. Prevalence of childhood anxiety disorders

The Centers for Disease Control reports the prevalence of anxiety disorders among children and adolescents to be 9.4% (https://www.cdc.gov/childrensmentalhealth/data.html). Mohatt et al. [11] reported that children and adolescents are often diagnosed with separation, generalized, and social anxiety disorders. The chapter sections will detail: (a) anxiety disorders in youth, (b) co-occurring anxiety in youth with ASD, (c) treatment for anxiety in youth populations, (d) CBT for youth with ASD, (e) CBT for youth with ASD and co-occurring anxiety, (f) computerized CBT for the treatment of anxiety, (g) computer-assisted models of treatment for youth, and (h) computer-assisted CBT for the treatment of anxiety in youth with ASD and co-occurring anxiety. The final section of the literature review will be the summary and conclusion.

3. Anxiety disorders in youth

The Diagnostic and Statistical manual of Mental Disorders (5th ed.; DSM-5; American Psychiatric Associated [12]) stated that pathological anxiety, across ages, may be described by persistent or extensive degrees of anxiety and avoidance associated with subjective distress or impairment. However, when it comes to children, normal and pathological anxiety can sometimes be hard to distinguish [13]. Oddly, the high rates of symptoms of anxiety disorders in children and adolescents may itself be responsible for this diagnostic difficulty. Because of its commonality within the community, with some portion of anxiety during childhood and adolescence deemed developmentally appropriate, clinicians may pay less attention to the issue and overlook clinically significant symptoms of the disorder [13]. Usually, children manifest various types of fears and anxieties in their normal course of development and these fears and anxieties are difficult to immediately characterize as pathological [14–16]. This makes distress an unreliable and inadequate criterion for establishing that children are experiencing pathological anxiety. This problem forms unique dilemmas when one attempts to distinguish among normal, subclinical, and pathological anxiety states in children. Beesdo et al. [17] claimed that children at younger ages might face problems with communicating cognition, emotions, and avoidance, as well as the associated distress and impairments to their parents, doctors, and diagnostic clinicians. This creates a new host of problems for detecting childhood anxiety disorders.

According to Beesdo et al. [17], it is during childhood and adolescence when anxiety symptoms and syndromes usually first materialize. In fact, childhood and adolescence are considered the core risk phases for individuals to develop anxiety-related illnesses, ranging from mild symptoms to significantly interfering anxiety disorders.

The nature of clinically-significant anxiety disorders as a whole almost guarantees that the individual, regardless of age, will have significant and negative impacts on their social and personal development, causing marked impairment of family life, academic achievement, and relationships with peers [18–20]. Because of poor social functioning, anxious youth tend to have fewer friends and less social support during childhood and adolescence, and experience victimization in many arenas [19]. Anxiety disorders in childhood and adolescence are not only extremely common but the resultant distress of living with both the symptoms and the functional consequences of the disorder are associated with lifelong psychiatric disturbance [21].

Prevalence of childhood anxiety disorders has been reported between 2.6 and 41.2% [22]. Children and adolescents are most commonly diagnosed with separation anxiety disorder (SAD), generalized anxiety disorder (GAD), and social phobia (SoP) [11]. Childhood anxiety disorders usually persist into adulthood, making children at risk of having psychiatric disorders in the future [17]. Anxiety disorders among children are linked to considerable developmental, psychosocial, and psychopathological complications.

4. Co-occurring anxiety in youth with ASD

ASD is a neurodevelopmental disorder that is multifaceted. Individuals with ASD evidence persistent deficits in social communication and social interaction across multiple contexts and restricted, repetitive patterns of behavior, interests, or activities [12]. In addition to the core deficits, individuals with ASD also struggle with many co-occurring features. Among children with ASD, it is estimated from 57.5% to 96.4% meet the criteria for at least one co-occurring psychiatric disorder [3, 23, 24]. The most recent United States Centers for Disease Control (CDC) report on prevalence rates of ASD suggested approximately one per 44 children (of 8-year-olds when the diagnosis can be reliably assessed, https://www.cdc.gov/ncbddd/autism/addm.html). This is an increase from an estimate of one per 68 children receiving an ASD classification by the CDC I 2014 [25].

5. Prevalence of co-occurring anxiety in youth with ASD

Children with ASD have been found to have higher rates of internalizing disorders compared to typically developing children or children with other primary diagnosis such as attention deficit hyperactivity disorder (ADHD) or conduct disorder [24, 26, 27]. Internalizing disorders are comprised of behaviors and emotions that are directed inwards and include mood disorders and anxiety disorders. Leo Kanner [28] first described infantile autism and noted common features among his cases were anxiety-related features. For example, Kanner [28] reported the insistence of sameness or repetitive behaviors were observed across cases. He wrote:

> *The child's behavior is governed by an anxiously obsessive desire for the maintenance of sameness that nobody but the child himself may disrupt... Changes of routine, of furniture arrangement, of a pattern, of the order in which every day acts are carried out, can drive him to despair. (p. 245)*

Current literature on anxiety in youth with ASD primarily focuses on individuals with HFA and AS [2, 4, 24, 29]. It has been estimated that nearly 40% of children and adolescents with a diagnosis of ASD meet clinical criteria for at least one co-occurring anxiety disorder [5]. Systematic reviews of the literature investigating the prevalence of anxiety in children and adolescents with ASD have been conducted [5–7, 30]. White et al. [6, 7] reviewed 40 publications. Of the 40 identified, 11 studies specifically examined the prevalence and reported rates of anxiety ranging between 11% and 84% in a population age range of 2–20 year-olds. In the review, only two studies were identified as reporting the prevalence of anxiety symptoms that met diagnostic criteria [1, 31], versus reports of clinical impairment or anxiety symptoms. MacNeil et al. [30] reviewed 13 studies with an age range of 2–19 years old. The mean prevalence rating of anxiety was neither scored nor reported due to the small number of identified studies and variation in outcome variables. It was concluded, however, across studies the findings were comparable in that youth with ASD experience increased levels of anxious symptomology that varied across types of anxiety [30]. van Steensel et al. [5] used a meta-analytic technique to review 31 studies. The review aimed to examine which of the primary anxiety diagnosis identified in the Diagnostic Statistical Manual (4th ed., text rev.; DSM-IV-TR; American Psychiatric Association [32]), occurs most in the ASD youth population. The researchers identified 10 additional studies that had been published since White et al. [6, 7] and MacNeil et al. [30]. Van Steensel et al. [5] reported across studies, a mean of 39.6% of children and adolescents with ASD meet the criteria for at least one co-occurring anxiety disorder according to DSM-IV diagnostic criteria. The meta-analysis of each specific anxiety disorder revealed the most frequently observed anxiety disorder in the ASD population less than 18 years of age, was specific phobia (SP) (29.8%). Furthermore, commonly occurring anxiety disorders also included obsessive-compulsive disorder (OCD) (17.4%) and SoP (16.6%) [5]. The prevalence rates of specific co-occurring disorders have differed by study. Researchers have also reported prevalence rates as follows: SP (8.5–44.3%), OCD (6.4–37%), SoP (7.4–29.2%), agoraphobia (6.4–7.9%), SAD (0.5–12%), GAD (2.4–13.4%), and panic disorder (1.1–10.1%) [1, 3, 31].

5.1 Models of anxiety in youth with ASD

Anxiety in children with ASD differs from anxiety in neuro-typical children due to behavioral manifestations and routine rigidity [33, 34]. Thus, the severity and typology of maladaptive behaviors exhibited by individuals with ASD in response to phobias and fears compound the difficulty of treating individuals with ASD compared to other groups [35]. Making diagnosis even more difficult is the fact that the presentation of anxiety is often atypical for youth with ASD relative to the DSM diagnostic criteria of said disorders [36]. As noted by Lecavalier et al. [37], the difficulty in diagnosing anxiety disorders in children and adolescents with ASD may stem from the fact that some maladaptive behaviors intrinsic to the diagnosis of ASD can make it unclear if such behaviors are the result of anxiety or are simply ASD related. For example, social avoidance is a factor in the diagnosis of children with social anxiety although it is intrinsic to the ASD diagnosis. Children with ASD are also likely to protest separation from caretakers, a behavior that, in a neuro-typical child might lead to a diagnosis of separation anxiety. Other common behaviors observed in youth with ASD relate to key features of anxiety disorders, such as the diagnostic criteria for sleep disturbance and simple phobia [37].

It is apparent that multiple factors impact the co-occurring nature of anxiety in youth with ASD. Common factors represented in the literature include: level of cognitive functioning or ability, age, and as previously stated, level of functioning on the autism spectrum as related to subgroups, and specific deficits or the presence of highly interfering behaviors [15, 16, 38–41].

5.2 Assessment of anxiety disorders in ASD population

The variability in prevalence rates of anxiety in youth with ASD can be attributed to a number of factors. Specifically, variations in assessment procedures and tools can produce differing prevalence estimates [42–44]. Also, core features of ASD overlap with diagnostic markers of anxiety that make it difficult for clinicians to determine if the anxiety symptoms are functioning independently of an ASD diagnosis [45]. Overall, psychometric assessment of measures used to identify co-occurring or comorbid disorders in ASD youth is lacking and greatly needed [46]. For these reasons it is important that a multimodal approach be used when assessing anxiety disorders in ASD youth [44].

Grondhuis and Aman [47] conducted a comprehensive review of the recent literature (2000–2011) specifically focusing on the assessment of anxiety in children and adolescents with ASD. The authors identified the most commonly used assessment tools and provided information on each of their strengths and weaknesses (see [47]). Ultimately, a total of 10 scales were identified as being the most commonly used tools to assess anxiety in ASD youth; Autism Comorbidity Interview—Present and Lifetime Version (ACI-PL), Anxiety Disorders Interview Schedule —Child and Parent reports ADIS-C/P, Autism Spectrum Disorders—Comorbid for Children (ASD-CC), Baby and Infant Scale for Children with Autistic Traits (BUSCUIT), Behavioral Assessment System for Children-2 (BASC-D), Child Behavior Checklist (CBCL), Child Symptom Inventory (CSI), Multi-dimensional Anxiety Scale for Children—child and parent report (MASC-C/P), Social Anxiety Scale for Children—Revised (SASC-R), and Spence Child Anxiety Scale—child and parent report (SCAS-C/P). Of the 10 instruments, only four (ACI-PL, ADIS, MASC, and SCAS) capture four or more dimensions of anxiety, whereas the remaining are limited in their ability to obtain a broader range of anxiety symptoms [47].

Given the complexities in assessing an internalizing disorder such as anxiety in youth with ASD, when selecting assessment measures, particularly a self-report measure, the individual's developmental level should be a key consideration [48]. When monitoring progress over time, the utility of multiple methods is necessary as children with ASD may have difficulty recognizing the change in their own behavior and typically report inconsistently with informant reports [48].

5.3 Impact of co-occurring anxiety on youth with ASD

The presence of anxiety in youth with HFA often exacerbates the deficits in social interactions and contributes to secondary behavioral difficulties [44]. A study by Eussen et al. [49] showed that lower quality social relations and lowered symptoms in children with high-functioning ASD led to higher levels of anxiety. The participants in the study were 134 school-aged children with ASD with and without a diagnosed anxiety disorder. The researchers discovered a positive relationship between low quality social relations, HFA, and high anxiety levels. The researchers reported that intelligence had no impact on the severity of anxiety symptoms. The authors ultimately suggested that future therapeutic interventions include the improvement of social relations as a goal in order to reduce levels or severity of anxiety in high-functioning children with ASD who demonstrate low social relation skills [49].

Individuals with ASD have difficulty in the area of social interaction, and often have difficulty engaging with others in a meaningful and developmentally appropriate manner. Their significant impairment in reciprocal social communication skills and high levels of anxiety with avoidant symptoms and atypical behaviors add an additional barrier to successful social functioning. Consequently, those with ASD may experience even more isolation from their neuro-typically developing peers [49–51].

In their study, Chang et al. [50] examined the link between anxiety and the degree of social functioning impairment in children with ASD. A total of 53 participants presented with a diagnosis of ASD and at least one anxiety disorder. SoP was the most prevalent disorder among the participants and according to the authors, the most problematic. If left untreated, SoP could extend through adolescence and into adulthood, impairing the development and maintenance of close relationships [50]. Although high-functioning children with ASD often have average cognitive abilities, their social impairment impedes their ability to interact with others. The study participants ranged in age from 7- to 11 years old and took a research evaluation to determine their levels of anxiety as well as depression and other disorders. They showed that SoP might have a greater negative functional impact than other types of anxiety on children with ASD. The researchers suggested CBT for children with ASD who are high functioning, noting that children without comorbid intellectual disabilities would make more progress through direct instruction [50].

6. Treatment for Anxiety in youth populations

The field of child psychology is faced with the critical issue of how to effectively treat and remediate the cognitive, behavioral, and emotional difficulties that are causing distress and psychopathology in childhood [52]. Before research being explicitly conducted with child participants, much of the framework for treating anxiety disorders in youth was derived from research with adult populations [53]. Currently, the most empirically supported modality of intervention for treating child anxiety disorders is CBT [54, 55]. CBT is an educational model that has been widely used to treat depressive and anxiety disorders [56]. The six central components of CBT include: (1) psychoeducation, (2) somatic management, (3) cognitive restructuring, (4) problem solving, (5) exposure, and (6) relapse prevention [57].

A primary goal of CBT for anxiety is to help the individual learn to recognize arousal and to use these signs as cues to implement anxiety-management strategies [58]. Psychoeducation provides information about common symptoms or problems associated with the individual's chief complaint [59]. Somatic management assists with further developing awareness and control over physiological and muscular reactions to anxiety. Typically, the individual is taught relaxation strategies such as deep breathing or progressive muscle relaxation. The exercises are intended to be utilized throughout the treatment protocol, initially requiring facilitation by a therapist, and eventually are performed independently by the individual. Cognitive restructuring teaches the individual to identify and modify any anxious self-talk in their internal dialog [60]. Problem-solving skills are taught to improve the client's ability to address concerns related to their condition. Problem-solving techniques are used to cope with anxiety symptoms. The individual learns that after recognizing and identifying the problem, they can then utilize learned techniques to manage their anxiety, weigh the consequences of each alternative, and ultimately choose and follow through with a plan [60]. Exposure provides systematic and controlled exposure to stimuli that have provoked anxiety in the past. Exposure tasks can be facilitated in session with the individual and therapist and can also be completed independently and documented as part of homework assignments. Exposure tasks allow the individual to practice skills, strategies, and problem-solving techniques in relevant contexts [60]. Relapse prevention is the final component to CBT and can be taught in a variety of ways. For children, it is often most beneficial to teach relapse prevention strategies with reinforcement and self-evaluation [61]. For example, a therapist might teach a child to judge the effectiveness of his/her efforts and reward him/herself accordingly. Relapse prevention strategies are taught to increase the repertoire of appropriate behaviors and responses of the individual [58]. By judging the effectiveness of their efforts, a child can learn to identify the favorable aspects of how he/she handled a situation as well as those things they may want to do differently [61].

6.1 Effectiveness of CBT in treating childhood anxiety

Currently, the first-line intervention for treating anxiety disorders in youth is CBT. Both group and individual CBT are considered efficacious interventions [62, 63]. Stuhlmiller and Tolchard [64] considered CBT to be the most effective nonpharmacological treatment for anxiety disorders. These and other positive results of CBT for treating childhood anxiety and other childhood disorders have led to an increase in demand for CBT interventions in this age group [62]. Kendall et al. [65] noted that approximately 60–65% of youth with anxiety disorders treated with CBT show an immediate and meaningful reduction in anxiety symptoms following treatment. Additionally, Donovan and March [66] note that 65–85% of children and youth no longer meet the criteria for diagnosis of their primary anxiety disorder after completing CBT.

Kendall [67] conducted the first RCT to investigate the effectiveness of CBT for children diagnosed with an anxiety disorder. Kendall [67] randomized 47 children aged 9–13 years with anxiety disorders (SAD, GAD, and SoP) to either an active treatment CBT group (n = 27) or a wait-list control group (n = 20). Diagnoses were determined using the ADIS-C/P [68]. For the treatment condition, the Coping Cat Workbook [67] was utilized for treatment procedures and the children utilized The Coping Cat Notebook to complete homework tasks. The individual therapy sessions occurred once a week for approximately 17 weeks and included education and facilitation of behavioral strategies to assist the child in (a) recognizing anxious feelings and somatic reactions to anxiety, (b) clarifying cognition in anxiety-provoking situations, (c) developing a plan to help cope with the situation, and (d) evaluating performance and administering self-reinforcement as appropriate.

For treatment outcomes, Kendall [67] utilized a 2 × 2 mixed factorial analysis of variance and the results revealed positive treatment outcomes for the active treatment of CBT condition. Children in the treatment condition demonstrated significant improvement from pre- to post-treatment on measures of self- and parent-reported distress and coping abilities, observation of anxious child behaviors, and overall diagnostic classification. Post-treatment 64% of participants in the treatment condition no longer qualified for an anxiety disorder diagnosis whereas only 5% of the participants in the wait-list condition did not qualify for an anxiety disorder diagnosis at the end of the waitlist period. These findings support the use of the Coping Cat protocol for the treatment of children with anxiety disorders [67]. Since the initial publication of evidence for the effectiveness of The Coping Cat treatment protocol in treating anxiety in youth, researchers have replicated results [67] with a variety of children with regards to ethnicity, gender [69] and cultures [70, 71]. Furthermore, long-term treatment gains have been demonstrated after 2 years post-completion of treatment [61].

Glenn et al.'s [72] study of CBT sought to determine the impact of treatment frequency and intensity and the extent of patient engagement on outcomes of CBT used in the treatment of anxiety disorders. The study sample consisted of 439 patients who

DOI: http://dx.doi.org/10.5772/intechopen.108223

voluntarily chose CBT as a treatment modality. The researchers compared high and low treatment dosage and high and low patient engagement and compared it to predictors of 12 and 18-month outcomes for patients who took part in a randomized controlled trial of the coordinated anxiety learning and management intervention and received CBT treatment for anxiety with and without medication in primary care settings. Data collected by the authors during and after treatment, determined that high attendance and completion of homework assignments predicted better outcomes across measures at both 12 and 18 months, and high commitment to CBT predicted high outcomes for all measures at the 18-month mark. Thus, the study suggested that high treatment dosage and high engagement in CBT for anxiety disorders could predict more considerable reductions in the symptoms of anxiety and depression. The study implied that the more engaged the client is in the intervention, and the more CBT they receive, the bigger the reductions of anxiety and depression symptomology.

Because anxiety disorders in childhood are among the most prevalent, financially burdensome, and psychologically distressing of childhood psychiatric disorders, the need for efficacious treatment protocols is a societal imperative [73]. In the results of Erford et al.'s [73] meta-analysis, the authors determined that by themselves, face-to-face counseling, medication, and psychotherapy have only a small to medium effect on the treatment of anxiety in children. However, after the thorough analysis of 80 clinical trials of CBT used with children and adolescents, they determined that both individual and group CBT was the most efficacious in the treatment of anxiety disorders in this population. The study researchers also found that long-term counseling/psychotherapy treatment had long-lasting positive effects beyond the treatment for anxiety and SP but acknowledged the need for research to fill the gap regarding the long-term effects of such therapeutic interventions. The use of CBT as an effective treatment for child and adolescent anxiety disorders within the typically developing population has become the first-line intervention for its effectiveness and overall positive impact on reducing symptom severity and improving global functioning [74].

7. The application of CBT for youth with ASD

The use of behavioral modification techniques is not new to the treatment of autism spectrum disorder, as theoretically-related applied behavioral analysis interventions have been successfully helping to reduce the maladaptive behaviors associated with the disorder [75]. There is now a body of literature that suggests CBT can be an effective intervention for youth and adults with ASD, but with considerations that still need to be resolved such as small to medium effect sizes, effect sizes that vary by measures used to assess the outcome, outcome measures assessed by self-report that may be biased toward small or non-significant effect sizes, and relatively small sample trials [76]. Moreover, CBT has been applied to persons with high-functioning autism (HFA) and Asperger syndrome (AS) who have sufficiently developed language and cognitive skills which, are heavily relied upon to successfully engage in CBT. Specifically, the ability to identify and understand emotions and cognitions in oneself and others, referred to as the theory of mind [77], are necessary to utilize tasks and strategies taught in CBT. These abilities are often core challenges for children with ASD [77] however, children with HFA and AS have been found to be similar in their abilities to perform theory of mind tasks when compared to typically developing children [78].

Hare [79] published the first study employing CBT methods to treat co-occurring symptoms in ASD. In a single case study, Hare [79] utilized CBT to treat depression and self-harm in a 26-year-old man with AS. Subject "B," had previously been diagnosed with schizophrenia, but at the time of the referral for treatment, he exhibited no psychotic symptoms nor was he taking anti-psychotic medication. B was diagnosed with AS in primary school, however, no practical help or interventions were received. B's intellectual abilities were reported in the low normal range at the ninth percentile level. B's speech was limited as was his nonverbal communication. His verbal comprehension, short-term, as long-term memory were reported as well developed and assessed by observation and psychometric assessment. Furthermore, B was reported to have adequate literacy skills. B was administered the Beck Depression Inventory (BDI) and obtained a score of 29, indicative of severe depression. At the time of referral, chief complaints and behaviors causing the most concern were self-harm in the form of cutting his forearms with broken glass and excessive drinking while alone. A clinical interview revealed B's self-harm behaviors were often preceded by negative thoughts and verbalized dysfunctional assumptions such as 'life says you should have a girlfriend' and that he had 'been dealt a bad hand' [79].

A treatment plan was individualized and consisted of 10 weekly, 30–60 minute sessions followed by five biweekly sessions. Therapy goals were elicited at the beginning of the intervention session and included the client being able to "make up his mind, to express his feelings, and not to be nervous with women and in social situations in general" ([79], p. 221). B completed a BDI before each session and the material for each session was based on his pattern of responding to the inventory [79]. B kept a diary during treatment and his retrospective entries were also built into the framework of each session's materials. B's diary entries were written in a naturalistic manner. Adaptations were made from the usual CBT protocol to individualize treatment for B. For example, the intervention method was chosen due to B's difficulty with face-to-face communication and sustained dialog and his interest in using numbers to describe his emotional state [79]. Additionally, B's key care worker was present throughout all of the sessions, and was encouraged to take on a co-therapists role.

Therapy consisted of drawing connections between B's actions and thoughts and the negative emotional states that preceded them. Dysfunctional assumptions were identified and challenged. B was instructed to state evidence for a particular belief and identified alternative ways to construct an event or situation. Through this approach, B was able to find accurate and appropriate sources of information upon which to base his emotional state. Lastly, B was introduced to alternative and non-injurious behaviors to cope with emotional discomforts such as anger and frustration. Journaling thoughts, exercise, distraction, and relaxation techniques were used as coping skills and alternatives to self-injurious behaviors [79].

The outcome of treatment for B was assessed in the following ways: BDI score, observation of self-harm behavior, and attainment of therapeutic goals [79]. Outcomes were assessed pre-treatment, throughout the course of treatment, and post-treatment. B's BDI scores evidenced significant stable reduction following the initial 6 weeks of the intervention. B's initial score of 29 on the BDI decreased to 13 at the end of the treatment stage. At 6 months post-treatment, B's BDI scores had slightly increased to 19, and at 8 months post-treatment, he scored 20 on the measure of depression. B's outcome results suggested his depression had improved at the final stage of treatment, then worsened following the end of the intervention phase, however, not to its pre-treatment level [79]. With regard to B's therapy goals, he had achieved two of his three stated therapy goals: being able to make up his mind (e.g., was able to make decisions related to looking for adult education classes) and being able to express his feelings (e.g., began to use writing to express his feelings and communicate with others). B did not meet his therapy goal of reducing social anxiety with females, as he was not able to generalize skills learned and practiced in the therapy session to real-life situations. In Hare [79], results suggested that the use of a CBT approach with the AS population could be useful. The findings paved the way for additional research examining the utility of CBT methods with the ASD population.

Since the publication of Hare [79], the use of CBT principles as effective interventions for youth with ASD has continued to be extensively examined. An intervention titled Program for the Education and Enrichment of Relationship Skills (PEERS) is an evidenced-based social skills program that utilizes the teaching methods of traditional CBT to teach social skills to adolescents with ASD and other social challenges [80]. The CBT treatment program has been examined through multiple clinical trials and reported to be effective in improving the social outcomes in youth with ASD [81–83].

The use of CBT, often with modifications, helps to make the modality more effective for use with this population [84]. The majority of studies employing CBT methods with the ASD population have been conducted with modifications [48]. Wood et al. [85] suggested using hands-on activities or visual aids to assist with facilitating concrete discussions and clarifying the lesson. Cardaciotto and Herbert [86] modified a CBT protocol to treat SoP by adding a social skills training component to the treatment. The modification Were done in the single case design to target the client's impairments in verbal, non-verbal, and paralinguistic communications. Assessment of SoP on outcome measures administered throughout treatment revealed a steady decline in SoP severity. Cardaciotto and Herbert [86] concluded that at the end of treatment the client no longer met diagnostic criteria for symptoms related to SoP.

Ames and Weiss [87] focused their study on the modifications necessary to treat anxiety in a child with ASD, aggression, and mild intellectual impairment with traditional CBT. CBT is the primary treatment for typically developing children and high-functioning children with ASD with anxiety and mood disorders. The study was qualitative and used one participant in a case-study format. The modifications necessary related to the participant's diagnosis of ASD, and included the use of visual aids, decreased verbal commands, role-play, the inclusion of special interests, visual social stories, direct parental participation, and physical play activities. The researchers determined that the use of modifications was useful in the treatment of ASD children, but acknowledged the lack of quantitative support for the modifications as the gains noted were anecdotal in nature. Although largely identified as an effective treatment for youth with ASD and co-occurring psychiatric or behavioral issues, researchers suggest that continued research is necessary to further strengthen the support that CBT is an efficacious modality for the population [88, 89].

8. CBT for youth with ASD and co-occurring anxiety

In the past decade, CBT has steadily emerged in the literature as an efficacious treatment modality for youth with ASD and co-occurring anxiety [85, 88, 90–92]. Across the current literature, positive outcomes are consistently reported, providing mounting evidence for CBT as an effective treatment modality for anxiety in individuals with ASD [85, 88, 90, 93–100].

Sofronoff et al. [90] published the first account of utilizing an RCT of a CBT intervention for anxiety in youth with AS. The study aimed to answer two primary questions, "whether a brief CBT intervention for anxiety would effectively reduce symptomology in children diagnosed with AS" ([90], p. 1157) and "whether there would be a positive effect of parent involvement on children's use of the strategies and therefore an increase in effectiveness." ([90], p. 1157). The study consisted of 71 child participants with AS aged 10–12 years. The presence of anxiety symptomology was established via parent report and the SCAS-P was used to obtain baseline anxiety level. Participants were randomized to one of three intervention groups: CBT intervention 1 (child only), CBT intervention 2 (child + parent), or waitlist control. Within each intervention group, participants were matched on age, sex, baseline anxiety level, IQ, baseline level of depression measured by the Children's Depression Inventory (CDI), and baseline level of AS symptomology measured by the Childhood Asperger Syndrome Test (CAST).

There were eight CBT intervention 1 groups and nine CBT intervention 2 groups that were each comprised of three participants and two therapists. Parents from the CBT intervention 2 groups formed two parent groups and were trained by a therapist to work as co-therapists in all components of the intervention. The waitlist group completed CBT intervention 2 following their final waitlist assessment. Graduate student therapists provided the CBT intervention for all groups and they received on-going supervision [90]. The intervention took place in a clinic setting and consisted of six weekly two-hour-long sessions. The first session included discussing happiness and relaxation, with activities to compare emotions in specific situations. Session two discussed the effects of anxiety and introduced the concept of a "tool box" to teach children various strategies to "fix" their negative emotions and anxiety. Session three focused on social and thinking tools, including cognitive restructuring techniques and how to get help from other people when feeling negative emotions or anxiety. In the fourth session, a "fear thermometer" was introduced to offer the children a visual aid in rating the level of anxiety in certain situations. Session five utilized social stories to teach emotion management strategies. Lastly, session six consisted of participants working together to create self-management plans.

Outcomes were measured by the SCAS-P, the Social Worries Questionnaire (SWQ), and a standardized observational measure of coping strategies generated by children called James and the Math Test. Assessment measures were completed at three time periods: Time 1 pre-treatment (baseline), Time 2 post-treatment, and Time 3 follow-up (6 weeks post-treatment). Scoring was completed by intervention-blind raters and yielded high inter-rater reliability (99%) [90].

The researchers used a series of repeated measures analyses of variance to compare parents' reports of child anxiety across time and between groups. Results from Sofronoff et al. [90] revealed significant reductions in parent-rated symptoms from Time 1 to Time 3 on both the total score and on all sub-scales of the SCAS-P and SWQ. Furthermore, James and the Math Test showed a significant increase in the number of adaptive coping strategies generated by each child to deal with anxiety-producing situations. There were also significant differences between the two CBT intervention groups, as measured by the SCAS-P, at Time 3 with the CBT intervention 2 group showing greater improvement, suggesting parent involvement in the program produced greater Outcome for the participants [90].

Overall, the results of this study demonstrated that CBT was effective in reducing symptoms in a child with AS [90]. The researchers reported that the CBT intervention was well accepted by the children and their parents. Some identified limitations of the study were focused on the nature of data collection. Outcome measures consisted of two parent report measures. As only parent report was utilized, parents may have expected their children to improve because of their participation in the program. The authors suggested that future research collect data from multiple informant measures and that behavioral change be assessed as well [90].

McNally Keehn et al. [93] conducted the first study to examine the effectiveness of the Coping Cat program in reducing anxiety in children with ASD. The researchers conducted a randomized control trial including 22 children ages 8–14 years old. The participants included in the study achieved an IQ ≥ 70 and met diagnostic criteria for one or more principal anxiety disorders (GAD, SoP, SAD). Twelve participants were randomized to the CBT condition and 10 were randomized to the waitlist/control (WL) condition. The study utilized the ADIS-P [68] as the primary outcome measure and the SCAS-C/P [101] and MASC-C/P [102] as secondary outcome measures to assess for clinically significant anxiety.

Results of the data analysis showed that ratings for principal anxiety disorders in the CBT group dropped below the clinical cutoff (<4) at post-treatment as measured by the primary outcome measure [93]. Specifically, 58% of children in the CBT condition no longer met the criteria for their primary anxiety diagnosis at post-treatment assessment while 100% of children in the WL condition continued to meet the criteria for the principal anxiety diagnosis at post-WL assessment. Furthermore, 36% of the CBT condition participants remained free from meeting diagnostic criteria for their primary anxiety diagnosis at the two-month follow-up suggesting that treatment gains from the modified Coping Cat program were maintained. Given the positive findings from the research study, the authors suggest that a modified version of the Coping Cat program could be a possible first line of treatment for children with ASD and co-occurring anxiety [93].

In another 12-week trial comparing CBT to treatment as usual (TAU) in 45 children, ages 7–11, Storch et al. [103] reported significant improvement in anxiety symptoms. After randomization, children in the CBT group were given 16 sessions of manualized CBT that included psychoeducation, cognitive components, exposure, homework, and parent meetings employing the Behavior Interventions for Anxiety with Autism [104]. Eighteen of 24 children in the CBT group improved relative to 3 of 21 children in the TAU group. Gains were was maintained for most of the CBT group at 3 months. A total of 38% (9/24) of children in the CBT group achieved clinical remission at post-treatment versus 5% (1/21) of those in the TAU arm ($p < .01$).

This same team also reported positive results in an older cohort of children and adolescents ages 11–16 [105]. In a similar randomized trial comparing sixteen weekly, CBT sessions, 11 of 16 in the CBT group showed significant improvement compared to 4 of 15 in the TAU group based on blind ratings of symptoms taken at prescreening, posttreatment, and a 1-month follow-up. Moreover, gains were generally maintained at follow-up.

Wood et al. [104] examined the efficacy of CBT for use with youth diagnosed with ASD and comorbid anxiety. They used a modified version of a modular CBT program originally designed for preteens with ASD, called Behavioral Interventions for Anxiety in Children with Autism (BIACA) to treat early adolescents with ASD co-occurring anxiety. The study participants included 33 adolescents between the ages of 11 and 15, whom the researchers randomly assigned to attend 16 CBT sessions or to be placed in the waiting list control group. The CBT group experienced 79% symptom improvement at the end of the study as measured by the Clinical Global Impressions-Improvement scale, as compared with 28% of the waitlist group. Their findings provided additional support that CBT was an effective treatment for ASD youth who have clinically significant levels of co-occurring anxiety.

Wise et al. [99] completed a small open trial of a manualized CBT program on seven 16–20 year-olds with ASD to treat anxiety. Over their 16-week trials that included psychoeducation, cognitive therapy, and exposure, significant improvement in anxiety was found on clinician-rated measures.

9. Computerized CBT for the treatment of anxiety.

Computerized CBT is a modern version of CBT developed to meet the needs of those who are diagnosed with or experience the symptoms of anxiety disorders and who, for a variety of reasons, do not use a therapist-guided CBT program. Barriers to treatment for anxiety include but are not limited to the accessibility of services, financial issues, lack of knowledge of appropriate services, and long waiting periods [106–108].

Andrews et al. [18] found that though treatment for anxiety has largely proved efficacious, low numbers of adults suffering from depression and anxiety actually seek therapeutic interventions. The researchers looked at the efficacy of the use of computer-based therapy for individuals with depression and anxiety. For their quantitative, retrospective cross-sectional study, the authors gathered 2670 abstracts on the subject of computer-based psychological treatment of depression, and anxiety disorders, calculated the effect size and determined the difference between the two conditions. Ultimately 22 studies were used in their analysis, and it was determined that even though the individuals had limited contact with a clinician, computerized CBT was a viable treatment for the disorders. When compared to face-to-face treatment, it offered the clients increased access to treatment, and had similar approval rates. Effect sizes obtained in the reviewed studies were substantial and the results indicated short-term and long-term benefits. The researchers concluded that computerized CBT is an efficacious and acceptable treatment [18].

A study by Amir and Taylor [109] noted that though GAD is a common and often debilitating disorder, many individuals who suffer from it do not seek or receive the most effective treatment. The quantitative research study included 21 participants who were seeking treatment for GAD and were willing to utilize a 6-week computerized home-based treatment program. The program contained two elements, an attention modification program (AMP) and a brief computer-delivered CBT module (cCBT). Of the 21 participants, 14 individuals, or 67% of participants, completed the program, and the treatment resulted in a clinically significant reduction in symptoms for program completers. The researchers reported considerably lower clinician and self-rated symptoms of GAD and 79% of the 14 study participants no longer met the DSM IV's criteria for GAD at the end of the program, with 36% classified as in remission.

Additionally, in their qualitative study, Barazzone et al. [110] found that computerized CBT programs build on certain features of the therapeutic alliance, such as the idea of empowerment, which helps to establish the therapeutic relationship and contribute to the achievement of positive mental health outcomes. Barazzone et al.'s [110] study used three online computerized CBT programs for depression to determine how well the therapeutic alliance was established and maintained electronically. The researchers analyzed data from the three computerized CBT programs using a deductive qualitative approach based on a matrix-based analytic method called framework analysis. The researchers looked for features within the three programs that could establish, develop, and maintain a therapeutic alliance. The study researchers determined that there was considerable evidence showing that the computerized therapy programs contained features associated with the establishment, development, and maintenance of the therapeutic alliance.

More recently, Bowler et al. [111] tested the prediction that computerized CBT and cognitive bias modification for interpretation (CBM-I) would reduce anxiety better than for a wait-list control group. The study participants were 63 mostly Caucasian adults who reported high levels of anxiety. Researchers randomly assigned participants to one of the three groups and obtained self-reported levels of anxiety, depression, attentional control, and threat-related interpretive bias at four time periods.

All participants, except those in the control group, reported clinically significant reductions in social and trait anxiety and depression levels.

Thus, combined studies reveal that computerized CBT is an efficacious and potentially cost-effective treatment for anxiety and depression when access to therapist-led, face-to-face cognitive behavioral therapy is limited [108, 110].

10. Computer-assisted models of treatment for youth

Multiple studies detailing the efficacy of using computerized CBT as a treatment for anxiety and depression in adults exist [18, 109–111]. There is also now a growing body of research focused on the efficacy of computerized CBT for use with youth [66, 112–117].

Craske et al. [112] describe a computer-assisted CBT program designed to provide evidence-based treatment for the four types of anxiety disorders usually observed in primary care settings. These anxiety disorders are panic disorder, posttraumatic stress disorder, GAD, as well as SoP. The researchers described the structure and format of this CBT program and showed evidence of the program's effectiveness. They gathered 13 clinicians utilizing this program and interviewed them about their perceptions of the program. The researchers found that the clinicians using the program all had positive views and see it as very helpful to the youth with these disorders. The patients showed great commitment to attendance and homework compliance with this program. The patients also understood the program material better and even acquired CBT skills.

Moreover, the clinicians who used the program reported that improvements were seen across the four types of principal anxiety disorders. Patients diagnosed with these different disorders showed improvements to the same degree as one another when it came to their self-ratings of self-ratings of anxiety, depression, and expectations for improvement. The researchers concluded that computer-assisted CBT programs could enable an effective practice-based system for spreading evidence-based mental health treatment across primary care settings while making sure that there would be treatment fidelity even in the hands of novice clinicians [118].

Holmes et al. [119] also discussed the effectiveness of using computer-based interventions as possible alternatives to treating children dealing with anxiety disorders. The researchers designed the study after identifying the gap in the literature exploring the feasibility and efficacy of computer-delivered treatment of anxiety in child patients as opposed to the frequently-studied adult populations. The researchers found that the internet might be an effective way of delivering CBT targeting children suffering from anxiety disorders since it has reportedly been effective for adults [119]. Computerized CBT programs can be effective either as a stand-alone internet treatment or a combined clinic and internet program. The researchers, however, questioned whether a computerized program is better than a clinic-based treatment program, especially for children. The researchers claimed that as of now, firm conclusions on this cannot yet be drawn, although it seems that internet approaches may be acceptable and beneficial for a significant proportion of children dealing with anxiety disorders, with their parents being satisfied with the process and outcomes [119].

In 2008 Kendell and Khanna introduced CCAL: The Coping Cat CD Rom [120, 121]. Khanna and Kendall [122] evaluated the feasibility and acceptable effects of CCAL, a computer-assisted CBT intervention for anxiety in youth based on the Coping Cat program framework. The researchers randomly assigned 49 children, 33 of whom are males from ages 7 to 13 and of different ethnicities, to CCAL, individual CBT (ICBT), and a computer-assisted education, support, and attention (CESA) condition. All therapists came from the community or were Psy.D. or Ph.D. trainees, some of whom were trained, others untrained, in practicing CBT for child anxiety. The researchers conducted independent diagnostic interviews and self-report measures at pre- and post-treatment and 3-month follow-up. At post-treatment, the researchers found that children who went through the ICBT or CCAL showed greater improvement than the children who underwent CESA. In addition, these improvements were sustained at follow-up, with no significant differences between the children who underwent ICBT and children who underwent CCAL [122]. At the 3-month post-treatment follow-up, 70% of those treated with CCAL, 81% of those who used the ICBT program, and 19% of those using the CESA program no longer met the criteria for their anxiety disorder. The parents of the children all provided satisfactory ratings for the treatments. However, the CCAL and ICBT children provided higher satisfaction ratings than the CESA children. Khanna and Kendall [122] concluded that CCAL is feasible, acceptable, and beneficial for children dealing with anxiety. This research provided further support for the effectiveness of computer-assisted modalities in delivering empirically supported treatments.

Spence et al. [123] compared online versus clinical delivery of CBT to treat anxiety disorders in adolescents. This comparison has been the question of most researchers in computer-assisted CBT treatment. Even though the safety and benefits of computer-assisted CBT treatments for children have been established by several researchers, they could not draw a firm conclusion as to whether computer-assisted treatments are better than clinical treatments. Spence et al. [123] tried to close this research gap. To determine this, they gathered 115 clinically anxious adolescents aged 12–18 years and their parent(s). Adolescents were randomly assigned to online delivery of CBT, clinic-based delivery of CBT, or WL control conditions. Those in the treatment groups were given equivalent CBT content. The researchers conducted clinical diagnostic interviews and questionnaire assessments 12 weeks after baseline and at 6- and 12-month follow-ups. They found that both online delivery and clinic-based delivery of CBT treatments are beneficial. Children in these two delivery modes of CBT experienced greater reductions in anxiety diagnoses and anxiety symptoms compared with the WL control. These improvements were maintained or further enhanced for both conditions, with minimal differences between them, at 6- and 12-month follow-ups. Therefore, the researchers cannot say online delivery is better than clinic-based delivery. In particular, 78% of those who underwent the online delivery program no longer met the principal anxiety diagnosis criteria at the 12-month follow-up. Around 80.6% of the patients in the clinic-based delivery group experienced the same. This shows that the two types of CBT treatments offer no relatively different outcomes and that both are effective. Ratings of treatment credibility from both parents and adolescents were high for both types of programs. Satisfaction ratings by adolescents were equivalent for the two types of CBT treatments [123]. However, parents of children in the clinic-based delivery of CBT treatments are a bit more satisfied than those whose children underwent the online delivery model. Still, the researchers concluded that online delivery of CBT, even if children experienced minimal therapist support, is equally efficacious as clinic-based, face-to-face therapy in treating anxiety disorders among adolescents [123]. The online-based treatment is also far more accessible [123]. This approach is an effective alternative for those who do not engage in face-to-face clinical treatment.

Blocher et al. [124] recognized that anxiety disorders are prevalent among children suffering from epilepsy and designed a study that would determine the efficacy, adaptability, and feasibility of a manual-based, computer-based CBT intervention for anxiety disorders in children with epilepsy. They gathered 15 children (aged 8–13 years) with epilepsy and dealing with anxiety disorder and asked them to complete 12 weeks of a manualized computer-assisted CBT. The children and their parents were interviewed at baseline with semi-structured questions. They were also asked to complete surveys before, during, and after treatment to determine their symptoms of anxiety, depression, and behavior problems. The researchers found that there were apparent reductions in symptoms experienced by the children in relation to anxiety and depression at the completion of the intervention and the 3-month follow-up. Aside from the children, the parents asserted that they observed fewer anxiety symptoms and a reduction in behavior problems. No adverse events were reported for any of the participants. The researchers, therefore, were able to conclude that computer-assisted CBT intervention for children with epilepsy and anxiety disorders is safe, effective, and feasible. They asked that this treatment form be included in future intervention studies dealing with children suffering from anxiety disorders.

A study by Donovan and March [66] determined the efficacy of a computerized CBT program for preschoolers with anxiety disorders. The computerized CBT program was parent-focused and therapist-assisted. The study authors required parents to complete a series of diagnostic interviews and parent-report questionnaires to determine the severity of anxiety symptoms of their combined 52 children ranging in age from 3 to 6-year-old. The researchers randomly placed the children into either the program group or informed them that they were on the waiting list, a group that then served as the control group. The parents participated in diagnostic interviews and filled out parent-report symptom severity questionnaires at the program's start and again after 6 months. Post-treatment assessments revealed that 39% of participants versus 25% of the control group showed significantly reduced symptoms at the end of the program. At the 6-month review, 70% of the preschoolers who had participated in the program group no longer had their initial anxiety disorder diagnosis. The results indicate that computerized CBT is efficacious for preschoolers with anxiety disorders.

Donovan et al. [106] detail how technology can decrease the barriers to treatment for children and adolescents, and study the benefits and weaknesses of using various computerized CBT programs to treat anxiety. Mentioned briefly was the efficacy of using a computer-based program for the treatment of adolescents with ASD. The study authors detailed a program called "BRAVE ONLINE," a computer-based CBT program for treating anxiety in children and adolescents. The program treats children aged 7–17 and has shown efficacy for both age groups. Although there is also a parent-based program for use with younger children, the results currently remain unpublished.

Ebert et al. [113] also studied the possibility of using computerized CBT treatments to alleviate the symptoms of anxiety and depression in children and adolescents. The researchers used data from 13 randomized trials that used 796 children and adolescents as participants to determine the effectiveness of symptom reduction when using computerized CBT programs to treat the symptoms of anxiety and depression in that population. They ultimately discovered that computerized CBT is an effective treatment modality relative to face-to-face treatment services for lessening anxiety and depression symptoms in young people up to age 25.

Researchers such as Vigerland et al. [116] suggested that most clinicians continue to lack the knowledge of or experience with the use of computerized CBT, even though computerized CBT has proven effective for treating anxiety in children and adolescents. In fact, many researchers believe that it should be the primary treatment for anxiety disorders in this age group [116]. In their 2014 study, Vigerland et al. [116] surveyed 156 mental health clinicians on their attitudes toward using computerized CBT to treat anxiety in children and adolescents. Although many clinicians (73%) viewed computerized CBT as an effective preventative measure, and 75% of the clinicians studied acknowledged its usefulness in the treatment of mild to moderate anxiety, most reported that they did not want computerized CBT to be freely accessible online. The mental health practitioners were reportedly concerned with the severity of symptoms, the age of the client, and the lack of human support during treatment. Thus, most clinicians wanted to see computerized CBT administered within a mental

Name of program and website	Ages	Facilitated support
Camp Cope-A-Lot https://www.workbookpublishing.com/camp-cope-a-lot.html	11–13	Professional and/or parent
SMARTCAT https://apps.apple.com/us/app/smartcat-3-0/id1511786912	7–13	Professional
Treasure Hunt https://www.treasurehunt.uzh.ch/en.html	9–13	Professional
BRAVE https://www.taptap.io/app/65756	8–12 9–13	Professional
Mayo Clinic Anxiety Coach https://anxietycoach.mayoclinic.org/anxiety/	Child/adol.	Self-help
REACH Patwardhan et al. [125]	9–11	Not specified
DARE	8–12	Therapist
https://apps.apple.com/us/app/dare-panic-anxiety-relief/id1034311206		
Cool Little Kids https://coollittlekids.org.au/login	3–6	Not specified
Pesky gNATs Island https://peskygnats.com/peskygnats/	9–17	Professional
Think, Feel, Do Stallard et al. [63]	11–16	Professional
Cool Teens Program https://www.c4tbh.org/program-review/cool-teens/	14–17	Professional
MoodGYM https://moodgym.com.au/	Not specified	Teacher
Unnamed; Tillfors [126]	Not specified	Professional
Kids-accident Cox et al. [127]	Not specified	Parents
Adapted from Tozzi et al. [115].		

Table 1.
Current evidence-based computer facilitated applications for treating anxiety in children.

health or primary care facility to ensure the involvement of face-to-face interaction in combination with the computerized CBT interventions [116].

Tozzi et al. [115] completed a meta-analysis of 197 articles with 19 meeting criteria for review of acceptable technology with treatment and prevention programs for anxiety in children and adolescents. Fourteen technology-based CBT treatments were identified as meeting efficacy standards. Seven were appropriate for children and seven for adolescents. The programs they identified can be seen in **Table 1**.

Despite questions of accessibility, the use of computerized CBT is now a growing trend in the treatment of anxiety disorders for children, adolescents, and adults alike [128–130], but the use of computerized CBT for children and adolescents with co-occurring ASD is not as prevalent. Thus, future research will likely include the efficacy of computerized CBT for use in youth populations with ASD [131].

11. Computer-Assisted CBT for the treatment of anxiety in youth with ASD and co-occurring anxiety

Children and adolescents with ASD have unique needs regarding the treatment of their disorder, and in most cases, behavioral analysis interventions were the preferred treatment [75]. The success of behavioral interventions combined for the treatment of ASD, and cognitive behavioral interventions for the treatment of co-occurring anxiety disorders are largely unknown and represent a significant gap in the research. Although it is known that CBT is an effective treatment for use with youth with co-occurring anxiety disorders and ASD, future research needs to determine the efficacy of computer-assisted CBT for the treatment of this population [117, 132–135]. Zabel recently completed a dissertation at Philadelphia College of Osteopathic Medicine, Department of Psychology, investigating the efficacy of CCAL CD Rom for treating anxiety symptoms in children with ASD. The single case study revealed inconsistent results on the overall reduction of anxiety symptoms in the participants diagnosed with ASD. The study utilized a small sample (n = 4) with no control group. According to Zabel [135] the 12-week CCAL intervention was "generally successful in decreasing some symptoms of anxiety for each of the participants" (p. 111). However, results on outcome measures yielded no statistically significant changes in symptom severity and were inconsistent across scales, subscales, and participants. The variability observed across outcome data was attributed to participant heterogeneity and a small sample size. Although quantitative data analysis did not reveal a statistically significant change in the participants' self and parent report outcomes measures, the researcher discussed valued qualitative information obtained during the study. For example, Zabel [135] discussed overall parent-reported satisfaction with the intervention and observed improvement in the participant's ability to approach their fears as they progressed through the intervention. Results from this first-known study on the efficacy of CCAL in treating anxiety in children with ASD offered valuable limitations identified that will benefit researchers wishing to continue examining the potential efficacy of CCAL, an empirically supported intervention program in youth with co-occurring ASD. To date, no known studies investigating the efficacy of CCAL have been conducted utilizing a larger sample size or RCT design.

Most recently, our group [95] reported the results of a crossover design showing the efficacy of a computer-assisted intervention program for youth with ASD who also experience co-occurring anxiety. The computer-assisted cognitive behavior program, CCAL was compared to control intervention, another computer-assisted program, The Social Express (TSE), that does not employ CBT nor is targeted for the treatment of anxiety. TSE is designed to improve social skills in youth with ASD. Participants had a principal anxiety disorder and a current diagnosis of ASD. Participants received 12 sessions of CCAL or 12 sessions of TSE. Outcome measures were obtained at intake, upon completion of the first intervention of the trial, and upon completion of the second intervention of the trial. CCAL was efficacious for treating anxiety. Participants who completed CCAL demonstrated significant clinical reductions in anxiety when compared to participants who completed TSE. The study obtained an NNT = 2.17 which is comparable or superior to those reported by pharmacological research examining evidence-based approaches to treating pediatric anxiety [136]. While a multi-modal treatment approach has been found most effective in treating anxiety in youth [136], there remains the potential for adverse events with psychopharmacological interventions. A small dropout rate for CCAL, and the intervention required minimal financial support interventions, CCAL and TSE, also both showed some limited improvement in social skills.

12. Conclusions

Anxiety is a frequent co-occurring condition in persons with ASD and particularly children and adolescents with ASD. During the past decade, multiple clinical trials have demonstrated significant evidence that CBT employed to treat anxiety in children and adolescents with ASD was generally effective and clearly constituted an evidence-based intervention treatment modality. Effect sizes, while significant, ranged from small to large depending on the study and particularly on outcome measures. Virtually all of the trials reported in this chapter were relatively small with treatment samples of less than 30 participants receiving CBT. This suggests the need for larger randomized trials.

Author details

Alan Lincoln[1]*, Shamiron Bales[1], Angela Woolard[1] and Felicia Pryor[2]

1 Alliant International University, San Diego, CA, USA

2 U.S. Army, USA

*Address all correspondence to: alincoln@alliant.edu

References

[1] de Bruin EI, Ferdinand RF, Meester S, de Nijs PF, Verheij F. High rates of psychiatric co-morbidity in PDD-NOS. Journal of Autism and Developmental Disorders. 2007;**37**(5):877-886

[2] Gillott A, Furniss F, Walter A. Anxiety in high-functioning children with autism. Autism. 2001;**5**(3):277-286. DOI: 10.1177/1362361301005003005

[3] Leyfer OT, Folstein SE, Bacalman S, Davis NO, Dinh E, Morgan J, et al. Comorbid psychiatric disorders in children with autism: Interview development and rates of disorders. Journal of Autism and Developmental Disorders. 2006;**36**(7):849-861

[4] Mattila ML, Hurtig T, Haapsamo H, Jussila K, Kuusikko-Gauffin S, Kielinen M, et al. Comorbid psychiatric disorders associated with Asperger syndrome/ high-functioning autism: A community- and clinic-based study. Journal of Autism and Developmental Disorders. 2010;**40**(9):1080-1093

[5] van Steensel FJA, Bögels SM, Perrin S. Anxiety disorders in children and adolescents with autistic spectrum disorders: A meta-analysis. Clinical Child and Family Psychology Review. 2011;**14**(3):302-317

[6] White SW, Ollendick T, Scahill L, Oswald D, Albano AM. Preliminary efficacy of a cognitive-behavioral treatment program for anxious youth with autism spectrum disorders. Journal of Autism and Developmental Disorders. 2009a;**39**(12):1652-1662. DOI: 10.1007/ s10803-009-0801-9

[7] White SW, Oswald D, Ollendick T, Scahill L. Anxiety in children and adolescents with autism spectrum disorders. Clinical Psychology Review. 2009b;**29**(3):216-229

[8] Bartolotti J, Sweeney J, Mosconi. Functional brain abnormalities associated with comorbid anxiety in autism spectrum disorder. Development and Psychopathology. 2020;**32**(4):1273-1286. DOI: 10.1017/S0954579420000772

[9] Qiao J, Li A, Cao C, Wang Z, Sun J, Xu G. Aberrant Functional Network Connectivity as a Biomarker of Generalized Anxiety. In: Disorder Machine Learning in Imaging Neurodevelopment and Neurodegeneration: Sec. Brain Imaging and Stimulation. Switzerland: Frontiers Media S.A.: Frontiers in Human Neuroscience. 2017;**11**:626. DOI: 10.3389/ fnhum.2017.00626

[10] Zhang Y, Li L, Yu R, Liu J, Tang J, Tan L, et al. White matter integrity alterations in first episode, treatment-naive generalized anxiety disorder. Journal of Affective Disorders. 2013;**148**:196-201. DOI: 10.1016/j. jad.2012.11.060

[11] Mohatt J, Bennett SM, Walkup JT. Treatment of separation, generalized, and social anxiety disorders in youth. American Journal of Psychiatry. 2014;**171**(7):741-748. DOI: 10.1176/appi. ajp.2014.13101337

[12] American Psychiatric Association. Diagnostic and Statistical Manual of Mental Disorders. 5th ed. Washington, DC: American Psychiatric Association; 2013

[13] Van Meter A, Youngstrom E, Youngstrom JK, Ollendick T, Demeter C, Findling RL. Clinical decision making about child and adolescent anxiety disorders using the Achenbach system of empirically based assessment. Journal of Clinical Child and Adolescent

Psychology. 2014;**43**(4):552-565. DOI: 10.1080/15374416.2014.883930

[14] Morris RJ, Kratochwill TR. Childhood fears and phobias. In Kratochwill, T.R., Morris, R.J. The Practice of Child Therapy. 2. New York: Pergamon. 1991

[15] Muris P, Merckelbach H, Mayer B, Meesters C. Common fears and their relationship to anxiety disorders symptomatology in normal children. Personality and Individual Differences. 1998;**24**(4):575-578

[16] Muris P, Steerneman P, Merckelbach H, Holdrinet I, Meesters C. Comorbid anxiety symptoms in children with pervasive developmental disorders. Journal of Anxiety Disorders. 1998b;**12**(4):387-393

[17] Beesdo K, Knappe S, Pine D. Anxiety and anxiety disorders in children and adolescents: Developmental issues and implications for DSM-V. Psychiatric Clinical North America. 2009;**32**(3):483-524. DOI: 10.1016/j.psc.2009.06.002

[18] Andrews G, Cuijpers P, Craske MG, McEvoy P, Titov N. Computer therapy for the anxiety and depressive disorders is effective, acceptable and practical health care: A meta-analysis. PLoS One. 2010;**5**(10):e13196. DOI: 10.1371/journal.pone.0013196

[19] Rapee RM. Nature and psychological management of anxiety disorders in youth. Journal of Pediatrics and Child Health. 2015;**51**(3):280-284. DOI: 10.1111/jpc.12856

[20] van Steensel FJA, Bögels SM. Anxiety and quality of life: Clinically anxious children with and without autism spectrum disorders compared. Journal of Clinical and Adolescent Psychology. 2012;**41**(6):731-738. DOI: 10.1080/15374416.2012.698725

[21] Creswell C, Waite P, Cooper PJ. Assessment and management of anxiety disorders in children and adolescents. Archives of Disease in Childhood. 2014;**99**(7):674-678

[22] Cartwright-Hatton S, McNicol K, Doubleday E. Anxiety in a neglected population: Prevalence of anxiety disorders in pre-adolescent children. Clinical Psychology Review. 2006;**26**(7):817-833

[23] Mukaddes NM, Hergüner S, Tanidir C. Psychiatric disorders in individuals with high-functioning autism and Asperger's disorder: Similarities and differences. World Journal of Biological Psychiatry. 2010;**11**(8):964-971

[24] van Steensel FJA, Bögels SM, de Bruin EI. Psychiatric comorbidity in children with autism spectrum disorders: A comparison with children with ADHD. Journal of Child and Family Studies. 2013;**22**(3):368-376

[25] Centers for Disease Control and Prevention. Prevalence of autism spectrum disorders-autism and developmental disabilities monitoring network, 11 sites, United States, 2010. Morbidity and Mortality Weekly Report. 2014;**63**:1-21. Available from: http://www.cdc.gov/media/releases/2012/p0329_autism_disorder.html

[26] Green J, Gilchrist A, Burton D, Cox A. Social and psychiatric functioning in adolescents with Asperger syndrome compared with conduct disorder. Journal of Autism and Developmental Disorders. 2000;**30**(4):279-293. DOI: 10.1023/a:1005523232106

[27] Lai MC, Kassee C, Besney R, Bonato S, Hull L, Mandy W, et al. Prevalence of co-occurring mental health diagnoses in the autism population: A systematic review and meta-analysis. The

Lancet Psychiatry. 2019;**6**(10):819-829. DOI: 10.1016/S2215-0366(19)30289-5

[28] Kanner L. Autistic disturbances of affective contact. Nervous Child. 1943;**2**(3):217-250

[29] Brereton AV, Tonge BJ, Einfeld SL. Psychopathology in children and adolescents with autism compared to young people with intellectual disability. Journal of Autism and Developmental Disorders. 2006;**36**(7):863-870

[30] MacNeil BM, Lopes VA, Minnes PM. Anxiety in children and adolescents with autism spectrum disorders. Research in Autism Spectrum Disorders. 2009;**3**(1):1-21

[31] Simonoff E, Pickles A, Charman T, Chandler S, Loucas T, Baird G. Psychiatric disorders in children with autism spectrum disorders: Prevalence, comorbidity, and associated factors in a population-derived sample. Journal of the American Academy of Child & Adolescent Psychiatry. 2008;**47**(8):921-929

[32] American Psychiatric Association. Diagnostic and Statistical Manual of Mental Disorders. 4th ed., text rev. ed. Washington, DC: American Psychiatric Association; 2000

[33] Bearss K, Taylor CA, Aman MG, Whittemore R, Lecavalier L, Miller J, et al. Using qualitative methods to guide scale development for anxiety in youth with autism spectrum disorder. Autism. 2015;**13**(62):361-315. DOI: 10.1177/1362361315601012

[34] Lau B, Leong R, Uljarevic M, Lerh J, Rodgers J, Hollocks M, et al. Anxiety in young people with autism spectrum disorder: Common and autism-related anxiety experiences and their associations with individual characteristics. Autism. 2020;**24**(5):1111-1126. DOI: 10.1177/1362361319886246

[35] Evans DW, Canavera K, Kleinpeter FL, Maccubbin E, Taga K. The fears, phobias and anxieties of children with autism spectrum disorders and down syndrome: Comparisons with developmentally and chronologically age matched children. Child Psychiatry and Human Development. 2005;**36**(1):3-26. DOI: 10.1007/s10578-004-3619-x

[36] Kerns CM, Kendall PC, Berry L, Souders MC, Franklin ME, Schultz RT, et al. Traditional and atypical presentations of anxiety in youth with autism spectrum disorder. Journal of Autism and Developmental Disorders. 2014;**44**(11):2851. DOI: 10.1007/s10803-014-2141-7

[37] Lecavalier L, Wood JJ, Halladay AK, Jones NE, Aman MG, Cook EH, et al. Measuring anxiety as a treatment endpoint in youth with autism spectrum disorder. Journal of Autism and Developmental Disorders. 2014;**44**(5):1128-1143. DOI: 10.1007/s10803-013-1974-9

[38] Farrugia S, Hudson J. Anxiety in adolescents with Asperger syndrome: Negative thoughts, behavioral problems, and life interference. Focus on Autism and Other Developmental Disabilities. 2006;**21**(1):25-35. DOI: 10.1177/10883576060210010401

[39] Meyer JA, Mundy PC, Van Hecke AV, Durocher JS. Social attribution processes and comorbid psychiatric symptoms in children with Asperger syndrome. Autism. 2006;**10**(4):383-402

[40] Pfeiffer B, Kinnealey M, Reed C, Herzberg G. Secondary modulation and effective disorders in children and adolescents with Asperger's syndrome.

American Journal of Occupational Therapy. 2005;**59**:335-345

[41] Weisbrot DM, Gadow KD, DeVincent CJ, Pomeroy J. The presentation of anxiety in children with pervasive developmental disorders. Journal of Child & Adolescent Psychopharmacology. 2005;**15**(3):477-496

[42] Kerns CM, Kendall PC. Autism and anxiety: Overlap, similarities, and differences. In: Davis TE III, White SW, Ollendick TH, editors. Handbook of Autism and Anxiety. Springer International; 2014. pp. 75-89. DOI: 10.1007/978-3-319-06796-4_6

[43] Moskowitz JL, Braconnier M. Assessing anxiety in youth with autism spectrum disorder. Psychology in the Schools. Pediatrics. 2016;137 Suppl 2:S115-23. DOI: 10.1542/peds.2015-2851J

[44] White SW, Schry AR, Maddox BB. Brief report: The assessment of anxiety in high-functioning adolescents with autism spectrum disorder. Journal of Autism and Developmental Disorders. 2012;**42**(6):1138-1145. DOI: 10.1007/s10803-011-1353-3

[45] Mayes SD, Calhoun SL, Murray MJ, Ahuja M, Smith LA. Anxiety, depression, and irritability in children with autism relative to other neuropsychiatric disorders and typical development. Research in Autism Spectrum Disorders. 2011;**5**(1):474-485

[46] Vasa R, Keefer A, Reaven J, South M, White S. Priorities for advancing research on youth with autism spectrum disorder and co-occurring anxiety. Journal of Autism and Developmental Disorders. 2017;**48**:925-934. DOI: 10.1007/s10803-017-3320-0

[47] Grondhuis SN, Aman MG. Assessment of anxiety in children and adolescents with autism spectrum disorders. Research in Autism Spectrum Disorders. 2012;**6**(4):1345-1365. DOI: 10.1016/j.rasd.2012.04.006

[48] Rotheram-Fuller E, MacMullen L. Cognitive-behavioral therapy for children with autism spectrum disorders. Psychology in the Schools. 2011;**48**:263-271. DOI: 10.1002/pits.20552

[49] Eussen ML, Van Gool AR, Verheij F, De Nijs PF, Verhulst FC, Greaves-Lord K. The association of quality of social relations, symptom severity and intelligence with anxiety in children with autism spectrum disorders. Autism. 2013;**17**(6):723-735. DOI: 10.1177/1362361312453882

[50] Chang YC, Quan J, Wood JJ. Effects of anxiety disorder severity on social functioning in children with autism spectrum disorders. Journal of Developmental and Physical Disabilities. 2012;**24**(3):235-245. DOI: 10.1007/s10882-012-9268-2

[51] Hallett V, Lecavalier L, Sukhodolsky DG, Cipriano N, Aman MG, McCracken JT, et al. Exploring the manifestations of anxiety in children with autism spectrum disorders. Journal of Autism and Developmental Disorders. 2013;**43**(10):2341-2352. DOI: 10.1007/s10803-013-1775-1

[52] Kendall PC. Cognitive-behavioral therapies with youth: Guiding theory, current status, and emerging developments. Journal of Consulting and Clinical Psychology. 1993;**61**(2):235-247. DOI: 10.1037/0022-006x.61.2.235

[53] Kendall PC, Chansky TE. Considering cognition in anxiety-disordered children. Journal of Anxiety Disorders. 1991;**5**(2):167-185. DOI: 10.1016/0887-6185(91)90027-q

[54] Albano AM, Kendall PC. Cognitive behavioural therapy for children and adolescents with anxiety disorders: Clinical research advances. International Review of Psychiatry. 2002;**14**(2):129-134

[55] Ollendick TH, King NJ. Empirically supported treatments for children with phobic and anxiety disorders: Current status. Journal of Clinical Child Psychology. 1998;**27**(2):156-167

[56] Beck AT, Emergy G, Greenberg RL. Anxiety Disorders and Phobias: A Cognitive Approach. New York: Basic Books; 1985

[57] Velting ON, Setzer NJ, Albano AM. Update on and advances in assessment and cognitive-behavioral treatment of anxiety disorders in children and adolescents. Professional Psychology: Research and Practice. 2004;**35**(1):42

[58] Butler G, Fennell M, Hackmann A. Cognitive-Behavioral Therapy for Anxiety Disorders: Mastering Clinical Challenges. Midtown Manhattan, New York: Guilford Press; 2010

[59] Khanna MS, Kendall PC. Computer-assisted CBT for child anxiety: The coping cat CD-ROM. Cognitive and Behavioral Practice. 2008;**15**(2):159-165. DOI: 10.1016/j.cbpra.2008.02.002

[60] Kendall PC, Hollon SD, editors. Cognitive-Behavioral Interventions: Theory, Research, and Procedures. Vol. 21. Cambridge, Massachusetts: Academic Press; 2013

[61] Kendall PC, Southam-Gerow MA. Long-term follow-up of a cognitive–behavioral therapy for anxiety-disordered youth. Journal of Consulting and Clinical Psychology. 1996;**64**(4):724-730. DOI: 10.1037/0022-006x.64.4.724

[62] Richardson T, Stallard P, Velleman S. Computerized cognitive behavioural therapy for the prevention and treatment of depression and anxiety in children and adolescents: A systematic review. Clinical Child and Family Psychology Review. 2010;**13**(3):275-290

[63] Stallard P, Richardson T, Velleman S, Attwood M. Computerized CBT (think, feel, do) for depression and anxiety in children and adolescents: Outcomes and feedback from a pilot randomized controlled trial. Behavioural and Cognitive Psychotherapy. 2011;**39**(03):273-284. DOI: 10.1017/S135246581000086X

[64] Stuhlmiller C, Tolchard B. Computer-assisted CBT for depression & anxiety: Increasing accessibility to evidence-based mental health treatment. Journal of Psychosocial Nursing and Mental Health Services. 2009;**47**(7):32-39, 8 p. DOI: 10.3928/02793695-20090527-01

[65] Kendall PC, Settipani CA, Cummings CM. No need to worry: The promising future of child anxiety research. Journal of Clinical Child & Adolescent Psychology. 2012;**41**(1):103-115. DOI: 10.1080/15374416.2012.632352

[66] Donovan CL, March S. Online CBT for preschool anxiety disorders: A randomised control trial. Behaviour Research and Therapy. 2014;**58**:24-35. DOI: 10.1016/j.brat.2014.05.001

[67] Kendall PC. Treating anxiety disorders in children: Results of a randomized clinical trial. Journal of Consulting and Clinical Psychology. 1994;**62**(1):100

[68] Silverman WK, Albano AM. Anxiety Disorders Interview Schedule for DSM-IV.: Parent Interview Schedule. Vol. 1. Cary, North Carolina: Oxford University Press; 1996

[69] Treadwell KR, Flannery-Schroeder, EC, Kendall PC. Ethnicity and gender

in relation to adaptive functioning, diagnostic status, and treatment outcome in children from an anxiety clinic. Journal of Anxiety Disorders. 1995;**9**(5):373-384

[70] Barrett PM, Dadds MR, Rapee RM. Family treatment of childhood anxiety: A controlled trial. Journal of Consulting and Clinical Psychology. 1996;**64**(2):333

[71] Barrett P, Turner C. Prevention of anxiety symptoms in primary school children: Preliminary results from a universal school-based trial. British Journal of Clinical Psychology. 2001;**40**(4):399-410

[72] Glenn D, Golinelli D, Rose RD, Roy-Byrne P, Stein MB, Sullivan G, et al. Who gets the most out of cognitive behavioral therapy for anxiety disorders? The role of treatment dose and patient engagement. Journal of Consulting and Clinical Psychology. 2013;**81**(4):639-649. DOI: 10.1037/a0033403

[73] Erford BT, Kress VE, Giguere M, Cieri D, Erford BM. Meta-analysis: Counseling outcomes for youth with anxiety disorders. Journal of Mental Health Counseling. 2015;37(1):63-94. DOI: http://dx.doi.org/10.17744/mehc.37.1.mgj66326868u33g2

[74] Dickson S, Kuhnert R, Lavell C, Rapee R. Impact of psychotherpy for children and adolescents with anxiety disorders on global and domain-specific functioning: A systematic review and meta-analysis. Clinical Child and Family Psychology Review. 2022;**25**:1-17. DOI: 10/1007/s10567-022-00402-7

[75] Smith T. Evolution of research on interventions for individuals with autism spectrum disorder: Implications for behavior analysts. The Behavior Analyst. 2012;**35**(1):101

[76] Weston L, Hodgelins J, Langdon E. Effectiveness of cognitive behavior therapy with people who have autism spectrum disorders: A systematic review and meta-analysis. Clinical Psychology Review. 2016;**49**:41-54. DOI: 10.1016/j.cpr.2016.08.001

[77] Baron-Cohen S, Leslie AM, Frith U. Does the autistic child have a "theory of mind"? Cognition. 1985;**21**(1):37-46

[78] Bauminger N, Kasari C. Brief report: Theory of mind in high-functioning children with autism. Journal of Autism and Developmental Disorders. 1999;**29**(1):81-86

[79] Hare DJ. The use of cognitive-behavioural therapy with people with Asperger syndrome: A case study. Autism. 1997;**1**(2):215-225. DOI: 10.1177/1362361397012007

[80] Laugeson EA, Mogil C, Dillon AR, Frankel F. Parent-assisted social skills training to improve friendships in teens with autism spectrum disorders. Journal of Autism and Developmental Disorders. 2009;**39**:596-606

[81] Laugeson EA, Frankel F, Gantman A, Dillon AR, Mogil C. Evidence-based social skills training for adolescents with autism spectrum disorders: The UCLA PEERS program. Journal of Autism and Developmental Disorders. 2012;**42**(6):1025-1036

[82] Laugeson EA, Park MN. Using a CBT approach to teach adolescents with autism spectrum disorder and other social challenges: The PEERS method. Journal of Rational Emotive Cognitive Behavioral Therapy. 2014;**32**:84-97. DOI: 10.1007/s10942-014-0181-8

[83] Schohl KA, Van Hecke AV, Carson AM, Dolan B, Karst J, Stevens S. A replication and extension of the PEERS

intervention: Examining effects on social skills and social anxiety in adolescents with autism spectrum disorders. Journal of Autism and Developmental Disorders. 2014;**44**(3):532-545. DOI: 10.1007/s10803-013-1900-1

[84] Ekman E, Hiltunen AJ. Modified CBT using visualization for Autism Spectrum Disorder (ASD), anxiety and avoidance behavior-a quasi-experimental open pilot study. Scandinavian Journal of Psychology. 2015;**56**(6):641-648. DOI: 10.1111/sjop.12255

[85] Wood JJ, Drahota A, Sze K, Har K, Chiu A, Langer DA. Cognitive behavioral therapy for anxiety in children with autism spectrum disorders: A randomized, controlled trial. Journal of Child Psychology and Psychiatry. 2009;**50**(3):224-234

[86] Cardaciotto L, Herbert JD. Cognitive behavior therapy for social anxiety disorder in the context of asperger's syndrome: A single-subject report. Cognitive and Behavioral Practice. 2004;**11**(1):75-81

[87] Ames M, Weiss J. Cognitive behavior therapy for a child with autism spectrum disorder and verbal impairment: A case study. Journal on Developmental Disabilities. 2013;**19**(1):61-69. DOI: 10315/27192/41015

[88] Chalfant AM, Rapee R, Carroll L. Treating anxiety disorders in children with high functioning autism spectrum disorders: A controlled trial. Journal of Autism and Developmental Disorders. 2007;**37**(10):1842-1857. DOI: 10.1007/s10803-006-0318-4

[89] Weiss JA, Thomson K, Burnham Riosa P, Albaum C, Chan V, Maughan A, et al. A randomized waitlist-controlled trial of cognitive behavior therapy to improve emotion regulation in children with autism. Journal of Child Psychology and Psychiatry, and Allied Disciplines. 2018;**59**(11):1180-1191

[90] Sofronoff K, Attwood T, Hinton S. A randomized controlled trial of a CBT intervention for anxiety in children with Asperger syndrome. Journal of Child Psychology and Psychiatry. 2005;**46**(11):1152-1160

[91] Sukhodolsky DG. Cognitive and behavioral interventions for anxiety in children with autism. Journal of the American Academy of Child and Adolescent Psychiatry. 2016;**10**(55):S325-S325. DOI: 10.1016/j.jaac.2016.07.368

[92] van Steensel FJA, Bögels SM. CBT for anxiety disorders in children with and without autism spectrum disorders. Journal of Consulting and Clinical Psychology. 2015;**83**(3):512-523. DOI: 10.1037/a0039108

[93] McNally Keehn RH, Lincoln AJ, Brown MZ, Chavira DA. The coping cat program for children with anxiety and autism spectrum disorder: A pilot randomized controlled trial. Journal of Autism and Developmental Disorders. 2013;**43**(1):57-67. DOI: 10.1007/s10803-012-1541-9

[94] Perihan C, Bicer A, Bocanegra. Assessment and treatment of anxiety in children with autism spectrum disorder in school settings: A systematic review and meta-analysis. School Mental Health. 2021;**14**:1-12. DOI: 10.1007/s12310-021-09461-7

[95] Pryor C, Lincoln A, Igelman R, Toma V, Iravani R. Efficacy of a computer-assisted cognitive-behavioral therapy program in treating youth with anxiety and co-occurring autism spectrum disorder: CAMP COPE A-LOT. Journal of Research on Autism Spectrum

Disorders. 2021;**83**:1-14. DOI: 10.1016/j.rasd.2021.101748

[96] Reaven J, Blakeley-Smith A, Culhane-Shelburne K, Hepburn S. Group cognitive behavior therapy for children with high-functioning autism spectrum disorders and anxiety: A randomized trial. Journal of Child Psychology and Psychiatry. 2012;**53**(4):410-419. DOI: 10.1111/j.1469-7610.2011.02486.x

[97] Sung M, Ooi YP, Goh TJ, Pathy P, Fung DS, Ang RP, et al. Effects of cognitive-behavioral therapy on anxiety in children with autism spectrum disorders: A randomized controlled trial. Child Psychiatry and Human Development. 2011;**42**(6):634-649. DOI: 10.1007/s10578-011-0238-1

[98] White SW, Ollendick T, Albano AM, Oswald D, Johnson C, Southam-Gerow MA, et al. Multimodal anxiety and social skill intervention for adolescents with autism spectrum disorder. Journal of Autism Developmental Disorder. 2013;**43**:382-394

[99] Wise JM, Cepeda SL, Ordaz DL, McBride NM, Cavitt MA, Howie FR, et al. Open trial of modular cognitive-behavioral therapy in the treatment of anxiety among late adolescents with autism spectrum disorder. Child Psychiatry and Human Development. 2019;**50**(1):27-34. DOI: 10.1007/s10578-018-0817-5

[100] Wood JJ, Ehrenreich-May J, Alessandri M, Fujii C, Renno P, Laugeson E, et al. Cognitive behavioral therapy for use with early adolescents with autism spectrum disorders and clinical anxiety: A randomized, controlled trial. Behavior Therapy. 2015;**46**:7-19. DOI: 10.1016/j.beth.2014.01.002

[101] Spence SH. A measure of anxiety symptoms among children. Behavior Research and Therapy. 1998;**36**(5):545-566

[102] Nauta M, Scholing A, Rapee RM, Abbott M, Spence SH, Waters A. A parent-report measure of children's anxiety: Psychometric properties and comparison with child-report in a clinic and normal sample. Behavior Research and Therapy. 2004;**42**:813-839

[103] Storch E, Arnold E, Lewin A, Nadeau J, Jones A, De Nadai A, et al. The effect of cognitive-behavior therapy versus treatment as usual in children with autism spectrum disorder. Journal of the American Academy of Child & Adolescent Psychiatry. 2013;**52**(2):132-142

[104] Wood JJ, Drahota A. Behavioral Interventions for Anxiety in Children with Autism. Los Angeles, CA: University of California– Los Angeles; 2005

[105] Storch E, Lewin A, Collier A, Arnold E, De Nadai A, Dane B, et al. A randomized control trial of cognitive-behavior therapy versus treatment as usual for adolescents with autism spectrum dirorders and comorbid anxiety. Depression & Anxiety. 2015;**32**:174-181. DOI: 10.1002/da.22332

[106] Donovan CL, Spence SH, March S. Using new technologies to deliver cognitive behaviour therapy with children and adolescents. In: Graham P, Reynolds S, editors. Cognitive Behaviour Therapy for Children and Families. New York: Cambridge University Press; 2013. pp. 351-382

[107] Jones R, Hussain F, Agha S, Weavers B, Lucassen M, Merry S, et al. Digital technologies to support adolescents with depression and anxiety: Review. BJPsych Advances. 2022:1-15. DOI: 10.1192/bja.2022.3

[108] Kaltenthaler E, Brazier J, De Nigris E, Tumur I, Ferriter M, Beverley C, et al. Computerized cognitive behaviour therapy for depression and anxiety update: A systematic review and economic evaluation. Health Technology Assessment. 2006;**10**(33):1-186. DOI: 10.3310/hta10330

[109] Amir N, Taylor CT. Combining computerized home-based treatments for generalized anxiety disorder: An attention modification program and cognitive behavioral therapy. Behavior Therapy. 2012;**43**(3):546-559. DOI: 10.1016/j.beth.2010.12.008

[110] Barazzone N, Cavanagh K, Richards DA. Computerized cognitive behavioural therapy and the therapeutic alliance: A qualitative enquiry. British Journal of Clinical Psychology. 2012;**51**(4):396-417. DOI: 10.1111/j.2044-8260.2012.02035.x

[111] Bowler JO, Mackintosh B, Dunn BD, Mathews A, Dalgleish T, Hoppitt L. A comparison of cognitive bias modification for interpretation and computerized cognitive behavior therapy: Effects on anxiety, depression, attentional control, and interpretive bias. Journal of Consulting and Clinical Psychology. 2012;**80**(6):1021-1033. DOI: 10.1037/a0029932

[112] Craske MG, Rose RD, Lang A, Welch SS, Campbell-Sills L, Sullivan G, et al. Computer-assisted delivery of cognitive behavioral therapy for anxiety disorders in primary-care settings. Depression and Anxiety. 2009;**26**(3):235-242

[113] Ebert DD, Zarski A, Christensen H, Stikkelbroek Y, Cuijpers P, Berking M, et al. Internet and computer-based cognitive behavioral therapy for anxiety and depression in youth: A meta-analysis of randomized controlled outcome trials. PLoS One. 2015;**10**(3):e0119895. DOI: 10.1371/journal.pone.0119895

[114] Temkin AB, Schild J, Falk A, Bennett SM. Mobile apps for youth anxiety disorders: A review of the evidence and forecast of future innovations. Professional Psychology: Research and Practice. 2020;**51**(4):400-413. DOI: 10.1037/pro0000342

[115] Tozzi F, Nicolaodou I, Galani A, Antoniades A. eHealth interventions for anxiety management targeting young children and adolescents: Exploratory review. JMIR Pediatrics and Parenting. 2018;**1**(1):e5. DOI: 10.2196/pediatrics.7248

[116] Vigerland S, Ljótsson B, Gustafsson FB, Hagert S, Thulin U, Andersson G, et al. Attitudes towards the use of computerized cognitive behavior therapy (cCBT) with children and adolescents: A survey among Swedish mental health professionals. Internet Interventions. 2014;**1**(3):111-117. DOI: 10.1016/j.invent.2014.06.002

[117] Wood JJ, Kendall PC, Wood KS, Kerns CM, Seltzer M, Small BJ, et al. Cognitive behavioral treatments for anxiety in children with autism spectrum disorder: A randomized clinical trial. JAMA Psychiatry. 2020;**77**(5):473-484. DOI: 10.1001/jamapsychiatry.2019.4160

[118] Reaven J, Moody EJ, Grofer Klinger L, Keefer A, Duncan A, O'Kelley S, et al. Training clinicians to deliver group CBT to manage anxiety in youth with ASD: Results of a multisite trial. Journal of Consulting and Clinical Psychology. 2018;**86**(3):205

[119] Holmes J, March S, Spence S. Use of the internet in the treatment of anxiety disorders with children and adolescents. Counseling, Psychotherapy,

and Health. 2009;**5**(1):187-231. The Use of Technology in Mental Health Special Issue

[120] Kendall PC, Khanna MS. Camp Cope-A-Lot: The Coping Cat CD Rom (Software). Ardmore, Pennsylvania: Workbook Publishing Inc.; 2008. Available from: www.workbookpublishing.com

[121] Kendall PC, Khanna MS. Coach's Manual for Camp Cope a-Lot: The Coping Cat CD Rom. Ardmore, PA: Workbook Publishing Inc; 2008

[122] Khanna MS, Kendall PC. Computer-assisted cognitive behavioral therapy for child anxiety: Results of a randomized clinical trial. Journal of Consulting and Clinical Psychology. 2010;**78**(5):737-745. DOI: 10.1037/a0019739

[123] Spence SH, Donovan CL, March S, Gamble A, Anderson RE, Prosser S, et al. A randomized controlled trial of online versus clinic-based CBT for adolescent anxiety. Journal of Consulting and Clinical Psychology. 2011;**79**(5):629

[124] Blocher JB, Fujikawa M, Sung C, Jackson DC, Jones JE. Computer-assisted cognitive behavioral therapy for children with epilepsy and anxiety: A pilot study. Epilepsy & Behavior. 2013;**27**(1):70-76

[125] Patwardhan M, Stoll R, Hamel DB, Amresh A, Gary KA, Pina A. Designing a mobile application to support the indicated prevention and early intervention of childhood anxiety. In: Proceedings of the Conference on Wireless Health. 2015. pp. 1-8

[126] Tillfors M, Andersson G, Ekselius L, Furmark T, Lewenhaupt S, Karlsson A, et al. A randomized trial of internet-delivered treatment for social anxiety disorder in high school students. Cognitive Behaviour Therapy. 2011;**40**(2):147-157

[127] Cox CM, Kenardy JA, Hendrikz JK. A randomized controlled trial of a web-based early intervention for children and theirparents following unintentional injury. Journal of Pediatric Psychology. 2010;**35**(6):581-592

[128] Basile V, Newton-John T, Wootton B. Remote cognitive-behavioral therapy for generalized anxiety disorder: A preliminary meta-analyis. Journal of Clinical Psychology. 2022:1-15. DOI: 10.1002/jclp.23360

[129] Bioulac S, de Sevin E, Sagaspe P, Claret A, Philip P, Micoulaud-Franchi JA, et al. What do virtual reality toold\s bring to child and adolescent psychiatry? L'Encephale. 2018;**44**(3):280-285. DOI: 10.1016/j.encep.2017.06.005

[130] Maskey M, Rodgers J, Ingham B, Freeston M, Evans G, Labus M, et al. Using virtual reality environments to augment cognitive behavioral therapy for fears and phobias in autistic adults. Autism in Adulthood: Challenges and Management. 2019;**1**(2):134-145. DOI: 10.1089/aut.2018.0019

[131] Kalvin C, Jordan R, Rowley S, Weis A, Wood K, Wood J, et al. Conducting CBT for anxiety in children with autism spectrum disorder during COVID-19 pandemic. Journal of Autism and Developmental Disorders. 2021;**51**:4239-4247. DOI: 10.1007/s10803-020-04845-1

[132] Conaughton R, Donovan C, March S. Efficacy of an internet-based CBT program for children with comorbid high functioning autism spectrum disorder and anxiety: A randomized controlled trial. Journal of Affective Disorders. 2017;**218**:260-268. DOI: 10.1016/j.jad.2017

[133] Hepburn S, Blakeley-Smith A, Wolff B, Reaven J. Telehealth delivery

of cognitive-behavioral intervention to youth with autism spectrum disorder and anxiety: A pilot study. Autism. 2016;**20**(2):207-218. DOI: 10.1177/1362361315575164

[134] Lee V, Roudarani F, Modica P, Pouyandeh A, Weiss J. Adaptation of cognitive behavior therapy for autistic children during the pandemic: A mixed-methods program evaluation. Evidenced-Based Practice in Child and Adolescent Mental Health. 2021;**7**(1):76-93. DOI: 10.1080/23794925.2021.1941432

[135] Zabel JA. The effectiveness of a computer-assisted, cognitive-behavior program for treating anxiety symptoms in children with autism spectrum disorder. In: PCOM Psychology Dissertations. Paper 334. 2015. Available from: http://digitalcommons.pcom.edu/cgi/viewcontent.cgi?article=1333&context=psychology_dissertations

[136] Strawn JR, McReynolds DJ. An evidence-based approach to treating pediatric anxiety disorders. Current Psychiatry. 2012;**11**(9):16-21

Chapter 13

Naturalistic Developmental Behavioral Interventions as Value-Based and Culturally Adapted EBPs for Autistic Individuals

Mian Wang, Rachel Schuck and Kaitlynn M.P. Baiden

Abstract

Naturalistic Developmental Behavioral Interventions (NDBIs) are child-centered and motivation-based interventions for autistic children. Though they hold great promise due to their naturalistic implementation and focus on children's strengths, there have been recent calls to improve NDBIs such that they are more aligned with the neurodiversity approach. Central to this argument is the notion that autistic clients and their families should find the intervention acceptable. This chapter describes how NDBIs differ from other behavioral interventions, what their strengths are, and how they can continue to be improved. More specifically, we focus on expanding target NDBI outcomes to include more distal, family centered variables (such as family quality of life); improving the social validity of NDBIs; and how NDBIs can be implemented using a tiered support system.

Keywords: naturalistic developmental behavioral intervention, motivation-based intervention, ASD, neurodiversity, social validity of intervention, evidence-based practice

1. Introduction

A steady increase in the prevalence of autism across the globe and growing demands for service and support have drawn increasing attention from policy makers, researchers, and practitioners in the field of health care, mental health care, and disability services. A recent systematic review, synthesizing 99 estimates from 71 studies of the prevalence of autism spectrum disorder (ASD) worldwide, suggests that approximately 1% of children are diagnosed with ASD around the world and that the prevalence data in 2012 and 2021 are not much different from a global point of view [1]. However, there are a number of countries (e.g., Australia, France, Korea, and the USA) reporting a noticeable ascending trend of autism prevalence. For instance, in the USA, the prevalence of autism has been rising, and it is rising very rapidly according to the CDC. When the CDC started systemic screening in

IntechOpen

2000, the ratio of 8-year-old children with ASD was about 1:166, and it has increased fourfold to 1:44 as of 2020 [2]. In response to the increasing autistic population and huge demands for high-quality service and support, there have been intensifying efforts in researching and developing effective intervention approaches for supporting autistic individuals to improve specific outcomes such as social communication and interaction skills and enhance holistic outcomes like quality of life. Over the last several decades, a wide array of psycho-educational interventions has been developed and researched, leading to the need for a systematic way of determining which of these interventions are most effective for autistic individuals. As such, the field has identified its own methods for identifying what we know as evidence-based practices (EBPs), which are seen as the "gold standard" in the field of autism intervention.

In this chapter, we will discuss current EBPs in the autism intervention literature. We begin with an introduction of the most commonly identified EBPs and a brief summary of some major methodological and ethical concerns of these psych-educational approaches. In the pursuit of potential remedies for addressing these issues and concerns, we introduce Naturalistic Developmental Behavioral Interventions (NDBIs; [3]), as a highly regarded intervention model with a strong evidence base, and potential value-based and culturally adapted evidence-based practices that can help address some of the underlying methodological and ethical concerns in autism interventions and support. We will then delineate both promises and limitations of NDBIs. Lastly, we evaluate the areas in which NDBIs need to be further improved, as well as implications for clinical practice and future research.

2. Evidence-based practices in autism interventions and support

There is a plethora of research on autism interventions that have been conducted in the last five decades. This research has sought to answer a critical question: how do we effectively support autistic individuals and their families? As a result of this research, the field has been able to identify a set of interventions that have proven to be effective and demonstrated positive outcomes for autistic individuals. The field knows these as evidence-based practices (EBPs). Currently, there are two main groups that have evaluated the extensive literature to determine which interventions and intervention packages qualify as evidence-based practice—the National Standards Project [4] and National Professional Development Center (NPDC) on autism spectrum disorders. Through a thorough literature review, NSP has identified 14 established evidence-based practices and 18 with emerging evidence [4]. The NPDC identified 27 evidence-based practices [5]. Most of these identified EBPs are based on behavioral principles.

Based on the NPDC standards, in order to meet the criteria as an evidence-based practice, there must be positive evidence to support the intervention strategy with at least two high-quality experimental or quasi-experimental group design studies that have been conducted by two different researchers or research groups, or at least five high-quality single-subject design studies conducted by at least three different researchers or research groups, totaling at least 20 participants. A practice could also meet this standard if there is one high-quality randomized or quasi-experimental group design study and a minimum of three high-quality single-subject design studies conducted by at least three different researchers or research groups across all studies [5]. The NSP standards for established evidence-based practices are similar and require either two group designs or four single-subject design studies that have a minimum of 12 participants with no conflicting results or a minimum of three group designs of six single-subject designs with a minimum of 18 participants, with no fewer than 10% of studies having conflicting results. Additionally, the NSP has a scoring system for ensuring these studies are of high quality [4].

Even with these standards, there have been criticisms of evidence-based practices used with autistic children from both methodological and ethical perspectives (e.g. [6]). These issues identified are not only with the literature base, but also with the practical implications of the use of EBPs in clinical settings. In terms of methodological issues, there have been concerns with both the quality of the review methods for determining the evidence-based interventions for autistic children, as well as issues with the quality of individual study designs and protocols. Specifically, Sandbank et al. [7] identified three major concerns with the reviews of the National Standards Project (NSP) and National Professional Development Center (NPDC) on Autism Spectrum Disorders: the attempt to blend evidence from different research design methodologies (single-subject and group designs) though there is no agreed upon way of doing so, limited information about the extent of intervention effectiveness and for which populations, and the lack of summarizing the effects of any given intervention. In addition to these clear issues with synthesizing the literature on autism interventions, there has been a multitude of common methodological issues that are seen across individual studies. Specifically, critics have expressed concerns over the strong focus on single-subject design versus group design and randomized controlled trials (RCTs) as well as the focus on short-term outcomes, with little attention paid to long-term effects [8]. On a similar note, an additional concern is that there is a lack of focus on adverse outcomes in the literature on autism interventions [9, 10]. Finally, there are concerns about who is conducting the research. This comes with the lack of autistic involvement in autism research, the lack of research on autistic input on evidence-based practices, and the limited social validation measures used in the autism intervention literature [11–13]. Moreover, researchers and research groups who are conducting this intervention literature often fail to identify any potential conflicts of interest (COI), though they are often relevant, calling into question the potential for bias within these studies [14].

Even more concerning than the methodological shortcomings are the ethical concerns that have been voiced by autistic self-advocates in recent years. We have identified a number of ethical concerns that have been brought up regarding the implementation of commonly used evidence-based practices for autistic children. Chief among these concerns are: the unethical history of behavioral intervention, the focus on normalization of autistic recipients, and the emphasis on compliance (a more detailed discussion is provided in a later section regarding limitations of Naturalistic Developmental Behavioral Interventions).

2.1 Naturalistic developmental behavioral interventions

One example of a manualized EBP approach for autistic children is Naturalistic Developmental Behavioral Interventions (NDBIs; [3, 15]). NDBIs are a set of intervention models that combine behavioral principles with insights from developmental psychology. Intervention models considered as NDBIs include pivotal response treatment (PRT; [16]), Early Start Denver Model (ESDM; [17–19]), Project ImPACT [20], incidental teaching (IT; [21]), enhanced milieu teaching (EMT; [22]), and Joint Attention Symbolic Play Engagement and Regulation (JASPER; [23]). All NDBIs emphasize child-centered learning focused on meeting the child where they are and using their interests to improve their motivation to learn [3]. NDBIs have built a large evidence base of both single-subject studies and randomized controlled trials, though methodological issues such as publication and detection bias and reliance on parent report measures [7, 24] weaken the evidence base. Nonetheless, a recent meta-analysis still found that NDBIs had the most promising evidence base compared to other interventions for autistic children [7].

Implementation of NDBIs should occur in natural environments, throughout the child's daily routines, at home, or at school. They were originally in part created to combat some of the issues clinicians saw with more typical, structured ABA, such as lack of motivation and generalization [25]. As such, all NDBIs share common components such as following the child's lead, shared control, natural reinforcement, and reinforcing non-perfect attempts. For example, if a child loves cars, playing with toy cars might be used to teach words such as "car," "go," or "fast." The child's interest in cars would thus motivate them to practice such words in a fun, enjoyable environment. It is also important in NDBI implementation to have shared control between children and adults, as opposed to more structured ABA, where the clinician usually directs interactions and has control over the materials [26]. This shared control gives the child agency but also allows the adult the chance to create learning opportunities (for example by holding out the car and asking the child, "what color is this?"). Natural reinforcement is also a hallmark of NDBIs. Natural reinforcement differs from external reinforcement in that the reinforcement is the *natural* consequence of whatever the child just did. For example, if the child wants to play with a car and says, "car," or answers the question about the color of the car, the adult contingently reinforces them with the car (*not* with candy, a sticker, or a token). Lastly, NDBIs encourage clinicians to reinforce *attempts*, as opposed to pushing for fully correct responses. For instance, a child might approximate the word car by saying "cah" or they might say a car is "pink" when it is actually red. By reinforcing these non-perfect attempts, children learn that it is the effort that matters to the adults in their lives.

3. Maximizing family intervention fit: cultural adaptations, neurodiversity, and strengths-based approaches

Family involvement is always a core aspect of NDBIs. Parents should be involved in goal setting as well as the intervention implementation; in fact, to maximize the use of the natural environment, most NDBIs specifically incorporate parent training such that parents can act as intervention providers [27]. However, simply involving parents in discussions about goals and teaching them to implement NDBIs does not guarantee that the interventions are meeting the families' needs. Therefore, researchers and clinicians must ensure that intervention recipients are involved in ways that are meaningful to them, whether that is more or less involved or involved in different ways. We present three areas that could lead to improvements in family intervention fit: adapting interventions to fit different cultures, incorporating a neurodiversity approach, and emphasizing strengths-based approaches.

3.1 Culturally adapted EBPs

Cultural adaptations of EBPs, which have emerged as an area of study in other fields (e.g., clinical psychology, see Lau [28]), seem to be absent as a focus of EBP discourse in the context of delivering quality service and support to autistic students for better life outcomes. In particular, a fundamental assumption about the universal applicability and effectiveness of EBP to all populations in the field of mental health care and service appears to be a flawed one when evidence of EBP effectiveness is solely based on the results of certain populations (e.g., White students of suburban middle-class families) [29]. Likewise, there seem to be similar issues about the legitimacy of implementation and dissemination of EBPs to populations of color in special education considering that most EBPs have been developed without even taking account of the cultural context of ethnic minority communities and cultural identity of those presumably being served (e.g., autistic individuals).

Castro and colleagues define the concept of cultural adaptation as: "a planned, organized, iterative, and collaborative process that often includes the participation of persons from the targeted population for whom the adaptation is being developed" ([30], p. 215). Cultural adaptation also concerns the process of adjusting an evidence-based intervention protocol by taking language, culture, and context into account to make it compatible with the cultural patterns, meanings, and values of those being served [31]. Culturally adapted EBPs for autistic individuals can help not only clarify and specify what ought to take place in adaptation for obtaining an optimal balance between adaptation and clinical implementation fidelity that leads to important implementation outcomes such as acceptability and appropriateness, but also define and clarify the necessary knowledge, skills, and roles of those facilitating the implementation process and the timeline and sequence of adaptations in the implementation process [32].

3.2 What is neurodiversity?

Many critiques of behavioral intervention can be tied to the fact that applied behavioral analysis (ABA) usually uses the medical model of disability to "treat" autism. Under this view, autism is seen primarily as a medical issue, with "reduction of autism symptoms" and appearing more "normal" as intervention targets. This is in direct contrast to the model of neurodiversity, which sees autism as a different—but not inherently bad—type of brain wiring. In her writing, Judy Singer [33], the sociologist who coined the term "neurodiversity," described it as similar to biodiversity, in that different types of brains contribute to the ecological fitness of a society. Harvey Blume's essay in *The Atlantic,* which introduced the term to the public in 1998, also used the word in this way: "Neurodiversity may be every bit as crucial for the human race as biodiversity is for life in general. Who can say what form of wiring will prove best at any given moment?"

Today, the term "neurodiversity" is used in multiple different ways [34]. The first is similar to the way Singer [33] and Blume [35] described neurodiversity: as a biological fact. Everybody's brain is different, which by default implies that there is diversity in human neurology (hence, *neuro-diversity).* The second way "neurodiversity" is often used refers to the ways this biological fact is utilized in everyday life (known as the neurodiversity *paradigm* (Walker [34] or neurodiversity *approach* [36]). According to Walker [34], there are three fundamental aspects of the neurodiversity paradigm/approach: neurodiversity is a beneficial form of diversity; there is no "average" or "normal" brain; and social dynamics affecting other forms of diversity (such as gender and race) are also at play when it comes to neurodiversity. Dwyer's [37] breakdown of the neurodiversity paradigm/approach is similar: there are no ideal minds; neurodivergent people should be accepted, not normalized; and society plays a large role in disabling neurodivergent individuals. Dwyer [36] also highlights that many advocates have adopted their own personal definitions of neurodiversity. For example, Bailin's [38] definition of the neurodiversity *approach* is inherently political: "primarily a call to include and respect people whose brains work in atypical ways, regardless of their level of disability." All of these definitions of neurodiversity relate back to autistic activist Jim Sinclair's [39] *Do not Mourn For Us* speech (see [40] for a historicization of this speech) where Sinclair implored parents to accept their autistic children and to stop seeing autism as a tragedy, explaining that autism is not something that can (or should) be removed from an individual. They highlighted that autism is a way of being (not an appendage or a "shell") and that autistic individuals are not stuck behind an impenetrable wall, incapable of building relationships with others. Sinclair acknowledges that parents may need to grieve the loss of their idea of an "ideal" child, but having an autistic child in and of itself is not a reason to grieve. This emphasis on acceptance of difference is the backbone of neurodiversity.

3.3 Common misconceptions about neurodiversity

Though neurodiversity hinges upon the biological fact of differences in brains, many misconceptions arise when the neurodiversity approach is applied to individuals with disabilities such as autism. Den Houting [41] brings up three common misconceptions. First, some critics feel that the neurodiversity approach views autism and other neurological disabilities as simply *differences* and not disabilities, implying that this approach effectively erases disability (e.g., [42]). Advocates highlight that this is just simply untrue—while the neurodiversity approach does see neurological variation as differences that should be respected, they still acknowledge the potentially disabling properties of such differences [38, 41, 43–45] (den Houting, 2018). While some contend that the disabling aspects are solely due to the social environment (e.g., [41]), others reject a strict social model and recognize that impairments localized in the individual can themselves be disabling (e.g., [37, 43]).

Another common critique is that the neurodiversity approach really only applies to those who have higher IQ and who can verbally self-advocate (e.g., [42]; numerous posts on the National Council for Severe Autism's blog, e.g., [46]). Den Houting [41] argues this ignores the fact that ability profiles of autistic individuals are not always consistent, or they might be great at something 1 day but struggle with it the next. Therefore, to assume that someone who can speak verbally is all-around "high-functioning" is incorrect. Ballou [43] and den Houting [41] also highlight that some neurodiversity self-advocates are in fact minimally verbal autistics (though den Houting acknowledges that there is a need for greater representation of non- or minimally speaking individuals within the movement). Ballou also makes the point that even if some individuals cannot traditionally self-advocate verbally, their other communicative acts should still be listened to and respected.

The last critique discussed by den Houting [41] is that, because neurodiversity advocates call for acceptance, they think neurodivergent people do not need any support. While this is not espoused by nearly any proponent of the neurodiversity paradigm, den Houting [41] sees this critique as stemming from a disagreement regarding the outcomes of support services. Those who support the neurodiversity approach call for supports that emphasize quality of life (e.g., [47]) and accommodations (e.g., [48]), whereas its critics tend to utilize the medical model wherein autistic individuals should be remediated and normalized. It is therefore a mischaracterization to say that neurodiversity proponents do not want disabled individuals to receive supports; they just want supports in place that are accepting and validating of one's neurotype.

3.4 Strength-based approaches to interventions/supports for autistic individuals

Though many early interventions for autistic individuals use the medical model to understand and "intervene upon" autism, there are researchers who feel that the neurodiversity paradigm and early intervention *can* coexist, particularly if clinicians listen to autistic perspectives regarding intervention goals, procedures, and outcomes [49–52]. Therefore, understanding neurodiversity is crucial for professionals who work with autistic people, as it can help the field move away from a focus on deficits and normalization and toward figuring out what autistic people actually want and need. One way for interventionists and support professionals to embrace neurodiversity in their practice is to use strengths-based approaches. Such approaches recognize that everyone, no matter what challenges they might face, has strengths and that such strengths must be acknowledged and leveraged in education, support services, and employment to ensure individuals enjoy a high quality of life.

In typical intervention/education for autistic children, deficits are identified through standardized tests and questionnaires, and plans such as individualized education programs (IEPs) are created in order to remediate these problem areas. These plans typically leave little room to document strengths [53], implying either that disabled children do not have strengths or that their strengths do not matter in comparison to their deficits. For example, a child's joint attention abilities may be overshadowed or even ignored if the child often needs to run and jump around the room while listening, as their IEP might call for them to sit still. Furthermore, some challenges faced by autistic individuals can be viewed as strengths depending on the context [54]. For example, perseverance on specific topics is often perceived as a problem, though it could be reconceptualized as excellent focus and expert knowledge. Autistic individuals have been shown to have a multitude of different strengths [55, 56], and capitalizing these interests and passions can be a way to motivate individuals to learn things they may have not been interested in doing previously [57, 58].

4. Promises and limitations of NDBIs

Despite cumulative evidence of the effectiveness of EBPs for autistic children suggested by several systematic literature reviews [4, 5], there are a great number of methodological and ethical concerns raised in the more recent meta-analytic review by adopting more sophisticated research methods with respect to the evidence base of EBPs in general (e.g., behavioral interventions) and NDBIs specifically [7, 14, 24]. NDBIs, emerging as valued-based approaches, have begun to address many of these methodological and ethical concerns in the implementation process of interventions and support for autistic children. NDBIs exhibit numerous promises in promoting strengths-based approaches, centering autistic voices, and eventually improving efficacy and effectiveness of interventions and support for autistic individuals in naturalistic settings, and also shed light on the future landscape of culturally adapted and value-based EBPs for helping and supporting autistic individuals to achieve better life outcomes.

4.1 Promises of NDBIs

NDBIs hold many promises, not just in their encouraging efficacy [7], but also in their philosophical underpinnings. As discussed above, NDBIs excel in their strengths-based approach to teaching children, focusing on what they can do and not what they cannot. Emphasizing child choice over clinician-directed tasks helps boost child motivation, which allows for a more positive, fun intervention environment. By demonstrating to children that effort is more important than perfection, children build confidence to try new things.

The use of naturalistic intervention settings and natural reinforcement also addresses some of the shortcomings of more traditional EBPs. By learning that good things happen during natural interactions, children are able to more easily generalize these skills across environments. For example, a child who learns during an NDBI intervention session that requesting a favorite toy result in getting that toy will find that that same behavior results in the same natural reinforcement at school. Furthermore, there is no need to constantly ensure that providers are all using the same external reinforcers across settings (e.g., making sure that teachers are using the same crackers at school as the interventionist uses at home), since the (natural) reinforcement is built into all learning opportunities. All these above-mentioned attributes of NDBIs attest to its strong embracement of the ecological perspective of child development and its applications in establishing child-centered and home-based interventions since NDBIs are typically implemented in autistic children's natural contexts (e.g., home and community settings) through everyday routine interactions with caregivers. This will likely improve the social and ecological validity of interventions and support for autistic children. In addition, NDBIs hold promises as developmentally appropriate practices which are broadly adopted in early childhood education and service for all children with exceptional learning needs given that the learning targets and objectives of NDBIs are guided by early developmental sequences. NDBIs also have the capability of being highly culturally responsive, as they emphasize setting goals that are important to the family [59, 60] and family professional partnership [61]. This emphasis on family thus should include intervention considerations related to culture. Several studies of culturally adapted NDBIs have shown promise. For example, researchers in China adapted the ESDM curriculum to emphasize vocal tones and include examples of eating relevant to Chinese society (e.g., pictures of chopsticks instead of forks) [62]. In India, Project ImPACT was adapted based on initial parent feedback. Changes included adding more psychoeducation about autism, teaching parents about play, and including extended family members as intervention providers [63]. Additionally, several NDBI manuals have been translated into languages other than English, such as Italian [64] and Chinese [65] versions of the ESDM manual.

Cultural context is also important when considering NDBIs' potential alignment with the neurodiversity approach. Some in the autistic community see themselves as part of an autistic cultural community that is distinct from other groups [66]. Just as NDBIs have the capability to be culturally adapted to fit other ethnic or racial groups, NDBIs have the potential to be culturally adapted to be aligned with autistic culture [52].

In contrast to most of the evidence-based behavioral interventions which predominantly focus on proximal outcomes of behavioral changes and skill acquisition, NDBIs cast emphasis on broader goals and long-term outcomes (e.g., social inclusion, rights, emotional, physical, and material well-being, self-determination, and quality of life). For example, PRT aims at training autistic children in their pivotal areas of motivation, self-initiation, and self-management that can lead to effective learning of both proximal outcomes such as cognitive, social, and other functional and life skills and distal outcomes like self-determination and quality of life.

4.2 Limitations of NDBIs

Apart from numerous promises that NDBIs can bring to improve outcomes of interventions and support for autistic children, we also acknowledge some limitations of NDBIs. Similar to those generic methodological issues identified with evidence-based practices in autism interventions above, NDBIs exhibit methodological limitations on the issues such as the quality of the review methods for determining the intervention effectiveness (e.g., primarily synthesizing the effects of the different interventions using a narrative approach and lack of using meta-analytic methods) and the quality of study designs and protocols (e.g., evidence base of NDBIs is primarily backed up by a research literature of plenty of single subject design studies and limited number of RCTs and rigorous group experimental design studies). NDBI RCTs are also hindered by the same methodological issues that autism intervention studies face more generally [24].

Another shortcoming in autism intervention studies is missing conflict of interest (COI) statements [9]. Chief among the potential COI issues are: (1) the author was the intervention model developer; (2) the author is employed to provide the intervention or is affiliated with an institution that provides said intervention; (3) the author receives direct payments for services or items related to the intervention (e.g., training materials, books, providing training); and (4) the study uses a commercially available measure that was developed by the author [9]. Lack of transparency in reporting these conflicts can cast doubt on the validity of the evidence base of the NDBIs interventions. It is important that researchers should adequately report any potential conflicts of interest in the NDBIs intervention studies.

Even more concerning than the methodological shortcomings are the ethical concerns that have been voiced by autistic self-advocates in recent years regarding the implementation of commonly used interventions for autistic children. Three major complaints stand out: the unethical history of behavioral intervention, the focus on normalization of autistic recipients, and the emphasis on compliance. While NDBIs in theory have attempted to address some of these problems, some of these concerns remain relevant to these more naturalistic approaches. More specifically, NDBIs have sought to improve upon the early iterations of behavioral interventions, focusing on reinforcement instead of aversive punishments.

However, goals of intervention, regardless of if it is through the use of NDBIs or more structured, traditional behavioral approaches, are often based on neurotypical standards defined by non-autistic people. This has been linked to autistic masking or camouflaging, the phenomenon that autistic people often feel the need to mask their autism traits in an effort to fit in (see [67, 68]). What is most concerning is that masking has been linked to poor mental health outcomes [69]. Though the implementation of NDBIs is not directly associated with the act of suppressing autistic traits, the common goals of these practices are. For instance, teaching vocal language or social conversational skills based on neurotypical norms are common goals of these interventions. In fact, most NDBI research focuses on improving "social communication" and "language" skills [24], with very few NDBI studies focusing on using alternative communication modalities [70].

The other major ethical concern with NDBIs is the issue of compliance [71]. This goes hand in hand with the focus on normalization, as autistic children are taught compliance around neurotypical behaviors, such as engaging in specific conversational behaviors, or forced eye contact, both of which have been known to be targets of NDBIs. Though there is no doubt that NDBIs seek to provide an increase in autonomy for children participating in the intervention (through the use of child choice/following a child's lead), the use of reinforcement to get children to do certain things or engage in certain behaviors can inadvertently place too much emphasis on compliance, even in these more gentle, naturalistic approaches. As such, NDBI researchers and clinicians need to pay attention to the practical ways in which they are using NDBIs to ensure that the client always maintains their autonomy and that skills being taught are meaningful to the client, so that quality of life and autonomy are prioritized over compliance.

Yet another concern lies with the positionality of the researchers. Historically, it has been neurotypical persons conducting research on interventions and delivering interventions for autistic people, with little involvement from the autistic community. This issue is relevant across all intervention research, including that of NDBIs. The evidence base for all interventions would be significantly strengthened with the increase of autistic researchers involved in these studies, as well as an increase in research and clinical practices that seek autistic feedback on intervention methods and practices to determine which practices are even found to be appropriate and effective by autistic people themselves.

The last concern on NDBIs intervention studies has to do with its historical focus on short-term outcomes, and lack of attention to long-term effects [7]. Though immediate effects of an intervention are of obvious importance, it is concerning that there have not been more longitudinal studies. This concern is of particular importance in light of the voiced concerns from autistic self-advocates that interventions for autistic children have resulted in trauma [72]. Moreover, given that autistic individuals are at a greater risk for mental health issues such as anxiety and depression in adulthood [73], there is a great need to evaluate the long-term effects of these interventions being deemed as "effective" in the short-term to ensure that long-term outcomes are just as positive. On a similar note, an additional concern is that there is a lack of focus on adverse outcomes in the literature on autism interventions [10, 14]. Just because something is found to be effective in terms of identified outcome measures, it does not mean that it is without adverse effects on its participants, and as such it is equally important to specifically evaluate these in all intervention studies.

In addition, it is noted that in systematic reviews and quantitative syntheses, positive outcomes proximal to intervention targets are often reported as evidence of intervention effectiveness for autistic children [24, 74]. Few studies conduct follow-up measures of child and family outcomes beyond 3–6 months after interventions and support are delivered to autistic children and their families [8]. Long-term outcomes of interventions for autistic adults are even more concerning. Some research results seem to portray a troubling picture on the long-term outcomes of adults with autism suggesting that adults with ASD have rather limited social integration, poor job prospects, and high rates of mental health problems and that overall outcomes for autistic adults in the areas of jobs, relationships, independent living, and mental health are considerably poorer than their same age neuro-typical peers [75]. A recent meta-analysis of studies of quality of life (QOL) for individuals with ASD across the lifespan suggests that autistic adults including those with higher intellectual and verbal functioning have poorer QOL than their peers without ASD [76].

5. Implications for future research and practice

Sandbank et al. [7] and Crank [24] both point out that, while NDBIs are a promising intervention type, evidence from randomized controlled trials indicates that the evidence base relies too heavily on parent report, which could inflate effect sizes. This must be addressed in intervention research. However, two important notes must be made: (1) parents may actually be able to detect subtle clinically significant changes in their children that are not picked up on by more standardized measures; and (2) even a "placebo-by-proxy" effect could lead to positive outcomes [77]. For example, parents might be highly encouraged after an NDBI trial because they saw improvements in their child's socio-communicative abilities that they had not witnessed before. Perhaps they then slightly overestimate their child's language improvements on a post-study questionnaire. While it is true that the effect size may be inflated by the parent's self-reported data, it is also possible that this family will continue to implement the intervention because they are so happy with it, which could lead to further language improvements. That said, future research can still do a better job of accurately capturing parent-reported outcomes. For example, qualitative methods such as interviews or free-response questions could be used to corroborate quantitative questionnaire data and explore *why* parents might be overestimating certain things. Furthermore, new questionnaires should be specifically developed to measure parent-reported changes in child behavior, as it is generally not considered psychometrically valid to use instruments in ways in which they were not originally intended and designed [78, 79]. Instead of using instruments designed as clinical diagnostic tools (e.g., the Vineland Adaptive Behavior Scales [80] or the Social Responsiveness Scale [81]), instruments must be specifically designed and validated to measure within-person, longitudinal change in parents' perceptions of their child's abilities.

Though context-bound outcomes can be useful [7, 82], researchers must ensure that they are also including outcome measures that evaluate generalization. For example, many PRT studies rely on parent–child interaction videos to evaluate changes in communication (e.g. [59, 60, 83, 84]). Though parents are not necessarily always instructed to implement PRT (e.g., Hardan et al. say that "parents were instructed to try getting the child to communicate as much as possible" (p. 886)), it is likely that parents knew they were instructed to use PRT, especially since these same videos were used to assess PRT fidelity, and the majority of parents did indeed meet fidelity. While these video clips are important in that they demonstrate that children are responsive to PRT while it is being implemented, it is not clear that improvements in socio-communicative skills would necessarily generalize to other environments where PRT was not being directly implemented, such as at home with their family or at school. Therefore, we suggest that other observational measures be included, such as interactions with adults not involved in or trained in the intervention, interactions with other children such as siblings or classmates, and/or natural interactions at home (e.g., see [85] for a discussion of using 16-h at-home recordings to analyze vocal reciprocity).

In addition to the importance of improving outcome measures of autistic children's generalized gains from interventions and support, there seem pressing needs to incorporate more distal outcomes of autistic individuals such as: changes of autism core characteristics, changes of the implementation process (e.g., person-centered and family centered planning that emphasizes preferences of autistic individuals and their families), and environment (e.g., sustainable family routine), and holistic measures of improved relationship and satisfaction with enhanced well-being (e.g., family and professional partnership and individual and family quality of life) in intervention effectiveness studies. More research needs to be conducted by including longer follow-up assessments of all above mentioned distal outcomes of autistic individuals and their families. Furthermore, future research ought to examine how different aspects of multicomponent intervention programs like NDBIs affect different types of outcomes. Additionally, adopting recent intervention research models like the Sequential Multiple Assignment Randomized Trial (SMART; [86]) in the future research of NDBIs can help researchers and interventionists not only systematize the application of a personalized approach to NDBIs [87] but also investigate the course of change for adapting the intervention processes to autistic children who are viewed either as a treatment "non-responder" or as "hidden victim" of adverse effects of the intervention [52]. By taking an additional measure to ensure the validity of NDBIs, we can benefit from employing participatory action research in the future research of NDBIs in which autistic individuals and their families are included in the process at all stages of the clinical trial or clinical program development.

5.1 Implications for practice

First, increased uptake of NDBIs is needed throughout the clinical community. Regrettably, many behavior interventionists have a limited understanding of NDBIs [88], and community implementation is lacking [89]. Further training is thus needed in how to implement NDBIs effectively. Furthermore, it is important for clinicians to understand the need to actively consider cultural adaptations, neurodiversity, and emphasizing strengths when working with autistic children and their families. Crucially, these should not be after-thoughts that are only addressed when NDBIs are implemented outside the United States or when a family points out that something is not in line with their values. Clinicians should bring these topics up from the beginning, regardless of the client's cultural background, in order to establish that these are meaningful aspects of the intervention that are taken seriously by the provider.

Clinicians must also always take autistic perspectives into account. As suggested by Schuck et al. [52], this may mean hiring autistic consultants or behavior analysts, or if that is not possible, staying up to date on what the autistic community is saying via academic literature and social media. This also applies to the perspective of the autistic intervention recipients themselves. If recipients are old enough and can communicate via speaking or writing, interviews or questionnaires can be administered to assess how clients are feeling about the intervention. For younger clients and/or those who use other means of communication, other types of treatment acceptability measures should be used (e.g., assessing child affect [90]).

Furthermore, intervention goals need to be neurodiversity affirming. That is, goals need to be based on autism acceptance and should not encourage children to go against an autistic way of being [52, 91]. Feedback from autistic adults can help clinicians and researchers develop more neurodiversity-friendly goals. For example, pushing children to exclusively use spoken language over other communication alternatives is seen by many to be pushing neurotypical standards on autistic children who have different communication needs (Schuck et al., under review). Additionally, autistic adults view many social intervention goals (e.g., improving communication skills; learning skills of conversation) skeptically (Baiden et al., under review). Relatedly, clinicians must always center autistic clients' strengths. Emphasizing strengths can improve children's self-esteem and confidence, lead to skill generalization, and ultimately lead to improvements in quality of life.

Apart from ensuring the appropriate and respectful goals of the interventions, it is crucial for both researchers and clinicians to examine if the implementation of NDBIs is appropriate and respectful and the intensity of NDBIs is appropriate as well. Autistic individuals and their families as well as professionals alike often expect to receive some common intervention recommendations (e.g., intervention variety and intensity). For example, it is noted that intensive behavioral interventions, delivered at 25–40 h per week, are the most frequently recommended intervention for young children with autism. However, Sandbank et al. [9, 14] contend the notion that "greater intervention intensities were associated with greater intervention gains" (p. 341). Research evidence shows that NDBIs, often provided at an intensity ranging typically from 10 to 20 h per week, can help autistic children achieve significant gains in multiple targeted and untargeted areas of interventions.

Author details

Mian Wang*, Rachel Schuck and Kaitlynn M.P. Baiden
Education Department, University of California, Santa Barbara, CA, USA

*Address all correspondence to: miwang@ucsb.edu

References

[1] Zeidan J, Fombonne E, Scorah J, Ibrahim A, Durkin MS, Saxena S, et al. Global prevalence of autism: A systematic review update. Autism Research. 2022;**15**(5):778-790

[2] Maenner MJ, Shaw KA, Bakian AV, Bilder DA, Durkin MS, Esler A, et al. Prevalence and characteristics of autism spectrum disorder among children aged 8 years—Autism and developmental disabilities monitoring network, 11 sites, United States, 2018. MMWR Surveillance Summaries. 2021;**70**(11):1

[3] Schreibman L, Dawson G, Stahmer AC, Landa R, Rogers SJ, McGee GG, et al. Naturalistic developmental behavioral interventions: Empirically validated treatments for autism spectrum disorder. Journal of Autism and Developmental Disorders. 2015;**45**(8):2411-2428. DOI: 10.1007/s10803-015-2407-8

[4] National Autism Center. Findings and Conclusions: National Standards Project, Phase 2. Randolph, MA: Author; 2015. Available from: https://www.nationalautismcenter.org/national-standards-project/results-reports/

[5] Wong C, Odom SL, Hume KA, Cox AW, Fettig A, Kucharczyk S, et al. Evidence-based practices for children, youth, and young adults with autism spectrum disorder: A comprehensive review. Journal of Autism and Developmental Disorders. 2015;**45**(7):1951-1966. DOI: 10.1007/s10803-014-2351-z

[6] Vivanti G. What does it mean for an autism intervention to be evidence-based? Autism Research. 2022;**15**(10):1787-1793. (n.d.); **n/a**(n/a). DOI: 10.1002/aur.2792

[7] Sandbank M, Bottema-Beutel K, Crowley S, Cassidy M, Dunham K, Feldman JI, et al. Project AIM: Autism intervention meta-analysis for studies of young children. Psychological Bulletin. 2020;**146**(1):1-29. DOI: 10.1037/bul0000215

[8] Wang M, Singer GH. *Supporting Families of Children with Developmental Disabilities: Evidence-Based and Emerging Practices*. Oxford, UK: Oxford University Press; 2016

[9] Bottema-Beutel K, Crowley S, Sandbank M, Woynaroski TG. Research review: Conflicts of interest (COIs) in autism early intervention research—A meta-analysis of COI influences on intervention effects. Journal of Child Psychology and Psychiatry. 2021;**62**(1):5-15. DOI: 10.1111/jcpp.13249

[10] Dawson M, Fletcher-Watson S. When autism researchers disregard harms: A commentary. Autism. 2022;**26**(2):564-566. DOI: 10.1177/13623613211031403

[11] Callahan K, Hughes HL, Mehta S, Toussaint KA, Nichols SM, Ma PS, et al. Social validity of evidence-based practices and emerging interventions in autism. Focus on Autism and Other Developmental Disabilities. 2017;**32**(3):188-197. DOI: 10.1177/1088357616632446

[12] D'Agostino SR, Douglas SN, Dueñas AD. Practitioner-implemented naturalistic developmental behavioral interventions: Systematic review of social validity practices. Topics in Early Childhood Special Education. 2019;**39**(3):170-182. DOI: 10.1177/0271121419854803

[13] Ledford JR, Hall E, Conder E, Lane JD. Research for young children

with autism spectrum disorders: Evidence of social and ecological validity. Topics in Early Childhood Special Education. 2016;**35**(4):223-233. DOI: 10.1177/0271121415585956

[14] Bottema-Beutel K, Crowley S, Sandbank M, Woynaroski TG. Adverse event reporting in intervention research for young autistic children. Autism. 2021;**25**(2):322-335. DOI: 10.1177/1362361320965331

[15] Hume K, Steinbrenner JR, Odom SL, Morin KL, Nowell SW, Tomaszewski B, et al. Evidence-based practices for children, youth, and young adults with autism: Third generation review. Journal of Autism and Developmental Disorders. 2021;**51**(11):4013-4032. DOI: 10.1007/s10803-020-04844-2

[16] Koegel LK, Ashbaugh K, Koegel RL. Pivotal Response Treatment. In: Lang R, Hancock TB, Singh NN, editors. *Early Intervention for Young Children with Autism Spectrum Disorder*. Switzerland: Springer International Publishing.; 2016. pp. 85-112. DOI: 10.1007/978-3-319-30925-5_4

[17] Rogers SJ, Dawson G. *Early Start Denver Model for Young Children with Autism: Promoting Language, Learning, and Engagement*. New York, NY: Guilford Publications; 2020

[18] Dawson G, Rogers S, Munson J, Smith M, Winter J, Greenson J, et al. Randomized, controlled trial of an intervention for toddlers with autism: The Early Start Denver Model. Pediatrics. 2010;**125**(1):e17-23. DOI: 10.1542/peds.2009-0958

[19] Rogers SJ, Dawson G, Vismara LA. An Early Start for Your Child with Autism: Using Everyday Activities to Help Kids Connect, Communicate, and Learn. Guilford Press; 2012

[20] Ingersoll B, Wainer A. Initial efficacy of project ImPACT: A parent-mediated social communication intervention for young children with ASD. Journal of Autism and Developmental Disorders. 2013;**43**(12):2943-2952. DOI: 10.1007/s10803-013-1840-9

[21] McGee GG. Incidental teaching. In: Encyclopedia of Behavior Modification and Cognitive Behavior Therapy: Educational Applications. Vol. 3. 2005. pp. 1359-1362

[22] Kaiser AP, Hester PP. Generalized effects of enhanced milieu teaching. Journal of Speech, Language, and Hearing Research. 1994;**37**(6):1320-1340

[23] Kasari C, Freeman S, Paparella T. Joint attention and symbolic play in young children with autism: A randomized controlled intervention study. Journal of Child Psychology and Psychiatry. 2006;**47**:611-620. DOI: 10.1111/j.1469-7610.2005.01567.x

[24] Crank JE, Sandbank M, Dunham K, Crowley S, Bottema-Beutel K, Feldman J, et al. Understanding the effects of naturalistic developmental Behavioral interventions: A project AIM Meta-analysis. Autism Research. 2021;**14**(4):817-834. DOI: 10.1002/aur.2471

[25] Koegel RL, Camarata S, Koegel LK, Ben-Tall A, Smith AE. Increasing speech intelligibility in children with autism. Journal of Autism and Developmental Disorders. 1998;**28**(3):241-251. DOI: 10.1023/a:1026073522897

[26] Smith T. Discrete trial training in the treatment of autism. Focus on Autism and Other Developmental Disabilities. 2001;**16**(2):86-92. DOI: 10.1177/108835760101600204

[27] Minjarez MB, Karp EA, Stahmer AC, Brookman-Frazee L. Empowering parents

through parent training and coaching. In: *Naturalistic Developmental Behavioral Interventions for Autism Spectrum Disorder*. Baltimore, MD: Paul H. Brookes Publishing Co.; 2020. pp. 77-98

[28] Lau AS. Making the case for selective and directed cultural adaptations of evidence-based treatments: Examples from parent training. Clinical Psychology: Science and Practice. 2006;**13**:295-310

[29] Aisenberg E. Evidence-based practice in mental health care to ethnic minority communities: Has its practice fallen short of its evidence? Social Work. 2008;**53**:297-306

[30] Castro FG, Barrera M Jr, Holleran Steiker LKH. Issues and challenges in the design of culturally adapted evidence-based interventions. Annual Review of Clinical Psychology. 2010;**6**:213-239

[31] Bernal G, Jiménez-Chafey MI, Domenech Rodríguez MM. Cultural adaptation of treatments: A resource for considering culture in evidence-based practice. Professional Psychology: Research and Practice. 2009;**40**:361-368

[32] Cabassa LJ, Baumann AA. A two-way street: Bridging implementation science and cultural adaptations of mental health treatments. Implementation Science. 2013;**8**:1-14

[33] Singer J. Why can't you be normal for once in your life? From a problem with no name to the emergence of a new category of difference. In: Corker M, French S, editors. *Disability Discourse*. Milton Keynes, UK: Open University Press; 1999. pp. 59-67

[34] Walker N. Neurodiversity: Some basic terms & definitions. 2014 Available from: https://neurocosmopolitanism.com/neurodiversity-some-basic-terms-definitions/

[35] Blume H. Neurodiversity: On the neurological underpinnings of geekdom. The Atlantic. 1998 Available from: https://www.theatlantic.com/magazine/archive/1998/09/neurodiversity/305909/

[36] Dwyer P. The neurodiversity approach(es): What are they and what do they mean for researchers? In: Human Development. 2022;**66**(2):73-92. DOI: 10.1159/000523723

[37] Dwyer P. On neurodiversity: Part III: What is the neurodiversity paradigm? In: Autistic Scholar. 2019 Available from: http://www.autisticscholar.com/what-is-neurodiversity/

[38] Bailin A. Clearing up some misconceptions about neurodiversity. Scientific American Blog Network. 2019 Available form: https://blogs.scientificamerican.com/observations/clearing-up-some-misconceptions-about-neurodiversity/

[39] Sinclair J. Don't mourn for us. Our Voice. 1993;**1**(3) Available from: http://www.autreat.com/dont_mourn.html

[40] Pripas-Kapit S. Historicizing Jim Sinclair's "Don't mourn for us": A cultural and intellectual history of Neurodiversity's first manifesto. In: Kapp SK, editor. *Autistic Community and the Neurodiversity Movement: Stories from the Frontline*. Singapore: Springer Nature; 2020. pp. 23-39 Available from: https://library.oapen.org/handle/20.500.12657/23177

[41] den Houting J. Neurodiversity: An insider's perspective. Autism. 2018;**23**(2):271-273. DOI: 10.1177/1362361318820762

[42] Jaarsma P, Welin S. Autism as a natural human variation: Reflections on the claims of the neurodiversity

movement. Health Care Analysis. 2012;**20**(1):20-30. DOI: 10.1007/s10728-011-0169-9

[43] Ballou EP. What the neurodiversity movement does—And doesn't—Offer. Thinking Person's Guide to Autism. 2018 Available from: http://www.thinkingautismguide.com/2018/02/what-neurodiversity-movement-doesand.html

[44] Chapman R. Neurodiversity, disability, wellbeing. In: *Neurodiversity Studies*. London, UK: Routledge; 2020. pp. 218-220

[45] Dwyer P. The social model and neurodiversity. In: Autistic Scholar. 2018 Available from: http://www.autisticscholar.com/social-model-neurodiversity/

[46] Armendariz R. The Autism Acceptance Hoax. National Council on Severe Autism; 2019 Available from: https://www.ncsautism.org/blog//the-autism-acceptance-hoax

[47] Robertson SM. Neurodiversity, quality of life, and autistic adults: Shifting research and professional focuses onto real-life challenges. Disability Studies Quarterly. 2009;**30**(1) Article 1. DOI: 10.18061/dsq.v30i1.1069

[48] des Roches Rosa S. I'm the parent of a "severe" autistic teen. I oppose the National Council on severe autism. Thinking Person's Guide to Autism. 2019 Available from: http://www.thinkingautismguide.com/2019/01/im-parent-of-severe-autistic-teen-i.html

[49] Fletcher-Watson S. Is early autism intervention compatible with neurodiversity? 2018. DART. Available from: https://dart.ed.ac.uk/intervention-neurodiversity/

[50] Lai M-C, Anagnostou E, Wiznitzer M, Allison C, Baron-Cohen S. Evidence-based support for autistic people across the lifespan: Maximising potential, minimising barriers, and optimising the person–environment fit. The Lancet Neurology. 2020;**19**(5):434-451. DOI: 10.1016/S1474-4422(20)30034-X

[51] Leadbitter K, Buckle KL, Ellis C, Dekker M. Autistic self-advocacy and the neurodiversity movement: Implications for autism early intervention research and practice. Frontiers in Psychology. 2021;**12**:1-7. DOI: 10.3389/fpsyg.2021.635690

[52] Schuck RK, Tagavi DM, Baiden KMP, Dwyer P, Williams ZJ, Osuna A, et al. Neurodiversity and autism intervention: Reconciling perspectives through a naturalistic developmental behavioral intervention framework. Journal of Autism and Developmental Disorders. 2021;**52**:4625-4645. DOI: 10.1007/s10803-021-05316-x

[53] Choi S, Schuck RK, Imm K. Redesigning deficit-laden assessments for neurodivergent students [chapter]. In: Handbook of Research on Challenging Deficit Thinking for Exceptional Education Improvement. Hershey, PA: IGI Global.; 2022. DOI: 10.4018/978-1-7998-8860-4.ch008

[54] Fung LK, editor. Neurodiversity: From Phenomenology to Neurobiology and Enhancing Technologies. Washington, DC: American Psychiatric Pub; 2021

[55] Armstrong T. Neurodiversity in the Classroom: Strength-based Strategies to Help Students with Special Needs Succeed in School and Life. Alexandria, VA. ASCD.; 2012

[56] Warren N, Eatchel B, Kirby AV, Diener M, Wright C, D'Astous V. Parent-identified strengths of autistic youth.

Autism. UK: Oxford; 2021;**25**(1):79-89. DOI: 10.1177/1362361320945556

[57] Donaldson AL, Krejcha K, McMillin A. A strengths-based approach to autism: Neurodiversity and partnering with the autism community. Perspectives of the ASHA Special Interest Groups. 2017;**2**(1):56-68. DOI: 10.1044/persp2.SIG1.56

[58] Lee EAL, Black MH, Falkmer M, Tan T, Sheehy L, Bölte S, et al. "We can see a bright future": Parents' perceptions of the outcomes of participating in a strengths-based program for adolescents with autism spectrum disorder. Journal of Autism and Developmental Disorders. 2020;**50**(9):3179-3194. DOI: 10.1007/s10803-020-04411-9

[59] Gengoux GW, Abrams DA, Schuck R, Millan ME, Libove R, Ardel CM, et al. A pivotal response treatment package for children with autism spectrum disorder: An RCT. Pediatrics. 2019;**144**(3):1-10 Academic Search Complete

[60] Gengoux GW, McNerney E, Minjarez MB. Selecting meaningful skills for teaching in the natural environment. In: Bruinsma Y, Minjarez MB, Schreibman L, Stahmer AC, editors. *Naturalistic Developmental Behavioral Interventions in the Treatment of Children of Autism Spectrum Disorder*. Baltimore: Paul H. Brookes; 2019. pp. 45-75

[61] Turnbull A, Turnbull HR, Francis G, Burke MM, Kyzar K, Haines S, et al. Families and Professionals: Trusting Partnerships in General and Special Education. 8th ed. New York, NY: Pearson; 2021

[62] Xu Y, Yang J, Yao J, Chen J, Zhuang X, Wang W, et al. A pilot study of a culturally adapted early intervention for young children with autism Spectrum disorders in China. Journal of Early Intervention. 2018;**40**(1):52-68. DOI: 10.1177/1053815117748408

[63] Sengupta K, Mahadik S, Kapoor G. Glocalizing project ImPACT: Feasibility, acceptability and preliminary outcomes of a parent-mediated social communication intervention for autism adapted to the Indian context. Research in Autism Spectrum Disorders. 2020;**76**:101585. DOI: 10.1016/j.rasd.2020.101585

[64] Vivanti G, Duncan E, Dawson G, Rogers SJ. (Eds.). *Implementazione dell'Early Start Denver Model in Gruppo (G-ESDM) per bambini con autismo in età prescolare*. Rome, Italy: Giovanni Fioriti Editore; 2019. Available from: https://www.fioritieditore.com/prodotto/implementazione-dellearly-start-denver-model-in-gruppo-g-esdm-per-bambini-con-autismo-in-eta-prescolare/

[65] Xu X, Wang Y. Early Start Denver Model for Young Children with Autism [Gu Du Zheng Yiu Er Zao Qi Jie Ru Dan Fe Mo Shi]. Shanghai: Shanghai Scientific Technology Publishing; 2014

[66] Straus JN. Autism as culture. The Disability Studies Reader 2013;**4**:460-484

[67] Bargiela S, Steward R, Mandy W. The experiences of late-diagnosed women with autism spectrum conditions: An investigation of the female autism phenotype. Journal of Autism and Developmental Disorders. 2016;**46**(10):3281-3294. DOI: 10.1007/s10803-016-2872-8

[68] Hull L, Petrides KV, Allison C, Smith P, Baron-Cohen S, Lai M-C, et al. "Putting on my best normal": Social camouflaging in adults with autism spectrum conditions. Journal of Autism and Developmental Disorders. 2017;**47**(8):2519-2534. DOI: 10.1007/s10803-017-3166-5

[69] Cage E, Troxell-Whitman Z. Understanding the reasons, contexts and costs of camouflaging for autistic adults.

Journal of Autism and Developmental Disorders. 2019;**49**(5):1899-1911. DOI: 10.1007/s10803-018-03878-x

[70] Gevarter C, Zamora C. Naturalistic speech-generating device interventions for children with complex communication needs: A systematic review of single-subject studies. American Journal of Speech-Language Pathology. 2018;**27**(3):1073-1090. DOI: 10.1044/2018_AJSLP-17-0128

[71] Sandoval-Norton AH, Shkedy G. How much compliance is too much compliance: Is long-term ABA therapy abuse? Cogent Psychology. 2019;**6**(1):1641258. DOI: 10.1080/23311908.2019.1641258

[72] McGill O, Robinson A. "Recalling hidden harms": Autistic experiences of childhood applied behavioural analysis (ABA). *Advances in Autism*, (ahead-of-print). 2020. DOI: 10.1108/AIA-04-2020-0025

[73] Hollocks MJ, Lerh JW, Magiati I, Meiser-Stedman R, Brugha TS. Anxiety and depression in adults with autism spectrum disorder: A systematic review and meta-analysis. Psychological Medicine. 2019;**49**(4):559-572. DOI: 10.1017/S0033291718002283

[74] Provenzani U, Fusar-Poli L, Brondino N, Damiani S, Vercesi M, Meyer N, et al. What are we targeting when we treat autism spectrum disorder? A systematic review of 406 clinical trials. Autism. 2020;**24**(2):274-284

[75] Howlin P, Magiati I. Autism spectrum disorder: Outcomes in adulthood. Current Opinion in Psychiatry. 2017;**30**(2):69-76. DOI: 10.1097/YCO.0000000000000308

[76] Van Heijst BF, Geurts HM. Quality of life in autism across the lifespan: A meta-analysis. Autism. 2015;**19**(2):158-167

[77] Grelotti DJ, Kaptchuk TJ. Placebo by proxy. British Medical Journal. 2011;**343**:d4345. DOI: 10.1136/bmj.d4345

[78] American Educational Research Association, American Psychological Association, & National Council on Measurement in Education. Standards for Educational and Psychological Testing. Washington, DC: American Psychological Association, Inc.; 2014

[79] Markus KA, Borsboom D. Frontiers of Test Validity Theory: Measurement, Causation, and Meaning. New York, NY: Routledge; 2013

[80] Sparrow SS, Cicchetti DV, Balla DA. Vineland Adaptive Behavior Scales: Second Edition (Vineland II), Survey Interview Form/Caregiver Rating Form. Livonia, MN: Pearson Assessments; 2005

[81] Constantino JN, Gruber CP. Social Responsiveness Scale: SRS-2 Software Kit. Torrance: Western Psychological Services; 2012

[82] Yoder PJ, Bottema-Beutel K, Woynaroski T, Chandrasekhar R, Sandbank M. Social communication intervention effects vary by dependent variable type in preschoolers with autism spectrum disorders. Evidence-Based Communication Assessment and Intervention. 2013;7(4):150-174. DOI: 10.1080/17489539.2014.917780

[83] Hardan AY, Gengoux GW, Berquist KL, Libove RA, Ardel CM, Phillips J, et al. A randomized controlled trial of pivotal response treatment group for parents of children with autism. Journal of Child Psychology and Psychiatry. 2015;**56**(8):884-892. DOI: 10.1111/jcpp.12354

[84] McGarry E, Vernon T, Baktha A. Brief report: A pilot online pivotal response treatment training program for parents of toddlers with autism Spectrum disorder. Journal of Autism and Developmental Disorders. 2019;**50**:3424-3431. DOI: 10.1007/s10803-019-04100-2

[85] McDaniel J, Yoder P, Crandall M, Millan ME, Ardel CM, Gengoux GW, et al. Effects of pivotal response treatment on reciprocal vocal contingency in a randomized controlled trial of children with autism spectrum disorder. Autism: The International Journal of Research & Practice. 2020;**24**(6):1566-1571 Academic Search Complete

[86] Collins LM, Murphy SA, Strecher V. The Multiphase Optimization Strategy (MOST) and the Sequential Multiple Assignment Randomized Trial (SMART): New methods for more potent eHealth interventions. American Journal of Preventive Medicine. 2007;**32**:5 (Suppl. S112-S118). DOI: 10.1016/j.amepre.2007.01.022.17466815.2062525

[87] Kasari C, Sturm A, Shih W. SMARTer approach to personalizing intervention for children with Autism Spectrum Disorder. Journal of Speech, Language, and Hearing Research. 2018;**61**(11):2629-2640. DOI: 10.1044/2018_JSLHR-L-RSAUT-18-0029.30418492.6693574

[88] Hampton LH, Sandbank MP. Keeping up with the evidence base: Survey of behavior professionals about naturalistic developmental behavioral interventions. Autism: The International Journal of Research & Practice. 2022;**26**(4):875-888 Academic Search Complete

[89] D'Agostino SR, Dueñas AD, Bravo A, Tyson K, Straiton D, Salvatore GL, et al. Toward deeper understanding and wide-scale implementation of naturalistic developmental behavioral interventions. Autism, 13623613221121428. 2022. DOI: 10.1177/13623613221121427

[90] Robinson SE. Teaching paraprofessionals of students with autism to implement pivotal response treatment in inclusive school settings using a brief video feedback training package. Focus on Autism and Other Developmental Disabilities. 2011;**26**(2):105-118. DOI: 10.1177/1088357611407063

[91] Dawson G, Franz L, Brandsen S. At a crossroads—Reconsidering the goals of autism early behavioral intervention from a neurodiversity perspective. JAMA Pediatrics. 2022;**176**(9):839-840. DOI: 10.1001/jamapediatrics.2022.2299

Chapter 14

An Intersubjectivity Parental-Based Intervention (I-PBI) for Preschoolers with ASD

Paola Venuti, Silvia Perzolli and Arianna Bentenuto

Abstract

Given the influence of parents' qualities and dyadic characteristics on child developmental outcomes, recent findings strengthened the importance of involving caregivers during the intervention to increase dyadic syntonization levels and to extend the acquisition of competencies in naturalistic contexts. The Intersubjectivity Parental-Based Intervention (I-PBI) presented throughout this chapter is delivered involving caregivers in two different modalities: first, in the therapeutic setting, together with the child to support interactions within the dyad. Second, the focus is on the parental representation of the child and the caregivers in their role. Trained psychologists deliver the intervention after receiving specific licenses on developmental intervention models for children with autism spectrum disorder (ASD). Finally, the team is constantly supervised at least once every month by an expert psychotherapist. Unlike parent-mediated intervention and parent training, the I-PBI does not require home assignments or fidelity schedules, and the therapist entirely delivers the intervention. Throughout this chapter, the structure and therapeutic techniques of the intervention will be presented. Further, results considering the child's developmental trajectories and changes in caregiver-child interaction will be discussed.

Keywords: autism spectrum disorder, intervention, parental involvement, caregiver-child interaction, Italian context

1. Introduction

Parents are genetically predisposed to intuitively capture and understand children's signals with typical development. However, parents may struggle to understand the signs and needs of children with autism spectrum disorder (ASD), and their approaches might not always be successful.

Given the influence of parents' qualities on child developmental outcomes, recent findings strengthen the importance of involving caregivers during the intervention to increase dyadic syntonization levels and extend the acquisition of competencies in naturalistic contexts (e.g., home) [1–4]. Currently, many guidelines [5, 6] recommend parental inclusion during intervention with children with ASD. A significant amount of research showed that involving the parent during the intervention enhances outcomes in children with ASD [3, 7–11]. Specifically, parental involvement during intervention seems to be extremely important in order to guarantee the adaptation to the child's difficulties and impairments, allowing the child to respond with enhanced communicative and social development [9], long-term symptom reduction [12], and to generalize these outcomes across settings [13]. Further, marked difficulties in social communication and responsiveness in parents of children with ASD might create a potential barrier to care for their children. In line with this, recent findings suggest that parental involvement was able to guarantee more noticeable results considering caregivers.

Interestingly, some research found a significant relationship between the degree of change in parental interaction and the rate of the child's improvement [14], underlying the importance of the dyadic relational aspects in child developmental outcomes. Because parents are central in ensuring success and a good prognosis, it is critical to include them throughout the intervention process. These findings shed new light on the idea that if parents are adequately informed during the intervention and if they constantly deliver intervention strategies in naturalistic contexts, the intensity of the intervention dwindles on intervention outcomes. In line with this, caregivers can continue to teach competencies to their children in the home context, improving parent-child interactions and increasing the amount of treatment they receive. Findings considering the evaluation of Naturalistic Developmental Behavioral Interventions (NDBI) are mainly focused on child outcomes demonstrating the improvements in both child's social engagement and cognitive development [4]. Child gains are predominantly assessed through outcome measures using standardized instruments such as Autism Diagnostic Observation Schedule [15] and Griffiths Scales [16–22]. Although empirical efforts have been made in this field, most of the research on interventions for ASD is focused on child outcomes more than parental outcomes [23]. However, a recent systematic review underlined the importance of a greater focus on both parents to provide tailored intervention [24]. Some evidence in this field showed that parents increased well-being and quality of life after being involved in the therapeutic setting with their children [25, 26].

2. Intersubjectivity parental-based intervention (I-PBI)

With this chapter, we want to present and describe an intervention plan that has been implemented in the Laboratory of Observation, Diagnosis, and Education (ODFLab) of the Department of Psychology and Cognitive Science, University of Trento (Italy). ODFLab is a clinical and research laboratory specialized in the multimethod assessment and evidence-based intervention programs for individuals with typical and atypical neurodevelopment. Specifically, the ODFLab is a national reference center for assessment and intervention for autism spectrum disorders (ASDs) and learning disabilities (LD). In the context of ASD, ODFLab implements an "Intersubjectivity Parental-Based Intervention" (I-PBI), which combines empirically validated scientific principles with guidelines following the Italian Health System [6, 27, 28]. This intervention integrates developmental and relationship-based principles with behavioral ones, taking inspiration from the elements of the American Early Start Denver Model [29, 30]. In addition, the I-PBI emphasizes the fundamental role of reciprocity between caregiver and child, supporting intersubjective exchanges and promoting the child's intentionality during interactions. The purpose of the intervention is to increase the intersubjectivity within the dyad, providing the child with the relational experience to reach several stages of development. The intervention allows children with atypical development to establish empathy relations with the parent and acquire essential primary communication skills. Furthermore, given possible caregivers-child maladaptive interactive circuits in dyads with children with ASD, the I-PBI involves caregivers in the therapeutic setting to allow parents to learn appropriate strategies to deal with their children. In addition, parents play a fundamental role in the generalization of child competencies. In fact, through parental involvement, caregivers may effectively use the acquired strategies in more naturalistic contexts (e.g., home). The intervention is adapted following the child's age, specific interests, and individual functional profiles. Further, intervention goals are constantly changed and revised depending on the child's developmental improvements. Moreover, unlike parent-mediated intervention and parent training, parental involvement does not require home assignments or fidelity schedules, and the therapist delivers the intervention entirely. In fact, during these weekly sessions, parents are not delivering the intervention, and therapists remain the key figures, structuring activities and creating opportunities for the caregivers and the child to interact and play together. Thanks to this, caregivers may have the opportunity to experience more functional interactions with their child characterized by more adequate proposals and significant awareness of the child's difficulties. This may lead to increased dyadic pleasure, increased parents' self-efficacy, and significant motivation to interact with their children while reducing stress and frustration. This intervention also refers to the highly validated Preschool Autism Communication Trial - PACT [9] procedure aimed to enhance parental sensitivity and responsiveness, and consequently, being beneficial in terms of more pronounced parental synchronous response to the child, child initiations with adults, and joint attention between parent and child. Considering the child, the intervention is based on three different levels: (1) Relationship, consisting of specific intervention on parent-child interaction; (2) Behavior, through learning adaptive modalities in the interaction with others by using alternative augmentative communication (CAA) and use of images or sounds in order to structure sequential organization of activities; (3) Development, consisting of individual rehabilitative interventions such as music therapy, psychomotricity, cognitive activation, speech therapy, and occupational therapy. Every intervention should be planned considering individual and specific characteristics. However, some primary indications are divided into four phases that would adapt to each child.

Phase 1 – Intensive Intervention: after diagnosis, the intervention should be intensive and highly structured, consisting of 6/8 hours per week (3/4 hours for individual rehabilitation and 3/4 involving parents during intervention). Further, meetings with parents alone are provided during this phase. The intensive intervention should last a minimum of 6 months, depending on each case. Generally, this first phase can be considered concluded when the adult can interact appropriately with the child and contain him/her.

Phase 2 – Consolidation of Intervention: this phase consists of a maximum of 4 hours of intervention per week in a group of peers to develop social play skills. However, during this phase, parents are supported by a psychotherapist or a psychologist through meetings every 2/3 weeks.

Phase 3 – "Conclusion" of Intervention: there is no actual conclusion of the intervention, and support for families is always present. When children acquire suitable and sufficient abilities, they may receive other direct interventions in specific moments, such as challenging situations or essential transitions in life.

2.1 Parental intervention

Considering parents, there are several phases below described in detail.

Phase 1 – Parent-Child Interaction: during this phase, the intervention setting is not highly structured to offer spontaneous and ecological interactions that are easily replicable at home or other contexts. The main goal of parent involvement in a therapy room is teaching adults to detect and promptly respond to the child's cues, decreasing the child's frustration and anxiety. During the first phase, especially during the first meetings, the therapist has a leading role in dealing with the child to comprehend which ways are appropriate and well accepted by the child, reactivating a synchronic interactive exchange. The therapist uses specific techniques to create an appropriate context within the dyad and help parents get closer to their children. The main focus of the intervention is the parent-child interaction and, in particular, the promotion of a synchronic and responsive interaction that acts as a framework for the child's development. Therefore, working on identifying dysfunctional interactive patterns is fundamental to understanding how to replace them with more adequate and effective interactive methods. Improvements in relationship quality imply constant support to the parents to help them acquire the ability to maintain a balance between the child's exploration and structured activities, respecting the timing and the methods of a child that follows different evolutionary paths. The main intervention objectives are:

- To increase the general *level of emotional availability* and the degree of reciprocal accessibility through a significant awareness to read and respond adequately to the partner's emotional cues.

- To increase synchrony levels in the exchanges that occur in *shared play moments*. Another salient aspect of the work is the play with the child. After carefully analyzing the child's level of functioning, the therapist selects the activities in line with the development and functional profile. The play activity can be without the object if the child can establish vis-a-vis or physical contact. The choice of the play is guided by the focus on the child's attention.

- When the child is interested, the therapist will try to engage the child as long as possible, initially *imitating* what the child does and then gradually introducing elements of differentiation such as a different rhythm and the amplification of behaviors. To build an intersubjective exchange with the child, the therapist uses the imitation of all vocal, expressive, and motor behaviors or functional use of objects. The child's imitation by the therapist allows the formation of primary intersubjectivity. The therapist's purpose is not to push the child to imitate but to experience the feeling of being with another at his level by activating a series of basic social behaviors such as eye contact.

- To promote exploration through *environmental structuring* in which the therapist allows the child to use all objects and spaces of the therapeutic context.

- To regulate emotions through *verbalization of emotional states.* The therapist reflects on the emotional states and the child's intentions with affective meaning. The therapist explains this verbally so that the child lives the experience of being understood by the other. At the same time, the parent begins to attribute meaning to some child's behaviors that often appear misunderstood, excessive, and inadequate.

DOI: http://dx.doi.org/10.5772/intechopen.108672

Phase 2 – Parental Representation: during this phase, every 2–3 weeks, parents meet another therapist, and through video recording technology, they discuss interactive moments with their children. The intervention provides specific work on parents' representations to build a more truthful image of the child and themselves as parents, enhancing their ability to reflect on their own and the child's behaviors. In addition, during these meetings, parents have the opportunity to share and discuss their difficulties, hopes, and worries. The intervention provides specific work on parents' representations to build a more truthful image of the child and themselves as parents, enhancing their ability to reflect on their own and the child's behaviors.

The meeting is divided into two phases: an initial one that follows the classic clinical interview method and a more structured one that involves video analysis. During the first phase, parents can talk freely about previous weeks' events. The therapist intervenes to share and process painful feelings and to support positive affects when the parents tell pleasant episodes connected to the relationship with the child. In addition, the therapist gives several concrete suggestions on supporting and managing certain aspects of the child's development. The therapist has previously selected clips of interaction that are first watched together and then commented on. The psychotherapist guides the parent in observing their behaviors' effects on the child (e.g., respecting the child's timing leads the child to respond to a request; or a too high-pitched voice causes the child's withdrawal behaviors). These events are of such a short duration that, generally, no attention is paid to them during the flow of the interaction. However, observing, evaluating, and discussing their presence are fundamental for truthful caregivers' representations.

Finally, parents are guided in the comprehension of their behavior through questions about feelings considering themselves and the child to promote their reflective function.

In summary, the therapist's objectives in this phase are:

- To reduce adverse effects
- To increase the ability to reflect on children's behavior
- To support a more realistic representation of the child
- To build a self-image as a parent

Phase 3 – Parent's group: in this phase, different parents of same-aged children discuss their difficulties and worries, support each other, and share thoughts and ideas about parenting. Thanks to the confrontation with families of children in the same condition, parents may feel understood in their difficulties and less alone.

3. Highlights

To sum up, the I-PBI focuses on:

1. To increase the ability to structure the environment to make it accessible to the child.
2. To reduce behaviors that hinder the processes of exploration and self-regulation.

3. To reduce negative effects such as boredom, disappointment, and hostility.

4. To increase the ability to reflect on the child's behaviors, capturing the mental states hidden behind some anomalies and bizarre features.

5. To build an aware and truthful representation of the child's difficulties and abilities.

6. To build an image of oneself as a more competent parent.

Trained psychologists deliver the intervention after receiving specific licenses on developmental intervention models for children with ASD. Finally, the team is constantly supervised at least once every month by an expert psychotherapist.

4. Evaluation of parental involvement during intervention with children with ASD

The heterogeneity in the symptomatology of ASD also reflects in several intervention outcomes [31]. Hence, it is difficult to identify one kind of intervention with the highest degree of efficacy compared with others, given that a specific intervention can be helpful for specific domains and patients but not for others [30, 32, 33]. A significant amount of research reported the efficacy of different kinds of intervention on the developmental trajectories of children with ASD during the intervention [19, 20, 22, 34]. Previous literature on parental involvement focused more on the evaluation of treatment response, considering the child outcomes demonstrating the improvements in both child's social engagement and their cognitive development [4], often without deepening dyadic and caregivers' variables associated with the response. Moreover, some research showed that without involving caregivers, a child's variables tend to remain more stable over time [9, 35]. Child gains are predominantly assessed through developmental outcome measures using standardized instruments such as Autism Diagnostic Observation Schedule [15] and Griffiths Scales [16]. However, these instruments, when used to assess the treatment outcomes longitudinally, might suffer from the issue of sensitivity to change. Standardized diagnostic and cognitive test items are, in fact, neither proximal to the treatment nor necessarily sensitive to small changes in social communication and interactive skills that may be occurring as treatment progresses. For this, the detection of change may be enhanced by using observational measures of social responsiveness [36]. In line with this, analyzing the dyad's interactive component through observational and behavioral measures might provide a sensitive-to-change perspective to investigate caregiver and child improvements in the relational context.

4.1 Changes in child developmental trajectories

In order to monitor preschool children with ASD during the parental-based intervention, children's developmental trajectories have been analyzed before and after treatment. Evaluating the developmental trajectories of about 30 preschool children with ASD, we found an improvement of both cognitive and socio-communicative domains [18]. We found a significant improvement in the general quotient of children exposed to the early intensive intervention line with previous literature [27, 29, 37].

Specifically, our data showed that linguistic-communication abilities present the most improvements.

This may be in line with the ground idea of developmental models of treatment for ASD that focus on a wide range of socio-communicative abilities instead of rehabilitating specific areas of cognitive development [4, 21]. These findings may also be explained by the parental involvement that supports parents in displaying appropriate strategies in different contexts of the child's life, extending effective social interactions in naturalistic settings besides the laboratory room, leading to better children's outcomes.

Another fundamental aspect is the decreased general behavioral expressions of ASD significantly, especially considering the socio-communicative area [38]. The social-affect area focuses on communicative abilities and social affect and considers different modalities and their integration. This supports the idea that treatment impacts developmental trajectories by improving a wide spectrum of socio-communicative abilities, including receptive and expressive communication, but also precursors of verbal communication such as gestures, imitation, and joint attention, fundamental elements to initiate or respond adaptively to the social exchange. Furthermore, in line with previous literature, interventions tend to focus more on supporting cognitive and social abilities rather than the restrictive and repetitive behaviors that tend to be more stable over time [39, 40]. Despite this, in the intervention group, we found a slight change considering this domain, probably associated with the targeted work on anxiety reduction, emotions, and self-regulatory mechanisms during the parental-based intervention.

This study shed new light on the developmental trajectories of children with ASD, strengthening the importance of specific work on early relationships to gain better outcomes and integrating different techniques during the intervention to optimize the child's improvements.

4.2 Changes in parent-child interaction

Considering the role of caregiver-child interactions for the child's development in both typical and atypical contexts, our intervention focused on relationship-based principles that aim to restore interactive circuits. Given the importance of parental involvement in the therapeutic setting and the paucity of studies highlighting parental and dyadic changes during the intervention, we analyzed caregiver-child dyads with ASD with several observative instruments that assessed the affective quality, play skill abilities, and parental speech.

An interesting result is a significant improvement in the mother's general level of sensitivity, especially in the domain of awareness of timing during the interaction, suggesting that mothers were more likely to wait for the appropriate moment to propose or interrupt the child during dyadic exchanges. In line with this, previous literature reported significant parents' acceptance and comprehension of the child and more positive dyadic patterns [3, 41].

Further, some findings suggest that parents show changes in their interactive strategies pre and post-intervention [42], besides evolutions in child's behaviors. In line with this, parents showed an increased ability to structure adequately the exchange with the child. Particularly, they seem to structure just the right amount according to the child's needs, using both verbal and non-verbal strategies. These results are especially relevant in the context of ASD. In fact, given the impairments in communicative abilities, the use of verbal indications displayed by parents may not be enough to scaffold an appropriate interaction effectively, and the use of nonverbal strategies plays a crucial role. While structuring is about guidance and mentoring, intrusiveness is the actual over-direction, over-stimulation, and interference in a child's behaviors and activities. In particular, parents seemed to be more able to follow the children's demands, interfering less with their activity. In line with this, verbal and physical interferences decreased significantly, indicating more suitability in dealing with children, which showed fewer signs indicating that the adult is intrusive in their activity. These results appear to be particularly relevant, considering that research in parenting in the context of neurodevelopmental disorders pointed out the tendency of caregivers to be more intrusive during interpersonal interchanges [43, 44]. Concerning the child, the increases found in the responsiveness domain might be influenced by more appropriate maternal behaviors during the intervention with parental involvement, which gives them the possibility to experience positive exchanges, first of all, mediated by the therapist and then gradually alone with the child. Therefore, the therapist gradually leaves space for the dyad, supporting them only when necessary to facilitate reciprocal attunement. By experiencing positive exchanges, parents might be more motivated and facilitated to reproduce specific social routines in the domestic context.

Another aspect that we took into consideration was play abilities during interactions since play skills are related to cognitive skills, and play is considered a primary opportunity for learning, especially when carried out in the context of child-adult interactions [45]. On this basis, dyadic play during intervention represents a key mediator of the whole interactive process [46]. After the intervention, parents' and children's play levels are more associated. In particular, the child's play was correlated with that of the parent after the intervention but not before, suggesting the presence of a greater ability for dyadic synchronization. This change reinforces higher levels of reciprocal syntonization, supporting the importance of directly intervening in the dyad to foster bidirectional exchanges.

Furthermore, considering the importance of parental linguistic elements in child development [47, 48], we also wanted to investigate longitudinal changes in parental speech pre and post-intervention. In fact, after the evaluation of affective and playful aspects during the intervention, we also aimed to examine how parents adapt their speech to their children over time. In line with the results considering increased relational affect, parents display more affective than informative speech after the intervention.

Further, parents increased their descriptions of the child's actions, suggesting an enhanced verbal structuring while sharing the attentive focus on what the child is doing during the exchange, supporting a non-intrusive linguistic style. It is relevant to note how sensitive and responsive modalities that parents acquired during the intervention also reflect on their linguistic speech directed to children. Linguistic and affective elements together seem relevant for the child's involvement.

5. Conclusion

The ground idea of the parental-based intervention is working with parents, rather than working for parents, to find personalized modalities to deal with a child with ASD. In fact, during treatment, parents acquire adequate strategies to respond to the child's signals, leading to more extended and more functional exchanges with the child. On the other side, it extends strategies in a more naturalistic setting, helping

DOI: http://dx.doi.org/10.5772/intechopen.108672

the child maintain and generalize competencies. During intervention with parental involvement, the therapist acts as a promoter of the exchange, supporting both the partners in establishing functional and adaptive social routines in which caregivers can experiment with themselves adequately and pleasantly, following their spontaneous adaptation to the child.

Coherently, after the intervention, the affective quality of the exchange results in enhanced syntonization to the child's needs with greater structuring abilities in a less interfering way. The involvement of caregivers should not only consider the work in the therapeutic setting with the child and the therapist, but a guided re-elaboration provided by the therapist to the parents alone is necessary for decoding strategies, observing the strengths and weaknesses of their child and themselves as parents. Thanks to this, parents may have better tools to understand the child's communicative signs. The increased awareness becomes a protective factor in preventing secondary deficits emerging from dysfunctional interactions when the fathers do not understand the child's difficulties.

Acknowledgements

We gratefully acknowledge the clinical staff of ODFLab and the families who participated in our studies.

Author details

Paola Venuti*, Silvia Perzolli and Arianna Bentenuto
Department of Psychology and Cognitive Science, Laboratory of Observation, Diagnosis, and Education (ODFLab), University of Trento, Italy

*Address all correspondence to: paola.venuti@unitn.it

References

[1] Green J, Garg S. Annual Research Review: The state of autism intervention science: Progress, target psychological and biological mechanisms and future prospects. Journal of Child Psychology and Psychiatry. 2018;**59**(4):424-443

[2] Nevill RE, Lecavalier L, Stratis EA. Meta-analysis of parent-mediated interventions for young children with autism spectrum disorder. Autism. 2018;**22**(2):84-98

[3] Oono IP, Honey EJ, McConachie H. Parent-mediated early intervention for young children with autism spectrum disorders (ASD): Parent-mediated early intervention for young children with autism spectrum disorders (ASD). Evidence Based Child Health. 2013;**8**(6):2380-2479

[4] Tiede G, Walton KM. Meta-analysis of naturalistic developmental behavioral interventions for young children with autism spectrum disorder. Autism. 2019;**23**(8):2080-2095

[5] World Health Organization. Transforming and Scaling Up Health Professionals' Education and Training. World Health Organization; 2013

[6] Istituto Superiore di Sanità. Il Trattamento dei Disturbi dello Spettro Autistico nei Bambini e Negli Adolescenti. Roma, Italy: Ministero della Salute; 2011

[7] McConnell SR. Interventions to facilitate social interaction for young children with autism: Review of available research and recommendations for educational intervention and future research. Journal of Autism and Developmental Disorders. 2002;**32**(5):351-372

[8] Wolery M, Garfinkle AN. Measures in intervention research with young children who have autism. Journal of Autism and Developmental Disorders. 2002;**32**(5):463-478

[9] Green J, Charman T, McConachie H, Aldred C, Slonims V, Howlin P, et al. Parent-mediated communication-focused treatment in children with autism (PACT): A randomised controlled trial. The Lancet. 2010;**375**(9732):2152-2160

[10] Kasari C, Siller M, Huynh LN, Shih W, Swanson M, Hellemann GS, et al. Randomized controlled trial of parental responsiveness intervention for toddlers at high risk for autism. Infant Behavior & Development. 2014;**37**(4):711-721

[11] Althoff CE, Dammann CP, Hope SJ, Ausderau KK. Parent-mediated interventions for children with autism spectrum disorder: A systematic review. The American Journal of Occupational Therapy. 2019;**73**(3):730

[12] Pickles A, Le Couteur A, Leadbitter K, Salomone E, Cole -Fletcher R, Tobin H, et al. Parent-mediated social communication therapy for young children with autism (PACT): Long-term follow-up of a randomised controlled trial. The Lancet. 2016;**388**(10059):2501-2509

[13] PACT-G Group, Green J, Aldred C, Charman T, Le Couteur A, Emsley RA, et al. Paediatric Autism Communication Therapy-Generalised (PACT-G) against treatment as usual for reducing symptom severity in young children with autism spectrum disorder: Study protocol for a randomised controlled trial. Trials. 2018;**19**(1):514

[14] Rogers SJ, Estes A, Vismara L, Munson J, Zierhut C, Greenson J, et al. Enhancing low-intensity coaching in parent implemented early start denver model intervention for early autism: A Randomized Comparison Treatment Trial. Journal of Autism and Developmental Disorders. 2019;**49**(2):632-646

[15] Lord C, Rutter M, DiLavore PC, Risi S, Gotham K, Bishop S. Autism Diagnostic Observation Schedule–Second Edition (ADOS-2). Los Angeles, CA, USA: Western Psychological Services; 2012

[16] Luiz DM, Foxcroft CD, Povey JL. The Griffiths scales of mental development: A factorial validity study. South Africa Journal of Psychology. 2006;**36**(1):192-214

[17] Fuller EA, Kaiser AP. The effects of early intervention on social communication outcomes for children with autism spectrum disorder: A meta-analysis. Journal of Autism and Developmental Disorders. 2020;**50**(5):1683-1700

[18] Bentenuto A, Bertamini G, Perzolli S, Venuti P. Changes in developmental trajectories of preschool children with autism spectrum disorder during parental based intensive intervention. Brain Sciences. 2020;**10**(5):289

[19] Simonoff E, Kent R, Stringer D, Lord C, Briskman J, Lukito S, et al. Trajectories in symptoms of autism and cognitive ability in autism from childhood to adult life: Findings From a Longitudinal Epidemiological Cohort. Journal of the American Academy of Child and Adolescent Psychiatry. 2020;**59**(12):1342-1352

[20] Szatmari P, Georgiades S, Duku E, Bennett TA, Bryson S, Fombonne E, et al. Developmental trajectories of symptom severity and adaptive functioning in an inception cohort of preschool children with autism spectrum disorder. JAMA Psychiatry. 2015;**72**(3):276

[21] Klintwall L, Eldevik S, Eikeseth S. Narrowing the gap: Effects of intervention on developmental trajectories in autism. Autism. 2015;**19**(1):53-63

[22] Venker CE, Eernisse ER, Saffran JR, Weismer SE. Individual differences in the real-time comprehension of children with ASD: Real-time comprehension in children with ASD. Autism Research. 2013;**6**(5):417-432

[23] Factor RS, Ollendick TH, Cooper LD, Dunsmore JC, Rea HM, Scarpa A. All in the family: A systematic review of the effect of caregiver-administered autism spectrum disorder interventions on family functioning and relationships. Clinical Child and Family Psychology Review. 2019;**22**(4):433-457

[24] Vasilopoulou E, Nisbet J. The quality of life of parents of children with autism spectrum disorder: A systematic review. Research in Autism Spectrum Disorder. 2016;**23**:36-49

[25] Due C, Goodwin Smith I, Allen P, Button E, Cheek C, Quarmby L, et al. A pilot study of social inclusion and quality of life for parents of children with autism spectrum disorder. Journal of Intellectual & Developmental Disability. 2018;**43**(1):73-82

[26] Ji B, Sun M, Yi R, Tang S. Multidisciplinary parent education for caregivers of children with autism spectrum disorders. Archives of Psychiatric Nursing. 2014;**28**(5):319-326

[27] Venuti P. Intervento e riabilitazione nei disturbi dello spettro autistico. Roma: Carocci Editore; 2012

[28] Venuti P, Bentenuto A. Studi di caso—Disturbi Dello Spettro Autistico. Trento, Italy: Erickson; 2017

[29] Dawson G, Rogers S, Munson J, Smith M, Winter J, Greenson J, et al. Randomized, controlled trial of an intervention for toddlers with autism: The Early Start Denver Model. Pediatrics. 2010;**125**(1):e17-e23

[30] Rogers SJ, Vismara LA. Evidence-based comprehensive treatments for early autism. Journal of Clinical Child and Adolescent Psychology. 2008;**37**(1):8-38

[31] Ben-Itzchak E, Watson LR, Zachor DA. Cognitive ability is associated with different outcome trajectories in autism spectrum disorders. Journal of Autism and Developmental Disorders. 2014;**44**(9):2221-2229

[32] Ospina MB, Krebs Seida J, Clark B, Karkhaneh M, Hartling L, Tjosvold L, et al. Behavioural and developmental interventions for autism spectrum disorder: A clinical systematic review. PLoS ONE. 2008;**3**(11):e3755

[33] Smith T, Iadarola S. Evidence base update for autism spectrum disorder. Journal of Clinical Child and Adolescent Psychology. 2015;**44**(6):897-922

[34] Nahmias AS, Pellecchia M, Stahmer AC, Mandell DS. Effectiveness of community-based early intervention for children with autism spectrum disorder: A meta-analysis. Journal of Child Psychology and Psychiatry. 2019;**60**(11):1200-1209

[35] Siller M, Hutman T, Sigman M. A parent-mediated intervention to increase responsive parental behaviors and child communication in children with ASD: A Randomized Clinical Trial. Journal of Autism and Developmental Disorders. 2013;**43**(3):540-555

[36] MacDonald R, Parry-Cruwys D, Dupere S, Ahearn W. Assessing progress and outcome of early intensive behavioral intervention for toddlers with autism. Research in Developmental Disabilities. 2014;**35**(12):3632-3644

[37] French L, Kennedy EMM. Annual research review: Early intervention for infants and young children with, or at-risk of, autism spectrum disorder: A systematic review. Journal of Child Psychology and Psychiatry. 2018;**59**(4):444-456

[38] Sandbank M, Bottema-Beutel K, Crowley S, Cassidy M, Dunham K, Feldman JI, et al. Project AIM: Autism intervention meta-analysis for studies of young children. Psychological Bulletin. 2020;**146**(1):1-29

[39] Wetherby AM, Woods J, Guthrie W, Delehanty A, Brown JA, Morgan L, et al. Changing developmental trajectories of toddlers with autism spectrum disorder: Strategies for bridging research to community practice. Journal of Speech, Language, and Hearing Research. 2018;**61**(11):2615-2628

[40] Shumway S, Farmer C, Thurm A, Joseph L, Black D, Golden C. The ADOS calibrated severity score: Relationship to phenotypic variables and stability over time: ADOS severity score. Autism Research. 2012;**5**(4):267-276

[41] Schreibman L, Dawson G, Stahmer AC, Landa R, Rogers SJ, McGee GG, et al. Naturalistic developmental behavioral interventions: Empirically validated treatments for autism spectrum disorder. Journal of Autism and Developmental Disorders. 2015;**45**(8):2411-2428

[42] Vismara LA, Young GS, Stahmer AC, Griffith EM, Rogers SJ. Dissemination of evidence-based practice: Can we train

therapists from a distance? Journal of Autism and Developmental Disorders. 2009;**39**(12):1636-1651

[43] Blacher J, Baker BL, Kaladjian A. Syndrome specificity and mother–child interactions: Examining positive and negative parenting across contexts and time. Journal of Autism and Developmental Disorders. 2013;**43**(4):761-774

[44] Freeman S, Kasari C. Parent–child interactions in autism: Characteristics of play. Autism. 2013;**17**(2):147-161

[45] Bretherton I. Emotional availability: An attachment perspective. Attachment & Human Development. 2000;**2**(2):233-241

[46] Wong C, Kasari C. Play and joint attention of children with autism in the preschool special education classroom. Journal of Autism and Developmental Disorders. 2012;**42**(10):2152-2161

[47] Haebig E, McDuffie A, Ellis WS. Brief report: Parent verbal responsiveness and language development in toddlers on the autism spectrum. Journal of Autism and Developmental Disorders. 2013;**43**(9):2218-2227

[48] Bottema-Beutel K, Park H, Kim SY. Commentary on social skills training curricula for individuals with ASD: Social interaction, authenticity, and stigma. Journal of Autism and Developmental Disorders. 2018;**48**(3):953-964

Chapter 15

What Therapy for My Child? Features, Strengths, and Gaps to Fill for the Implementation of Early Autism Interventions

Giulia Purpura and Annarita Contaldo

Abstract

Scientific literature suggests the neurobiological value of early intervention for children at risk of ASD and of other neurodevelopmental disorders, because it is based on the promotion of brain plasticity mechanisms in an ecological, noninvasive, and evidence-based way. Moreover, several authors suggest the greatest efficacy of early rehabilitation programs, involving both the parents and the children, is to improve not only sensory-motor and cognitive outcomes but also child-parent interactions and the wellness of the familiar system. In this chapter, the neurobiological fundaments and features for the early intervention and the most recent early approaches for children at risk of ASD (behavioral, developmental, naturalistic developmental behavioral, and parent-mediated interventions) will be explained.

Keywords: autism spectrum disorder, early intervention, behavioral interventions, developmental interventions, naturalistic developmental behavioral interventions, parent-mediated interventions

1. Introduction

During the last two decades, new findings and data about neurobiological features, clinical characteristics, and impact on quality of life of autism spectrum disorder (ASD) were incredibly bloomed and these new pieces of knowledge also influenced the idea of taking charge and rehabilitation of children, adolescents, and adults with ASD. Moreover, the biopsychosocial ICF-CY perspective contributed to a change of view on this topic because it was demonstrated as this perspective can efficiently capture functional abilities and disabilities in developing individuals for tailored intervention planning [1].

About this, Palisano and colleagues [2] marked the importance of considering the health of individuals with childhood-onset neurodevelopmental conditions as an emergent set of capacities that develop over a lifetime to enable them to interact successfully within their biological, physiological, psychological, and social environments and realize their potential and well-being. According to these authors, rehabilitation

IntechOpen

programs must take into consideration that health development is a nonlinear adaptive process. It occurs through person-environment transactions that can be transformative in enabling individuals with neurodevelopmental conditions to actively participate in their social environment. In this way, every different period of life can contribute in different ways to the construction of a developmental trajectory, in line with the needs, priorities, concerns, opportunities, and experiences of the individual with a disability and his/her family in order to reach desired social roles [2, 3].

Obviously, the first periods of life are particularly important and difficult in this process; parents must cope with a series of unforeseen stresses and readapt their life on the basis of ASD, from the diagnosis to the choice of the rehabilitation program. If on one hand, the great growth of pieces of knowledge allowed a big improvement of early and specific approaches for children at risk of ASD, on the other hand, the parents are often confused and isolated in the understanding of what is the best type of intervention for their child.

As a matter of fact, the presence of high levels of stress in parents of children with ASD was widely demonstrated [4, 5], and also for these reasons early interventions could have the potential value, as well as exploiting the greater predisposition to modify itself of the brain during developmental age, also of ensuring parents have the resources they need to manage stress associated with caring for their child.

The developmental process occurring in the human brain during fetal life and during early childhood is the result of an intricate continuous interaction between genes and environment, activity, and experiences [6]. In particular, in early childhood, individuals go through the most complex, dramatic, and important phases of maturation, although brain changes and adaptation are part of a long-lasting process that continues throughout the whole life [7]. During this stage of neurodevelopment, cognitive and social behaviors cannot be understood in isolation, but their development is strictly interlinked to sensory-motor systems and motives and opportunities of the child in their environment [8]. So, in line with these points, in this chapter, the neurobiological fundaments and features for the early intervention and the most recent early approaches for children at risk of ASD will be explained.

2. Neurobiology of early intervention in ASD

The term "early intervention" includes all measures aimed at preventing developmental disabilities, ensuring neuroprotection, and providing optimal environmental conditions [9].

Their implementation is strongly related to the concept of neural plasticity which is a fundamental property of the central nervous system (CNS) and denotes several capacities including the ability to adapt to changes in the environment and to store information in memory associated with learning [10]. For this reason, experience-dependent neural plasticity is increased in the developing brain than in the adult brain, and it is usually adaptive and beneficial for permitting neurodevelopment during fetal life and during the first three postnatal years. Some of its basic mechanisms (for example, neurogenesis, programmed cell death, myelinations, and others), although started before birth, continue to be very high in the first-year post-term [6]. Moreover, it was widely demonstrated that specific time windows, named critical periods, are present and staggered throughout the first years of postnatal life for the most important brain functions (for sensory systems, motor development, language, and higher cognitive functions), and, in these periods, the corresponding neural circuits display a heightened sensitivity to acquire instructive and adaptive signals from the external environment for its maturation [11].

The effect of sensory experience on brain sensitivity is addressed by numerous researchers in understanding how to maximize the extraordinary potential of brain plasticity in neurorehabilitation for possible restorations in presence of brain dysfunctions. Since this, refinement and maintenance of appropriate neural connections have been made possible in laboratory by paradigms specifically devoted to increasing the quality and intensity of environmental stimulation, such as environmental enrichment (EE). EE is "a combination of complex inanimate and social stimulations", and its main goal is to improve the animal's quality of life by providing them with a combination of multisensory/cognitive stimulation, increased physical activity, and enhanced social interactions and by eliciting natural explorative behaviors [12].

The possibility of modifying neural circuitry through environmental experiences suggested the idea of taking advantage of the EE in several conditions: the benefits of EE on synaptic plasticity, sensory development, and cognitive processes have been investigated in developing, adult, and aging animals and at a later stage in animals with several neurologic and genetic disorders [13–16]. In many cases, EE enhanced brain weight, neurogenesis, dendritic branching, synapse formation, and neuroanatomical components, with consequent changes also in behavior and learning [17].

These findings were very important for the field of pediatric neurorehabilitation because the EE paradigm is ecological, noninvasive, and well thought-out to enhance the neuroplasticity through experience, and for this reason, several research groups investigated and demonstrated the profound and positive effect of intensive and multisensory stimulation during early stages of life on the human brain [18].

For example, some authors suggested the effect of early multisensory stimulation on visual development of infants at risk of developmental disorders [19–21], and Pineda and collaborators also underlined the presence of a growing body of evidence supporting the use of early sensory interventions in the neonatal intensive care units, which can be safe and potentially important for optimizing infant and parent outcomes [22].

More recently, this line of research is expanding in order to understand if this type of early approach can have effects on social abilities and also, in this case, results appear very promising. In animal models, profound and long-term beneficial effects of early social environmental stimulation were found, encouraging the use of non-pharmacological interventions for the treatment of social defects in neurodevelopmental diseases [23–25].

Consequently, all these findings inspired the development of new protocols for children at risk of ASD, in which sensory-motor and social impairments are the most distinguishable symptoms in early stages: for example, recently Whittingham and colleagues [26] published the ENACT protocol (ENvironmental enrichment for infants; parenting with Acceptance and Commitment Therapy), which is the first randomized controlled trial to test a very early intervention for infants at risk of ASD (infants with one or more biological siblings or a biological parent diagnosed with ASD). It is implemented within the first six months of life and structured by a combination of parent-mediated very early intervention with parental mental health support.

In conclusion, it is widely supported by neurobiological and behavioral findings, the positive value of early intervention for children at risk of ASD and of other neurodevelopmental disorders. For these reasons, several evidence-based models were developed and implemented in the last twenty years.

3. Contemporary approaches for young children at risk of ASD

Taken as a whole, these data highlight the importance of early intervention in the rehabilitation process of children with neurodevelopmental disorders, although several questions remain open regarding some characteristics, such as intensity, focus, setting, and participants.

From a metanalysis of Fuller and Kaiser [27] emerges that the mean study age (of analyzed manuscripts) was associated with treatment effect size on social communication outcomes and that optimal social communication outcomes were observed when the mean age of the participants was 3.8 years, with positive effects diminishing somewhat after that age. However, clinical and experimental findings suggest that to be maximally effective, early intervention must be intensive, active, and tailored for each individual and family-centered [17].

Already Bonnier [9] underlined the greatest efficacy of programs involving both the parents and the children, to improve not only cognitive outcomes but also child-parent interactions. Moreover, an important point to consider is the fact that the families are now well informed, in particular thanks to Internet and social networks, and they know earlier about the risk of neurodevelopmental disabilities; this, on one hand, is an important aspect for a good success of the prevention and early detection programs, on the other hand, it could increase anxiety level of the parents, especially of children at risk of ASD. As a matter of fact, raising children with ASD can have a profound impact on caregivers, who, if guided by professionals, can benefit from strengths-based, future-focused supports early in their parenting experience [28].

According to Zwaigenbaum and collaborators, the central role of parents has been emphasized in the context of intervention of young children with or at risk of ASD: interventions could be designed to incorporate learning opportunities into everyday activities, capitalize on "teachable moments," and facilitate the generalization of skills beyond the familiar home setting [29].

Rehabilitation, therefore, must be individualized to not only the infant and his/her brain dysfunctions but also to the family circumstances, and it should provide support to parents, on account of their fundamental role in child's development. To this end, Novak and Morgan [30] recently suggested the "key drivers of plasticity and learning" in context of early intervention for children at risk of neurodevelopmental disabilities (see **Figure 1**): (1) training-based interventions harnessing experience-dependent plasticity, which means using interventions that specifically train an infant to perform a skill; (2) environmental enrichment that includes toys and exercise equipment to promote voluntary, self-initiated actions and learning and motivating but a repetitive challenge in an ecological context; (3) parent-child interactions, for promoting parent-child bonding, responsive parenting and the wellness of the familiar system.

Based on these requirements, the main approaches currently used in the context of early intervention for children at risk for ASD are described below.

3.1 Behavioral interventions

Behavioral interventions were among the first developed and clinically tested approaches for improving outcomes for ASD children and are based on operant learning [31]. They are characterized by discrete stimulus presentation, prompted exhibition of the desired response, and provision of positive feedback [6]. Although this type of

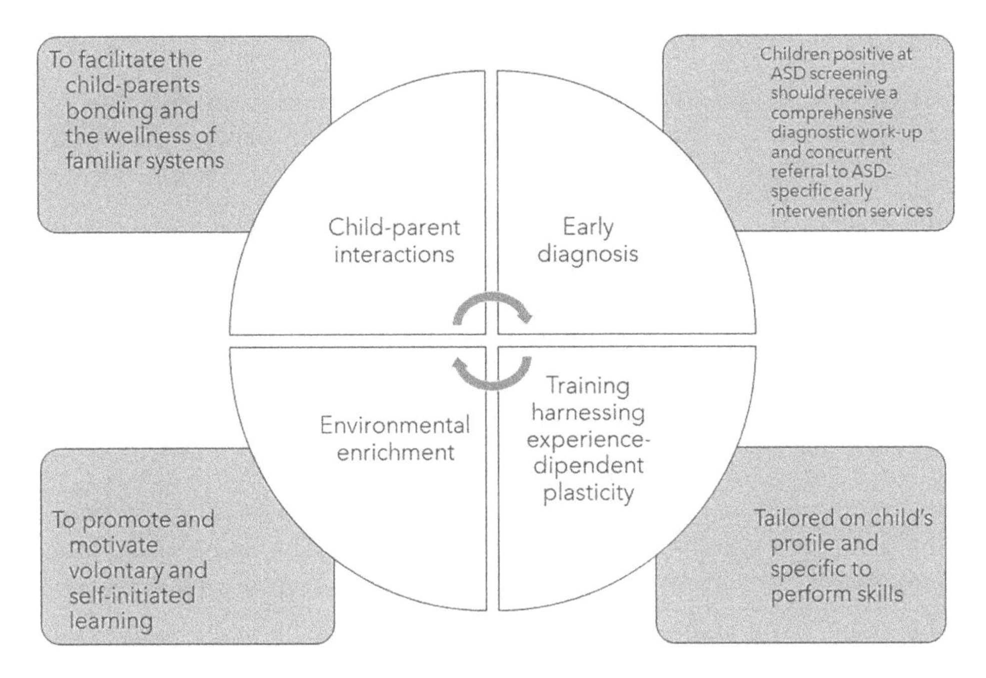

Figure 1.
Graphic representation of main elements for the implementation of early intervention, according to Novack and Morgan [30].

intervention is profoundly changed in comparison with the first models of the years '60 and '70, also now behavioral approaches maintain some fundamental characteristics, in particular, the high intensity of the hours of therapy and the use of reinforcement to increase skills and reduce "autistic behaviors". The most commonly used behavioral program that provides direct intensive service to young children with ASD and their families is the "Early Intensive Behavioral Intervention" (EIBI), implemented under the supervision of personnel trained in applied behavior analysis (ABA) procedures [32]. EIBI uses a specific teaching procedure with a 1:1 adult-to-child ratio and the implementation in either home or school settings for a range of 20 to 40 hours per week, with children from one to four years old. In this model, the analysis of functional behavior is used to develop individualized intervention targets where complex behaviors are broken down into specific steps and reinforced to gradually approximate the desired behavior and ultimately enhance learning [33, 34].

In 2018, a Cochrane Systematic Review focused on the evidence of the effectiveness of EIBI in increasing functional behaviors and skills, decreasing autism severity, and improving intelligence and communication skills for young children with ASD [35]. The evidence supports the use of EIBI for some children with ASD, especially with discrete effects on the adaptive behavior, cognitive functions, and language. No evidence was found about the improvement of autism severity or problem behaviors. However, the authors suggested interpreting the results with caution since the quality of the evidence of these studies is low and the methodological rigor remains a weak point, above all for the small sample size in the studies analyzed and for the use of non-randomized research designs [35]. So further research is necessary to estimate the effect of this rehabilitative approach.

3.2 Developmental interventions

Developmental interventions are based on the idea that emotional development plays a key role in areas such as language, cognition, visuo-spatial processing, and motor development. For this reason, these interventions focus on improving the synchrony, reciprocity, and duration of parent-child or child-child interactions as a pathway for ameliorating deficits in social communication and generating cascading improvements in developmentally related skills. These approaches are primarily delivered in the context of everyday routines such as play, and intervention goals are chosen based on the typical sequences of social communication and language development [31].

In this context, certainly "Developmental, Individual-differences, Relationship based (DIR) Floortime Model" is the most known. DIR was developed by Greenspan and Wieder for children between two and 12 years [36]. It aims in the first instance on affection and, according to this model, the parental engagement is an essential element for child improvement [37]. During the implementation of model, the use of "floor-based play" technique with the child addresses the main purpose of the intervention; floortime sessions are guided by the child, focusing on pretend play and conversation, and the intervention is tailored to the child's specific needs in addition to an individualized and strength-based program for the child [38].

Although some high-quality studies suggest that developmental-based interventions can improve some core challenges associated with ASD, particularly difficulties in social communication [31], both DIR model and the other developmental models were not specifically implemented for young children, and this point could be considered a limitation. For this reason, Solomon and collaborators implemented the "Play and Language for Autistic Youngsters (PLAY) Project Home Consultation program", based on DIR model by Greenspan and Wieder, but specific for young children ages three to five years old with ASD [39]. These authors, by a randomized controlled trial (RCT), demonstrated positive effects of this model on parent's abilities to sensitively respond and effectively engage their child, on shared attention and initiation of ASD children during play, and on improvement of autism symptomatology.

3.3 Naturalistic developmental behavioral interventions

Recently, the increasing of naturalistic developmental behavioral interventions (NDBIs), rooted in both applied behavioral and developmental sciences, has become imponent. NDBIs use natural environments, behavioral strategies, and personal interests to motivate the child and teach developmentally appropriate skills. Moreover, these models utilize several techniques for exploiting all possible opportunities for learning for the child and employ individualized treatment goals; they focus on child-initiated teaching episodes, capitalize on natural reinforcement and child motivation, and can include adult imitation of the child [40]. In NDBIs, reciprocal imitation is considered a useful strategy to promote social engagement in children with ASD, particularly in children with low developmental levels [41].

Examples of early intervention based on this approach are "Pivotal Response Treatment" (PRT) for children between two and seven years [42–44], "Early Start Denver Model" (ESDM) from 12 months to 48 months of life [45, 46], "Joint Attention Symbolic Play, Engagement Regulation" (JASPER) for children between one and eight years [47, 48], and "Reciprocal Imitation Training" (RIT) recently implemented also for toddlers from birth to three years [49].

Some NDBIs are focused interventions designed to address a specific and crucial behavioral area, others are comprehensive interventions that target the entire range of developmental domains, including cognition, social abilities, language, play, and motor systems, considering both abilities in emergency and vulnerabilities of children. Skills are usually not taught discretely or in isolation, but rather in the course of the child's typical daily interactions, experiences, and routines, with multiple materials and by multiple people [50]. Through these early intervention models, it is occurring as a shift of the main goal away from the reduction of core autistic traits and toward the improvement of well-being and optimization of individual potential [40].

Sandbanck and collaborators in a recent review [31] highlighted the presence of several RCTs in support of NDBIs. These studies suggest that NDBIs may be not only particularly useful for supporting development of social communication, language, and play but also for reduction of caregiver stress and for improvement of parental abilities.

3.4 Parent-mediated interventions

Parental involvement is good early treatment practice for ASD because it is one of the factors associated with a better outcome for children, but this type of approach may also support family outcomes, including parent-child interactions and caregiver empowerment [51]. In parent-mediated interventions, parents are taught a combination of techniques to promote the child's social engagement, language, imitation, and play skills. Parents are also trained to become more responsive to the children's communication style and needs, with an effect also in emotional regulation [52].

Many of the early interventions explained above, both NDBI types, such as ESDM and JASPER, and development-based, such as DIR and PLAY models, despite being implemented through direct contact with the child, involve the parent in the session. As a matter of fact, several studies about this type of interventions showed many effects both in children and parent outcomes [39, 53–56].

Moreover, in 2013, a Cochrane systematic review found some evidence for effectiveness of parent-mediated interventions for young children with ASD, most particularly in proximal indicators within parent-child interaction but also in more distal indicators of child language comprehension and reduction of autism severity [51].

In this context, there are also models involving exclusively the work with the parents and in which the aim of the intervention is first to increase parental sensitivity and responsiveness to child communication, to reduce mistimed responses, and to promote new strategies in them, with a secondary increment of the child's communication. These parent-mediated interventions utilize techniques such as modeling and video-feedback; some examples are the "PArent-mediated Communication-focused Treatment in children with autism" (PACT), for parents of ASD children from two to eight years [57], and a model implemented in "British Autism Study of Infant Siblings, based on Video Interaction for Promoting Positive Parenting program" (iBASIS-VIPP), for parents of children with an age range of 7–12 months of life [58]. Studies about these two types of models found a clear benefit for parent-child dyadic social communication, an improvement of attention of the infant to parent, and of adaptive behavior.

4. Future directions

The new pieces of knowledge about brain functions and dysfunctions have profoundly changed the methods of detection, diagnosis, and intervention of neurodevelopmental disorders, such as the ASD. Moreover, the available evidence suggests that skills improve when they are practiced intensively in a playful daily caregiving setting, in which families must have an active role in the promotion of the health of their child [6].

It is also true that research in this field is complex and continually ongoing, also because manifestations of ASD, outcome measures, and contexts may be extremely heterogeneous. Although data about early intervention are promising, especially for daily living and sensory-motor skills of these children, the results must be considered with caution, for this great variability of measures, subjects, and types of intervention [59]. Certainly, it is widely recognized that greater implementation of RCTs in this field of rehabilitation is needed to provide better indications to professionals and parents.

However, as suggested by Vivanti [60], the concept of "evidence-based" is multifaceted, especially in the field of ASD, and *"being able and willing to keep up with the evidence requires an appreciation that the evidence base in the field reflects a provisional state of affairs, rather than an unmodifiable truth".*

Maybe, parents and professionals should understand that it does not exist a perfect and effective intervention for all children, but the choice can depend on a lot of variables, such as the symptoms' severity, the age of child, the presence of co-occurring disorders, the environmental factors, the learning opportunity and the environmental adversities, and others. However, a relevant intervention target should be to avoid the "normalization of the autistic behavior", and rather take into consideration the well-being of individuals and their families, respecting their neurodiversity, but at the same time, trying to optimize the individual potential and the reach of the desired role within the society [40].

Conflict of interest

The authors declare no conflict of interest.

Author details

Giulia Purpura[1*] and Annarita Contaldo[2]

1 School of Medicine and Surgery, University of Milano Bicocca, Monza, Italy

2 Department of Developmental Neuroscience, IRCCS Fondazione Stella Maris, Pisa, Italy

*Address all correspondence to: giulia.purpura@unimib.it

References

[1] de Schipper E et al. Ability and disability in autism spectrum disorder: A systematic literature review employing the international classification of functioning, disability and health-children and youth version. Autism Research. 2015;**8**(6):782-794. DOI: 10.1002/aur.1485

[2] Palisano RJ et al. Life course health development of individuals with neurodevelopmental conditions. Developmental Medicine and Child Neurology. 2017;**59**(5):470-476. DOI: 10.1111/dmcn.13402

[3] Palisano RJ et al. Promoting capacities for future adult roles and healthy living using a lifecourse health development approach. Disability and Rehabilitation. 2020;**42**(14):2002-2011. DOI: 10.1080/09638288.2018.1544670

[4] Baykal S, Karakurt MN, Çakır M, Karabekiroğlu K. An examination of the relations between symptom distributions in children diagnosed with autism and caregiver burden, anxiety and depression levels. Community Mental Health Journal. 2019;**55**(2):311-317. DOI: 10.1007/s10597-018-0343-8

[5] Purpura G, Tagliabue L, Petri S, Cerroni F, Mazzarini A, Nacinovich R. Caregivers' burden of school-aged children with neurodevelopmental disorders: Implications for family-centred care. Brain Sciences. 2021;**11**(7):1-12. DOI: 10.3390/brainsci11070875

[6] Hadders-Algra M. Early diagnostics and early intervention in neurodevelopmental disorders—age-dependent challenges and opportunities. Journal of Clinical Medicine. 2021;**10**(4):1-24. DOI: 10.3390/jcm10040861

[7] Cioni G, Sgandurra G. Normal psychomotor development. Handbook of Clinical Neurology. 2013;**111**:3-15. DOI: 10.1016/B978-0-444-52891-9.00001-4. PMID: 23622146

[8] Von Hofsten C. Action in development. Developmental Science. 2007;**10**(1):54-60. DOI: 10.1111/j.1467-7687.2007.00564.x

[9] Bonnier C. Evaluation of early stimulation programs for enhancing brain development. Acta Paediatric International Journal of Paediatry. 2008;**97**(7):853-858. DOI: 10.1111/j.1651-2227.2008.00834.x

[10] Johnston MV. Plasticity in the developing brain: Implications for rehabilitation. Developmental Disabilities Research Reviews. 2009;**15**(2):94-101. DOI: 10.1002/ddrr.64

[11] Hensch TK, Bilimoria PM. Re-opening windows: Manipulating critical periods for brain development. Cerebrum. 2012;**2012**:11. Available: http://www.ncbi.nlm.nih.gov/pubmed/23447797%0Ahttp://www.pubmedcentral.nih.gov/articlerender.fcgi?artid=PMC3574806

[12] Baroncelli L, Braschi C, Spolidoro M, Begenisic T, Sale A, Maffei L. Nurturing brain plasticity: Impact of environmental enrichment. Cell Death and Differentiation. 2010;**17**(7):1092-1103. DOI: 10.1038/cdd.2009.193

[13] Cancedda L, Putignano E, Sale A, Viegi A, Berardi N, Maffei L. Acceleration of visual system development by environmental enrichment. The Journal of Neuroscience. 2004;**24**(20):4840-4848. DOI: 10.1523/JNEUROSCI.0845-04.2004

[14] Fischer FR, Peduzzi JD. Functional recovery in rats with chronic spinal cord injuries after exposure to an enriched environment. The Journal of Spinal Cord Medicine. 2007;**30**(2):147-155. DOI: 10.1080/10790268.2007.11753926

[15] Polito L et al. Environmental enrichment lessens cognitive decline in APP23 mice without affecting brain sirtuin expression. Journal of Alzheimer's Disease. 2014;**42**(3):851-864

[16] Begenisic T et al. Environmental enrichment decreases gabaergic inhibition and improves cognitive abilities, synaptic plasticity and visual functions in a mouse model of down syndrome. Frontiers in Cellular Neuroscience. 2011;**5**(December):1-22. DOI: 10.3389/fncel.2011.00029

[17] Cioni G, Inguaggiato E, Sgandurra G. Early intervention in neurodevelopmental disorders: Underlying neural mechanisms. Developmental Medicine and Child Neurology. 2016;**58**:61-66. DOI: 10.1111/dmcn.13050

[18] Purpura G, Cioni G, Tinelli F. Multisensory-based rehabilitation approach: Translational insights from animal models to early intervention. Frontiers in Neuroscience. 2017;**11**:430. DOI: 10.3389/fnins.2017.00430

[19] Guzzetta A et al. Massage accelerates brain development and the maturation of visual function. The Journal of Neuroscience. 2009;**29**(18):6042-6051. DOI: 10.1523/JNEUROSCI.5548-08.2009

[20] Purpura G, Tinelli F, Bargagna S, Bozza M, Bastiani L, Cioni G. Effect of early multisensory massage intervention on visual functions in infants with Down syndrome. Early Human Development. 2014;**90**(12):809-813. DOI: 10.1016/j.earlhumdev.2014.08.016

[21] Fontana C et al. Effects of early intervention on visual function in preterm infants: A Randomized Controlled Trial. Frontiers in Pediatrics. 2020;**8**(June):1-9. DOI: 10.3389/fped.2020.00291

[22] Pineda R, Guth R, Herring A, Reynolds L, Oberle S, Smith J. Enhancing sensory experiences for very preterm infants in the NICU: An integrative review. Journal of Perinatology. 2017;**37**(4):323-332. DOI: 10.1038/jp.2016.179

[23] Oddi D et al. Early social enrichment rescues adult behavioral and brain abnormalities in a Mouse Model of Fragile X Syndrome. Neuropsychopharmacology. 2015;**40**:1113-1122. DOI: 10.1038/npp.2014.291

[24] Garbugino L, Centofante E, D'Amato FR. Early social enrichment improves social motivation and skills in a monogenic mouse model of autism, the Oprm1 -/- Mouse. Neural Plasticity. 2016;**2016**:1-11. DOI: 10.1155/2016/5346161

[25] Chen YS et al. Early environmental enrichment for autism spectrum disorder Fmr1 mice models has positive behavioral and molecular effects. Experimental Neurology. 2022;**352**:114033. DOI: 10.1016/j.expneurol.2022.114033

[26] Whittingham K, McGlade A, Kulasinghe K, Mitchell AE, Heussler H, Boyd RN. ENACT (ENvironmental enrichment for infants; Parenting with Acceptance and Commitment Therapy): A randomised controlled trial of an innovative intervention for infants at risk of autism spectrum disorder. BMJ Open. 2020;**10**(8):1-10. DOI: 10.1136/bmjopen-2019-034315

[27] Fuller EA, Kaiser AP. The effects of early intervention on social

communication outcomes for children with autism spectrum disorder: A meta-analysis. Journal of Autism and Developmental Disorders. 2020;**50**(5):1683-1700. DOI: 10.1007/s10803-019-03927-z

[28] Miller L et al. Impact of 'early intervention' parent workshops on outcomes for caregivers of children with neurodisabilities: A mixed-methods study. Disability and Rehabilitation. 2022;**20**:1-12. DOI: 10.1080/09638288.2022.2143579

[29] Zwaigenbaum L et al. Early intervention for children with autism spectrum disorder under three years of age: Recommendations for practice and research. Pediatric Collective Autism and Spectoral Disorders. 2021;**2021**:269-290. DOI: 10.1542/9781610024716-part06-ch023

[30] Novak I, Morgan C. High-risk follow-up: Early intervention and rehabilitation. Handbook of Clinical Neurology. 2019;**162**:483-510. DOI: 10.1016/B978-0-444-64029-1.00023-0. PMID: 31324326

[31] Sandbank M et al. Project AIM: Autism intervention meta-analysis for studies of young children. Psychological Bulletin. 2020;**146**(1):1-29. DOI: 10.1037/bul0000215

[32] MacDonald R, Parry-Cruwys D, Dupere S, Ahearn W. Assessing progress and outcome of early intensive behavioral intervention for toddlers with autism. Research in Developmental Disabilities. 2014;**35**(12):3632-3644. DOI: 10.1016/j.ridd.2014.08.036

[33] Howard JS, Sparkman CR, Cohen HG, Green G, Stanislaw H. A comparison of intensive behavior analytic and eclectic treatments for young children with autism. Research in Developmental Disabilities. 2005;**26**(4):359-383. DOI: 10.1016/j.ridd.2004.09.005

[34] Frazier TW, Klingemier EW, AndersonCJ, GengouxGW, YoungstromEA, Hardan AY. A longitudinal study of language trajectories and treatment outcomes of early intensive behavioral intervention for autism. Journal of Autism and Developmental Disorders. 2021;**51**(12):4534-4550. DOI: 10.1007/s10803-021-04900-5

[35] Reichow B, Hume K, Barton EE, Boyd BA. Early intensive behavioral intervention (EIBI) for young children with autism spectrum disorders (ASD). Cochrane Database of Systematic Reviews. 2018;**5**:2018. DOI: 10.1002/14651858.CD009260.pub3

[36] Greenspan SI, Wieder S. A functional developmental approach to autism spectrum disorders. Journal of Association Persistant with Handicap. 1999;**24**(3):147-161. DOI: 10.2511/rpsd.24.3.147

[37] Praphatthanakunwong N, Kiatrungrit K, Hongsanguansri S, Nopmaneejumruslers K. Factors associated with parent engagement in DIR/Floortime for treatment of children with autism spectrum disorder. Genetic Psychiatry. 2018;**31**(2):1-9. DOI: 10.1136/gpsych-2018-000009

[38] Boshoff K et al. Child development outcomes of DIR/floortime TM-based programs: A systematic review. Canadian Journal of Occupational Therapy. 2020;**87**(2):153-164. DOI: 10.1177/0008417419899224

[39] Solomon R, Van Egeren LA, Mahoney G, Quon Huber P, Zimmerman MS. PLAY project home consultation intervention program for young children with autism spectrum

disorders: A Randomized Controlled Trial. Journal of Developmental and Behavioral Pediatrics. 2014;**35**(8):475-485. DOI: 10.1097/DBP.0000000000000096

[40] Schuck RK et al. Neurodiversity and autism intervention: Reconciling perspectives through a naturalistic developmental behavioral intervention framework. Journal of Autism and Developmental Disorders. 2022;**52**(10):4625-4645. DOI: 10.1007/s10803-021-05316-x

[41] Contaldo A, Colombi C, Narzisi A, Muratori F. The social effect of 'being imitated' in children with autism spectrum disorder. Frontiers in Psychology. 2016;**7**(MAY):726. DOI: 10.3389/fpsyg.2016.00726

[42] Gengoux GW et al. A pivotal response treatment package for children with autism spectrum disorder: An RCT. Pediatrics. 2019;**144**(3):1-10. DOI: 10.1542/peds.2019-0178

[43] Duifhuis EA, den Boer JC, Doornbos A, Buitelaar JK, Oosterling IJ, Klip H. The effect of pivotal response treatment in children with autism spectrum disorders: A non-randomized study with a blinded outcome measure. Journal of Autism and Developmental Disorders. 2017;**47**(2):231-242. DOI: 10.1007/s10803-016-2916-0

[44] Koegel RL, Bradshaw JL, Ashbaugh K, Koegel LK. Improving question-asking initiations in young children with autism using pivotal response treatment. Journal of Autism and Developmental Disorders. 2014;**44**(4):816-827. DOI: 10.1007/s10803-013-1932-6

[45] Dawson G et al. Randomized, controlled trials of an intervention for toddlers with autism: The Early Start Denver Model. Pediatrics. 2010;**125**(1):e17-e23. DOI: 10.1542/peds.2009-0958

[46] Vivanti G, Dissanayake C. Outcome for children receiving the early start denver model before and after 48 months. Journal of Autism and Developmental Disorders. 2016;**46**(7):2441-2449. DOI: 10.1007/s10803-016-2777-6

[47] Chang YC, Shire SY, Shih W, Gelfand C, Kasari C. Preschool deployment of evidence-based social communication intervention: JASPER in the Classroom. Journal of Autism and Developmental Disorders. 2016;**46**(6):2211-2223. DOI: 10.1007/s10803-016-2752-2

[48] Waddington H, Reynolds JE, Macaskill E, Curtis S, Taylor LJ, Whitehouse AJO. The effects of JASPER intervention for children with autism spectrum disorder: A systematic review. Autism. 2021;**25**(8):2370-2385. DOI: 10.1177/13623613211019162

[49] Ibañez LV, Scott S, Stone WL. The implementation of reciprocal imitation training in a Part C early intervention setting: A stepped-wedge pragmatic trial. Autism Research. 2021;**14**(8):1777-1788. DOI: 10.1002/aur.2522

[50] Schreibman L et al. Naturalistic developmental behavioral interventions: Empirically validated treatments for autism spectrum disorder. Journal of Autism and Developmental Disorders. 2015;**45**(8):2411-2428. DOI: 10.1007/s10803-015-2407-8

[51] Diggle TTJ, Mcconachie H. Parent-mediated early intervention for young children with autism spectrum disorder. Cochrane Database of Systematic Reviews. 2013;**4**:2013. DOI: 10.1002/14651858.CD003496.pub2

[52] Hendrix NM, Pickard KE, Binion GE, Kushner E. A systematic review of emotion regulation in parent-mediated interventions for autism spectrum disorder. Frontiers in Psychiatry. 2022;**13**(1):2118. DOI: 10.3389/fpsyt.2022.846286

[53] Rogers SJ et al. Enhancing low-intensity coaching in parent implemented early start denver model intervention for early autism: A Randomized Comparison Treatment Trial. Journal of Autism and Developmental Disorders. 2019;**49**(2):632-646. DOI: 10.1007/s10803-018-3740-5

[54] Abouzeid N, Rivard M, Mello C, Mestari Z, Boulé M, Guay C. Parent coaching intervention program based on the Early Start Denver Model for children with autism spectrum disorder: Feasibility and acceptability study. Research in Developmental Disabilities. 2020;**105**:103747. DOI: 10.1016/j.ridd.2020.103747

[55] Harrop C, Gulsrud A, Shih W, Hovsepyan L, Kasari C. The impact of caregiver-mediated JASPER on child restricted and repetitive behaviors and caregiver responses. Autism Research. 2017;**10**(5):983-992. DOI: 10.1002/aur.1732

[56] Pajareya K, Nopmaneejumruslers K. A pilot randomized controlled trial of DIR/FloortimeTM parent training intervention for pre-school children with autistic spectrum disorders. Autism. 2011;**15**(5):563-577. DOI: 10.1177/1362361310386502

[57] Green J et al. Parent-mediated communication-focused treatment in children with autism (PACT): A randomised controlled trial. Lancet. 2010;**375**(9732):2152-2160. DOI: 10.1016/S0140-6736(10)60587-9

[58] Green J et al. Parent-mediated intervention versus no intervention for infants at high risk of autism: A parallel, single-blind, randomised trial. The Lancet Psychiatry. 2015;**2**(2):133-140. DOI: 10.1016/S2215-0366(14)00091-1

[59] Daniolou S, Pandis N, Znoj H. The efficacy of early interventions for children with autism spectrum disorders: A systematic review and meta-analysis. Journal of Clinical Medicine. 2022;**11**(17):5100. DOI: 10.3390/jcm11175100

[60] Vivanti G. What does it mean for an autism intervention to be evidence-based? Autism Research. 2022;**15**(10):1787-1793. DOI: 10.1002/aur.2792

Chapter 16

Perspective Chapter: "The Knowing How to Regulate Oneself"– Transversal Competence between Parenting Skills, Biological Determination, Deficits in Primary or Secondary Disorders, and the Role of Specific Rehabilitation in Developmental Age

Francesco Cerroni, Raffaella Salatiello,
Paola Alessandra Albano and Ludovica Cira Nocerino

Abstract

The regulation underlies numerous developmental processes during the life cycle and intervenes in sensory processing, attachment, management of the self in relation to the other and the environment, the attunement of the affects, experimentation of interactions, the configuration of relationships, resilience, and intersubjectivity. The regulation typically occurs from the earliest stage of life. The child defines his interactive style mediated by his motor dimension through appropriate processing of stimuli adapting himself to the physical and social environment through the tonic dialogue and he also reaches the ability to manage, control, and attunement of affects and emotional states within complex dynamics in adulthood with more developed cognitive skills through the "tonic dialogue". The construct emerges on a neurobiological and neuroanatomical basis, which describes the individual subject's peculiar way of reacting and relating to the world: the temperament. The relational and reactive style modifies and defines itself in a strictly individual manner based on the subject's life experiences, especially of social nature. The interactive modes, the ruptures, and the repairs that characterise the relationship with the primary caregiver leave an imprinting that the subject retains throughout his life which will define his relational style, as much as it may change according to the interacting part. From the pathological front, regulatory disorders require a global, highly specific rehabilitative treatment which aims at the developmental needs of the child. Neuro and psychomotor therapy of developmental age intervenes in all aspects of regulatory disorders and plays a role that is not only rehabilitative and abilitative but also preventive, as reduces the risk that the disorder may evolve into further clinical conditions, especially of a psychopathological nature.

Keywords: regulation, attunement, neuro and psychomotor therapy of developmental age, transversal competencies, regulatory disorders, setting

1. Introduction

Regulation deficit frequently occurs in comorbidity in clearly nosographic-defined neurodevelopmental disorders. Nevertheless, the difficulty of isolating regulatory disorders in developmental age, and proceeding with exclusive diagnoses of the disorder, often undermines its progressive assessment and its evolution into disorders that continue in the development of the subject under evaluation and treatment. Regulatory disorders are therefore alterations that are present but not always classified as main disorders as much as secondary and they require accurate reading abilities and identification as they invoke concepts such as intricacy, mutability, and transience.

2. Affects regulation and tonic dialogue—self and hetero regulation and RM

The regulation is a construct that is intrinsic to every individual and in every era of life, regardless of whether the developmental trajectory can be identified as typical or not.

The regulation intervenes in a plurality of conditions; among these appears to be particularly relevant the capability to congruously elaborate internal and external stimuli of sensory, perceptive, or social nature, to develop appropriate and adaptive responses.

Hill [1] speaks of affect regulation, the affects are distinguished into two categories: the primary affects which are defined as the somatic representation of the organism's state, namely that which produces a sensation from the arousal signalling of our internal organs and the categorial affects, which are identified in emotions.

During development, as well as at every stage of life, it is necessary to structure stable affections that can create favourable conditions for implementing new skills and allow attunement to others because of the social necessity that characterises the human being. Recognising the affections, building them, and keeping them steady over time is an indispensable condition for the basis of an individual's development. The state of homeostasis occurs, in fact, when we are regulated within the boundaries of our "*window of tolerance*". The concept of "*window of tolerance*" is systematised by D. Siegel in [2], who defines it as that ideal space, graphically included between two parallel lines, in which the subject oscillates daily in a variable manner; boundaries of our window of tolerance are represented by the two lines, one leaning towards the high state of arousal (hyper-arousal) and the other one leaning towards a low state of arousal (hypo-arousal). On the other hand, when the threshold of the arousal decreases or increases transcending the abovementioned boundaries, we are in a state of "*dis-regulation*". What enables us to come back to an optimal state of regulation is the personal ability of resilience, defined by Cicchetti as "*the ability of individuals to recover their functioning after exposure to stress-induced dysregulation*". Freud [3] speaks of *a* "*protective shield against stimuli*", a barrier with which the child is naturally endowed and it protects himself from external stimuli that could potentially exceed his threshold of sensory analysis. More recently, we come to Erikson [4], who states that the little child, like everyone else, possesses certain optimal levels of stimulation, below which stimulation will be sought and above which it will be avoided.

The child actively regulates the exchange with the outside world, as everyone does at all ages. Individuals with different psychiatric disorders seem to have different thresholds, typically higher or lower concerning the quantity and duration of tolerated stimulation.

Becoming dysregulated is a common occurrence in daily living. Adaptive functioning is maximised when a controlled condition can be recovered effectively. The subject should have primarily well-regulated loved ones since only in this way he can engage in new and fruitful situations and relate to others more effectively since his relational availability is implemented. This availability out to be a condition that is not always experienced optimally in various disease patterns, as it could also be altered secondarily precisely because of atypicality and dysfunctional regulation processes. If there is dysregulation of loved ones there could be a condition of ineffectiveness and fallibility of relationships and pasts, as well as a negative condition that could lead to the development of inappropriate response strategies to the condition of insecurity in relationships.

The regulation skills are built over time by structuring themselves above a neurobiological and genetic substratum such as temperamental profile and the subject's experience, especially of the social nature with the caregiver of reference. *Temperament*, which has a not negligible neurobiological matrix, is defined by how the subject approaches his surroundings, stably delineating the reactive quality that characterises the child, and regulating the responses given to environmental and social stimuli.

The relationship with the parent, especially in the neonatal period, is crucial in the definition of *hetero-regulatory processes*, which take time to shape since at birth there are only primitive forms of *self-regulation* such as self-consolation, thumb sucking, and then moving on to strategies such as distraction management. The role of the other in the process of defining regulation is not only limited to that containing availability that shapes the attachment bond but is also important for the modelling mechanisms that the subject uses from the observations of others to be able to delineate his peculiar regulation strategies.

Mother and child learn in their interactive exchange, to take turns and read each other's signals, maturing progressively finer modes of interpretation. These experiences are for Bowlby [5] translated into *Internal Operating Models* (I.O.M) of Attachment, which can be defined as a "package" of cognitive-affective-relational interpersonal behaviours that mediate attachment relationships throughout life. These mother-child interactive modes develop as internalised actions managed by implicit processes, constituting an automated mode of relating to the attachment figure. The I.O.M also fulfils an assimilative function, which in principle has an adaptive value that is not always realised. Social experiences are filtered and absorbed and on the bases of performed expectations, relationships are interpreted. This condition, which leads to the management of attention, perception, and representation, enables what happens to the individual to be read and interpreted based on experiences. There are primary and secondary attachment models, depending on the specific attachment figure. The ability to regulate emerges from the attachment relationship, which is precocious and pre-verbal and is defined starting from a state of non-autonomy by the child.

The structuring of regulation strategies follows, clearly, the subject's overall development trajectories: the child refines his emotional and behavioural reading skills of the other, gives meanings and relates in a progressive more coherent manner.

Communicative-linguistic development also provides an increasingly valid and effective tool for the child to channel the emotions and his emotional and affective contents on this channel. Cognitive development, which from 18 months onwards, by the Piagetian memory, proceeds more and more towards the structuring of the symbolic capacity, gives the child an important tool for structuring congruent self- and hetero-regulatory strategies. The first real form of modulation of one's states of regulation mediated by others is the *tonic dialogue*. In the earliest stages of development, being able to modulate oneself in relation first to the other and then to the environment occurs through contact exchange in the early construction of the mother-child dyad.

In the early stages, regulation passes through the condition of exclusively exchanging muscle tone, where it is typically the mother who initially modifies herself according to the child's "questions and reactions". Over time, the child perceives a modification of the Other according to the expression of his needs, observing the purely motor aspects. The tone acts as a balancer of the exchange, adapting to the child's needs, and acts as means of communication in which conditions such as safety, stability, boundaries, and affection are involved. Subsequently, the child will gradually use the tonic dialogue through the exercise of mutual regulation with the mother, to engage in expressive and receptive communication with the environment, express needs, consciously modified his muscle tone, and regulate emotions and adaptive responses according to the appropriately processed stimulus.

These milestones of human development pass through five major areas of adaptive child development, within the first early interactions that are:

1. *Biological regulation*: the ability to regularise all biological processes, including nutrition and sleep-wake rhythm. It occurs during the first month of a child's life and allows the first social encounters to take place, which need to be regulated and made stable and to which the child is naturally predisposed as demonstrated by his innate sensitivity and reactivity to the caregiver's voice, expression, and gestures. Within this first phase, it is relevant to speak of "*modelling*", to which reference must be made and to which both the parental couple and the infant are subjected. Modelling consists of specific "adjustments", that are unique to each relationship; therefore, it is appropriate to recall Sander's [6] theory of "*Cross-Fostering*", whereby mutual adaption occurs specifically for each parent-child pair. The progressive evolution of the first social exchanges is also mediated by early imitative processes, which take on a much higher social value than the mere repetition and motor and gestural learning: neonatal imitation is constituted as a social and primarily communicative linking tool, which is conveyed in order or not to accept the behaviour of the CG. A deficit condition in the abovementioned skills produces cascading alterations in motor, communicative, cognitive, and social learning.

2. *Vis-à-vis exchanges*: the ability to adjust one's facial expression in relation to what is proposed in front of our field of vision or about specific sensory stimuli. This competence is present from the age of 2 months since we need to allow our visual sense organ to mature so that we can move from paying attention only to the contours of stimuli to an increase in visual acuity. The first socialising smiles appear at this stage, progressing into more direct and prolonged visual contact. This development passes through the mother's modulation of the levels of activation and synchronisation of the child's gaze, which will lead to the developmental maturation around the seventh month of the no longer

indiscriminate smile. At this stage of development, the "*Turn Taking*", the alternation of roles, is experienced; it is later observed more in vocal exchanges, as the child and parent influence each other. The aim is to create a very early form of "conversation" untethered from tonic dialogue to keep the created interaction stable. The main characteristic of the exchange is contingency, understood as the temporal dimension of the exchange, characterised by rhythmic behaviour, matching, and mirroring, which in interactive experiences emerge facilitating self-regulation and dyadic regulation in the child and the dyad, and laying the foundations for empathic competencies. The communicative-social tool that defines these relationships is the *referential gaze;* looking at each other and imitating facial expressions are the manifestation of the interactive coordination established in the dyad. This condition, which Trevarthen calls "*primary intersubjectivity*", is realised through neonatal imitation and proto-conversations and is based on brain circuits capable of integrating expressing eye, mouth, voice, hand movements, and posture.

3. *Sharing of topics*: a progressive form of regulation that consists of the beginning to shift the attention to situations outside the dyad but needing to share them first through the gaze, and later with the capacity for attention and action on the same. This stage, which appears in typical development from the age of 5 months, provides a condition of increased flexibility in the child's attention capacity, who will be able to shift attention towards an element outside the dyad; at the same time, motor-fine skills also allow this form of experimentation, in line with cognitive development. Initially, the child will experiment alone with the object, and later he will integrate the new experience with the object and the caregiver. This is where the skills of "*co-orientation*" appear, leading to two or more people dwelling on the same common focal point. This is the key to start of the structuring of what Trevarthen calls "*secondary intersubjectivity*".

4. *Reciprocity*: a condition that leads to the emergence of the interest in and recognition of the Other, so that it begins to be more flexible in finding a common focus. It is the stage that appears between 8 and 9 months and allows the child to engage simultaneously in different activities, which previously could only be experienced through a single experience, without being able to integrate perceived stimuli. Reciprocity brings the child to the experimentation of playing roles with the partner that is now coordinated and exchangeable. Reciprocity must be implemented by the concept of "*intentionality*", which allows one to plan one's behaviour and anticipate its consequences so that the child can fully participate in social interactions. This condition must provide from the child's point of view, flexibility and elasticity in managing the regulation of affections and emotionality such as can support him in the first real social relationships in experimentation. The qualitative refinement of the second dimension of intersubjectivity, combined with the physiological maturations that the child experiences from the cognitive point of view, makes him aware that the other also has his attentional focus and thus inserts him into an exchange articulated by requesting and declarative messages. The maturation of secondary intersubjectivity allows the subject to mature from what was once a form of attention definable as "*mutual*", whose main focus is the other in its physicality and expressiveness, called "*joint*" (or shared), which is precisely the condition in which both partners focus their attentional resources on a common focus interest.

5. *Symbolic representation*: an area with strong connotations linked to both cognition and language development. It is defined as the child's ability to use verbal and symbolic tools in relationships and exchanges with others, in order not only to be able to carry out an exchange in the present but also to reflect on them once they are concluded. This last stage begins to develop between 9 and 10 months, but is consolidated once discrete levels of communication have been reached; the ultimate aim is to impose oneself based on social references read in the environment. Trevarthen, in connection with this, argues that the language which the child acquires after the first year of life is the cumulative effect of the maturation of primary and secondary subjectivity. The child looks around him for clues, both in expression and in the behaviour of others, which should lead to his assessment of the situation. This process must include the ability to process the understanding of the event, whereby the child must through the acquisition of sensory perceptions and also the sum of all the reactions produced by others towards oneself and towards the environment, implements one's own search for social references. From 9 months onwards, the child experiences a real evolutionary drive in the motor, cognitive, emotional, social, and communicative spheres. He becomes fully aware of the physical and mental differentiation from the other; however, the child's regulatory strategies seem to be strictly dependent on the dyadic system in which he is embedded. Intersubjectivity can also be understood also from a dynamic systems perspective, as self-awareness goes beyond mere bodily boundaries to include the other who self-regulates himself [7, 8].

During interactions with the adult, the child often experiences "*mismatches*", which are moments of dyssynchrony that generate negative emotions and stress. This stress, which is typical of every relationship, can be caused by various conditions, such as lack of emotional synchronisation, unclear signals or not being understood correctly. Most mother-child dyads constantly reach a state of mismatch, which they manage to repair in subsequent interactions. The stress that is spoken of as resulting from the lack of synchronisation is, however, a springboard to go on to build what are "*coping*" strategies, which are functional to the structuring of the child's character, and, in successful cases, capable of providing the child with an important sense of efficacy and competence; they can then be generalised in different contexts, with an important adaptive value.

In case of unsuccess, the child experiences many failures and to equally curb the negative feelings resulting from the mismatch, he structures self-regulatory strategies that limit the interactive-social capabilities.

Various coping strategies can be experienced by the child, chosen based on elements which are not only contextual but also purely temperamental; summarised by Gianino into the following:

- *Signalling,* which can be positive, neutral or negative, while maintaining the objective of remaining in the sharing;
- *Attention elsewhere*, on an object or on himself;
- *Self-consolation,* using one's own body includes: oral stimulation, rocking, intertwining fingers;

- *Withdrawal;*
- *Escape;*
- *Gaze avoidance/visual exploration.*

When the child uses strategies which are different from signalling, renounces both social involvement and sometimes involvement with objects, trying to self-regulate. The individual differences that characterise the children and their modes of expression in terms of emotional manifestations and the prevailing mood tone seem to originate from the way of functioning of the adult-child dyad, who are partners in an affective communicative exchange.

The goals that the child sets include social, relational, and self-centred goals, such as achieving internal homeostasis. The driving force behind the activity is always the motivation, which resides in the final idea that the child structures, and is fuelled by the emotional equipment (positive and negative) that animates the child. The set goals are not always successfully achieved, and the experiences of fallibility that the child may experience are not uncommon. However, the negative experience of failure, with its negative emotional corollary, is an ambivalent experience which can lead both to reshape of the strategy resulting in success and also to renunciation. The child does not have all the resources he would need to achieve all his goals, and this is a risk factor for experiencing repeated failures, and consequently repeated negative emotional experiences. Nevertheless, this does not happen, as the child is placed in an interactive context, in a system of affective communication, in which the child's efforts are read, interpreted, and supported by the CG; from a functional point of view, the messages that the child sends to its CG are called by Tronick and Gianino "*hetero-directed regulatory behaviours*", emphasising their regulatory function in relation to the behaviour of the interacting subject.

On the other hand, behaviours such as self-stimulation or averting one's gaze are referred by the same to as "*self-directed regulatory behaviour*", that the child engages to regulate, control, and modify its affective state. The distinction between self-directed and hetero-directed regulatory behaviour is not always clear; what is certain is that these are behaviours that are part of the child's repertoire for dealing with stressful situations that can generate negative affections and excessive positive affections that can turn into distress situations.

These behaviours are so important because they act to allow the child to contain the potentially disruptive effects of his emotions, the uncontrolled expression of which could interfere with the implementation of strategies aimed at the fulfilment of the child's goals. Both self-directed and hetero-directed regulatory behaviours allow the child to exercise control over his emotional state, interact with those around him and act on the world around him.

Children and adults are placed in mutually coordinated interactions, where the child quickly takes an active part in communication with a global emotional involvement that can have positive and negative connotations. However, developmental trajectories are highly individual and singular, and this has been explained by Tronick and Gianino as an outcome of the differences and qualitative characterisations of the communication systems in which the subjects are embedded, and by the number and manner in which negative and positive emotional experiences are lived and dealt with. Normally, both conditions are experienced and then balanced towards a positive connotation of the interactive experience; in abnormal experiences, however, there is a longer duration of periods of interactive failure. The authors suggest that the full experience of success-failure-repair of interactive errors and the transformation of negative affect into positive affect, of interactional-transformative errors of negative affection into positive, produce beneficial effects on the child's development, enhancing their hetero-directed affective and communicative competence, increasing self-regulatory skills and contributes to delineating differentiation with the outside world, and self-identification.

On the contrary, as might be expected, the chronic experience of failure in abnormal interactions produces negative effects on the child's development.

Adopting a self-directed style of regulation, the child changes his focus and turns his attention to the control of negative affects and their effects on disorganised behaviour. Focusing on this strongly self-centred goal limits the experiential repertoire on the external world, not only in relational terms but also in exploratory terms leading to a potential slowdown in cognitive development. The effect on self-esteem is then not negligible: the child will have an image of himself as ineffective, thus tendentially negative self-esteem. The attachment bond will undoubtedly be disturbed: the parent will be perceived as unreliable.

This developmental trajectory is never determined by a single event, but rather by the slow accumulation of interactive and affective experiences with different people and events.

In order for the attunement (regulation of arousal) between Mother and Child to take place there are a series of stimulations, especially at the sensory level, that stimulate different behaviours in each type of relationship:

- *Predictable and tolerable form of Hyper-stimulation;*
- *Intolerable forms of Hyper-stimulation;*
- *Intolerable forms of Hypo-stimulation;*

These three forms generate different responses according to each pair being examined, they often reduce to being as variables as predictable but also unpredictable.

The processes of attunement with the other involve numerous states, such as:

- *Lack of attunement,*
- *Selective attunement,*
- *Imperfect attunement,*
- *Modulations,*
- *Inauthentic attunement,*
- *Excessive attunement.*

Attunement is the key to opening the door to the intersubjectivity between people, which can be used both to enrich one's mental life through the partial union with another and to impoverish it by keeping a part of one's inner experience strictly to oneself. Thanks to his early emotional-cognitive-social skills, the child can establish intersubjective connections with others from an early age. The process of emotional attunement, together with infants' early imitative capacities, enables them to connect with their caregivers. Infants, in fact, precociously enter into social interactive sequences, through vocalisations, gestures, and glances, in a progressively more attuned manner with caregivers of reference. In the structuring of intersubjectivity, the motor matrix cannot assume a marginal role; "*intercorporeality*" is a fundamental aspect of it. It includes, in fact, a mechanism of recognition of the other's body as similar to one's own, due to the sharing of similar aims and purposes towards which we direct ourselves. Intersubjectivity is properly defined as an experience of "mental contact with the other that takes place during interpersonal communication" [9, 10] (Trevarthen, 1998). Attachment and intersubjectivity are closely related; being attached to someone implies the possibility of developing an intersubjective connection, just as the intersubjective connection with someone can be the first step in forming an attachment bond with that person.

Intersubjective interactions are organised in developmental sequences according to Singer and Hein [11], who speak in particular of four sequences:

- *Emotional contagion*: this occurs when an emotion (e.g., sadness expressed through crying) is transferred to another person (e.g., a child cries when he hears another do so in turn), without being aware that the emotion felt originates from another person.

- *Empathy*: occurs when the individual, aware of the difference with the other, shares the other's emotions.

- *Compassion:* it arises when there is not only an understanding of the other person's emotions but also a feeling of sorrow and a drive to improve the other person's situation.

- *Theory of mind*: is the ability to attribute mental states (beliefs, intents, desires, emotions, knowledge) to oneself, and others, and to understand that others have mental states different from one's own [12].

Manenti [13] speaks of intersubjectivity as a dimension that matures after the individuals involved in the relationship pass through prior relational dimensions. The subject, in fact, needs the others not to be a subject but to live as a subject. Arriving at an intersubjective dimension is a condition that goes beyond the idea that human beings are intrinsically open to sociality since it describes a situation in which the subject is open to the relationship to define not only the relationship but also himself. The intersubjective dimension is composed of mutual changes and exchanges of personal resources, which delineate and define the identity of the involved subjects.

Specifically, Manenti [13] speaks of:

- *The Relational Dimension of the Self*: it conveys the readiness of the I to open up to build social relationships with a "you". To open up means to give oneself to confrontation, exchange ideas, and cooperate.

- *Interpsychic dimension*: it takes place at the moment when the "Selves" open to the relationship have entered into contact, which is not yet at a level where the "Self" reciprocally exchanges information about themselves. The contact could be regulated by norms that, on the contrary, isolate the individual "Self" even more, protecting them from mutual interferences.

- *Interpersonal dimension*: it is a dimension that marks a step forward. The two "Selves" available to the relationship, once in contact have established exchanges, characterised by mutual regulation, reciprocity, acceptance, and understanding.

- *Intersubjective dimension*: this is the dimension that goes beyond empathy, sharing, and acceptance. In the intersubjective dimension, the two "Selves" not only have a contact that leads them to have exchanges but also show themselves to be available to each other to allow themselves to be changed, transformed and redefined, thus building a new identity. In the relational fusion, the "Self" fades into the background.

The model that explains how in the above-mentioned interactive experiences there is structuring and evolution of regulation skills is the *Mutual Regulation Model*. The Mutual Regulation Model [14, 15] theorises that during mother-infant interaction the partners have interactional goals and, to achieve them, have different skills at their disposal. The ultimate goal is mutual regulation, which is identified as an interpersonal state of pleasure and attachment. To establish this condition, both must jointly regulate the interaction through interactive behaviours, namely affective manifestation. Thus, the child actively participates in this condition, using the tools at his disposal (smiles, vocalisations, postural adjustments) and his affective system, differentiated already at birth.

Despite this, the mutual regulation process contemplates and recognises the possibility that interactions may encounter physiological failures, due to misunderstanding of the other's behaviour or the implementation of inappropriate behaviour. These conditions, identifiable as "*mismatch*" in their physiological occurrence, generate negative affections (anger, contempt, sadness) in the child and motivate him to adapt and seek the most functional means of repairing the mismatch and relieving the experience of positive affection (joy, demonstrated interest). However, this can only be achieved in the presence of a sufficiently sensitive partner. Positive and negative affections allow the child to regulate the interaction to achieve the aforementioned reciprocal regulation.

The Regulation Model, defines that the actions carried out by the child through the use of his affective apparatus are used to regulate his interaction, this implies the ability on the part of the child to regulate his affective responses, since within the interaction he has to regulate two aspects of the affect:

- The *Qualitative Dimension*: what the child feels and expresses about the interaction;

- The *Quantitative Dimension*: all those temporal or intensity parameters of affection that are usually measured through parameters such as threshold, latency, ascending time, intensity, and recovery time of an affective manifestation.

In accordance with the mutual regulation model, when there is a disconnection between the partners, the child signals to the partner to change the mismatched behaviour, and the responsive and sensitive partner modifies the stressful condition, relieves the child's distress, and helps the child to regulate his affective state.

For this reason, self-regulation and interactive regulation are complementary to each other, just as they should be understood as sides of the same coin when assessing the child's social behaviour.

3. Regulatory disorders

Alterations in regulation are transversely present in every clinical picture in developmental age with peculiar ways of expression. Immaturity in the ability to self-regulate can lead to the expression of oppositional, impulsive, aggressive behaviour. This condition may fade naturally, following the child's psychological growth and development trajectory, or it may exacerbate to become a fully disordered condition.

De Gangi, Porge, Sickel, and Greenspan, in a longitudinal study conducted on a population of 4-year-old children, described the progression of dysregulation symptoms towards a pathological trajectory in terms of developmental, sensorimotor, and/or emotional-behavioural deficits at 4 years of age, suggesting that children with an untreated regulatory disorder may not overcome behavioural difficulties.

To be able to distinguish between actual symptoms of the disorder (which may result in psychopathology) and the transient phase of life, age-specific diagnostic criteria would be required. Since these diagnostic criteria do not currently exist, the disorder category has not yet been included in standardised nosography systems such as DSM 5 or ICD-10.

The first to have formulated diagnoses for regulatory disorders was Greenspan [16] who defined regulatory disorders as the co-presence of three fundamental characteristics that negatively affect sensory processing abilities and are expressed through:

- Sensory difficulties,
- Sensory-motor difficulties,
- Information processing difficulties.

These characteristics are due to an excessive or limited reactivity to sensory stimuli, which qualitatively impairs it and the expression of motor skills, and has an impact both at the level of coordination and movement planning. This manifests itself as a clear difficulty in organising movements in sequence.

In regulation disorders, a specific behavioural pattern is usually present, characterised by:

- Disorders concerning the control of action,
- Attention disorders,
- Behavioural disorders,
- Disturbance in the modulation of affective states and interaction with others.

Regulation disorders are characterised by difficulties in regulating behaviour, physiological process, attention, motor skills, and in organising a calm, vigilant or positive affective state. A child with a regulatory disorder is particularly difficult to manage from the earliest days.

Soon, this generalised dysregulation has negative side effects on the family environment and can lead to chronic stress in parents, which will be further reflected in the quality of the child's responses.

The child may present dysregulation in sleep regulation, feeding or sphincter control, as well as in the area of gross or fine motor skills, in the ability to maintain attention on a detail (or conversely persist on a specific detail), in affects (abrupt transitions from serenity and joy to sadness and anger), in behaviour (aggressive/impulsive).

An early and important dysfunction in the process of affective regulation, inhibitory control, behavioural regulation, etc. can impact functions such as sleep, feeding, and sensory reactivity, predisposing the child to structure relational disorders and symptoms that can be traced back to psychopathological conditions. Clinical symptoms include hypersensitivity, impulsivity, irritability, and hyper/hypo reactivity, with an impact on sleep and feeding. In addition, regulatory disorders may be present and persist even at school age.

The diagnosis of these conditions is complex and also requires the presence of specific sensory difficulties (perception and proprioception of stimuli).

Considering among the causes, children with the most difficult temperament, those with regulatory disorder correspond to a minority at the extreme of this category. These problematic characteristics are generally of a constitutional or maturation nature, but it should not be forgotten that the quality of care may accentuate the difficulties or, on the contrary, diminish them. In the first case, children are exposed to a very high risk of developing other behavioural disorders in later childhood.

These conditions are relatively rare and data on their prevalence in the population are relatively inaccessible, due to the recent diagnostic framing, and certain clinical configurations can be difficult to distinguish from other early developmental difficulties. Treatment consists of providing the best support to the parents, who will have to transfer their regulatory strategies to the child. A successful diagnostic framing, as always, proves to be fundamental and can prevent problematic behavioural and social patterns from developing in the future.

According to what can be deduced, given that regulation is implicated in all stages of growth and development and continues through development, it allows us to tune in to all the stimuli to which the individual is constantly subjected; it can only be stated, that in addition to specific regulation disorders, there is a strong presence of alterations in motor, affective, emotional, mentalising regulation, and all conditions concerning higher cognitive processes such as executive functions, in the comorbidity of developmental and neurodevelopmental diagnoses.

The six capacities of Emotional and Social Functioning are:

- *Attention and regulation* (the beginning is typically observed between birth and 3 months): the infant observes and pays attention to what is happening around him with all senses, such as looking, listening, touching, and moving. The infant can remain sufficiently regulated to maintain attention and interact without hypo or hyper-reacting to external or internal stimuli. As the child, over time, reaches higher levels of functioning, his ability to maintain a sustained and continuous flow of interactions provides evidence of his capacity for age-appropriate attention and regulation.

- *Formation of relationships or mutual engagement* (the beginning is typically observed between 3 and 6 months): the infant develops a relationship with an emotionally available caregiver for the primary purpose of comfort, security, and pleasure. As development progresses, through the support of the caring environment, the infant becomes able to experience the full range of positive and negative emotions, remaining engaged in the relationship.

- *Two-way intentional communication* (the beginning is typically observed between 4 and 10 months): the infant uses gestures, including purposeful displays of affection, to initiate a mutual "conversation". Simple gestures, such as reaching out to be picked up or pointing to an object that is interesting to him, become a more complex sequence of gestures during the second year of life. Two-way communication becomes a real conversation as the child develops verbal language.

- *Complex gestures and problem solving* (the beginning is typically observed between 10 and 18 months): the child uses emerging symbolic skills and language to acquire what he wants or desires—namely to solve problems. Single gestures are replaced by complex sequences of gestures and actions (e.g., leading a parent towards the desired object). As soon as the child develops language, he uses words and gestures for communication and problem-solving.

- *Use of symbols to express thoughts and feelings* (the beginning is typically observed between 18 and 30 months): the child, using imaginative play and language, begins to express thoughts, ideas, and feelings through symbols. A child can communicate what he imagines through role play, dressing up, and playing with dolls. Imaginative play can represent real-life experiences and stories that the child has known through stories, books, videos, and television. In play scenarios, the child projects his feelings into the characters and actions.

- *Logical connection of symbols and abstract thinking* (the beginning is typically observed between 30 and 48 months): the child can logically connect and process sequences of ideas. He uses logically interconnected ideas in preservations concerning everyday life events and imaginary stories. The stories of children who have reached this level of functioning typically have a beginning, middle, and end. The child can understand abstract concepts, reflect on feelings, and articulate lessons learned from experience.

Attention must be given to all diseases into which a particular regulation problem may develop in childhood, later puberty, and adulthood, in addition to the presence of comorbidity with other diagnoses.

The Diagnostic Classification 0–3 and later the 0–5, proposes different types of regulation disorders that mainly concern the dysregulation of certain basic rhythms (sleep, feeding) and sensory processing, which may however be part of a phenomenal expression of broader and more complex pathologies affecting neurodevelopment.

All disorders related to regulation deficits found in the Diagnostic Classification DC:0–3 and DC:0–5 as well as in the Diagnostic and Statistical Manual of Mental Disorders are proposed below:

Disorders of regulation about sensory processing for Diagnostic Classification DC:0–3 are reported:

- *Sensory processing regulation disorder* which is divided into three forms:

- *Hypersensitive (Type A Fearful-Cautious);*
- *Hypersensitive (type B Negative-Provocateur);*
- *Hyposensitive/Hyporesponsive (Type A distracted-hard to engage);*
- *Hyposensitive/Hyporesponsive (type B self-centred);*
- *Impulsive looking for sensory stimulation.*

For the diagnostic classification DC:0–5 we include among the main disorders of sensory processing regulation:

- *Sensory Hyperresponsiveness Disorder;*
- *Sensory Hyporesponsiveness Disorder;*
- *Other Sensory Processing Disorder.*

Sleep-Wake Regulation Disorders for the Diagnostic Classification DC:0–3 are reported:

- *Sleep Behaviour Disorder;*
- *Falling Asleep Disorder;*
- *Night Waking Disorder.*

The Diagnostic Classification DC:0–5 adds:

- *Partial Arousal Sleep Disorder;*
- *Childhood Nightmare Disorder.*

Regulation Disorders in relation to Anxiety Disorders for the Diagnostic Classification DC:0–3 are reported:

- *Separation Anxiety Disorder;*
- *Generalised Anxiety Disorder;*
- *Social Phobia.*

The Diagnostic Classification DC:0–5 adds to DC:0–3:

- *Selective Mutism;*
- *Inhibition to Novelty Disorder;*

- *Other Childhood Anxiety Disorder*

Eating Regulation Disorders for the Diagnostic Classification DC:0–3 are reported:

- *Feeding Disorder Related to Regulatory Status;*
- *Feeding Disorder Related to Caregiver-Child Reciprocity;*
- *Childhood Anorexia;*
- *Sensory Aversion to Food;*
- *Eating Disorder associated with co-existing medical conditions;*
- *Eating Disorder associated with insults of the gastrointestinal tract.*

The Diagnostic Classification DC:0–5 adds to DC:0–3:

- *Hyper-Eating Disorder;*
- *Hypo-Eating Disorder;*
- *Atypical Eating Disorder.*

Mood Regulation Disorders for the Diagnostic Classification DC:0–3 are reported:

- *Childhood Depression;*
- *Major Depression;*
- *Depressive Disorder NOS.*

In the Diagnostic Classification DC:0–5, there is a transition into:

- *Depressive Disorder of Childhood;*
- *Other childhood mood disorders;*
- *Anger and aggression dysregulation disorder of childhood.*

This disorder may later evolve into:

- *Conduct Disorder;*
- *Oppositional Defiant Disorder (ODD);*
- *Disruptive Behaviour Disorder or irritability.*

Regulation Disorders in attachment and adaptation for both Classifications DC:0–3 and DC:0–5 are reported:

- *Adjustment Disorder.*

While only for DC:0–5 there is present:

- *Reactive Attachment Disorder.*

Regulation Disorders in affective and relationship disorders for Classification DC:0–3:

- *Relationship and Communication disorder;*
- *Regulation Disorder in Affective Disorders.*

While only for DC:0–5 there is:

- *Childhood Specific Relationship Disorder.*

Disorders *of Regulation in Multisystemic Developmental Disorders (DC:0–3) or Neurodevelopmental Disorders:*

- *Autism Spectrum Disorder (ASD);*
- *Attention Deficit/Hyperactivity Disorder (ADD/ADHD);*
- *Developmental Coordination Disorder (DCD).*

4. Rehabilitative conclusion and setting

The Regulation Disorder, because of the mistake in attunement and the lack of recovery of it, generates in the child conditions of strong frustration both towards the environment in which he lives and especially towards his parents. In fact, *the term "regulation" indicates, in a very general way, the child's ability to adapt to environmental requests in ways that respond to contextually defined expectations. This capacity depends on a series of variables that can be schematically ascribed to three categories:*

- *the threshold of sensory receptors responsible for collecting environmental stimuli;*
- *The efficiency of the central control processes in charge of stimulus processing;*
- *The modulation of affective states activated by different stimuli.*

It is necessary to consider the transversality of the construct in every phase of any subject's life, and in developmental age, it is precisely the condition that assumes an important adaptive value in the process of cognitive and emotional growth. From the perspective of therapeutic treatment, it is crucial to remember not only the extreme precocity onset of the RD but also the frequent alterations in regulation skills that may be seen in distinct nosographic images.

In rehabilitation, this disorder, as far as the treatment of the child is concerned, has a strong "*habilitative*" connotation, since the aim is to create new capacities in the child, who experiences and has experienced the difficulty of being able to tune in with the Other.

DOI: http://dx.doi.org/10.5772/intechopen.109536

The "*re-habilitative*" connotation is aimed at the parent, who is *disorganised, unregulated/untuned* to the specific requests of the child and in the most extreme situation *disturbed* in reading and experiencing the relationship itself.

In any sort of treatment, it is effective to rely on Therapists who use the reading and the conducting of the treatment in an integrated manner. A good therapist must be able to balance the needs of the child, which must be focused on experimenting with a new attunement of affections; and the delicate nature of working with the parent, who must be able to recognise and become aware of his attunement challenges with the child, and then gradually succeed in re-entering into an appropriate relationship with the therapist's assistance.

The main objectives of the initial phases of treatment are:

- the *Quality of the Interaction* between therapist and child is aimed at encouraging the stimulation of potential areas of development and supporting the integrative processes necessary for self-regulation;

- The *Profile Building, Monitoring and Checking* of the child's growth path.

The rehabilitation process aims at the condition of regulation "from the outside" facilitated by the therapist to allow the child to progressively access self-regulation and subsequently, at the mentalisation of affective states as a premise for the realisation of full awareness of the Self. The therapeutic approach favoured in the developmental age to act on regulation is *bottom-up*; the regulation of affection is mediated by the bodily dimension, to try to create a stabilisation of a relationship that evolves on a tonic, postural, spatial, temporal, and motor level, experienced especially in the sensorimotor setting, where a form of implicit communication takes place.

Furthermore, a *top-down* dialogic and reflexive approach should not be neglected, which is not universally applicable in developmental rehabilitation. Therapeutic change first passes through the implicit and automatic dimensions and then reaches the conscious, reflexive, and verbal processes.

To be able to objectively and congruously define a developmental disorder, it is necessary to define the child's Functional Profile, which will allow the formulation of the Rehabilitation Project. This last comes with specific short-medium and long-term objectives, to which the use of strategies and facilitations will be added; this will make it possible to achieve the objectives specified for a particular treatment.

The functional profile defines the characteristics of the disorder for which the child is being observed, but also outlines the child's areas of strengths and weaknesses in all functional areas, taking into account the peculiarities of his significant environment. For the definition of the functional profile there are two fundamental moments:

- The *evaluation*, extended from the disorder to the child and more generally to the context. It is a process of knowledge, which also involves the adoption of specific assessment tools;

- The *translation* of the elements that emerge from the assessment into codified categories (ICF codes) so that they can be transferred to a notation sheet that can be read instantly by all the members of the rehabilitation team. The team can identify the therapy goals thanks to the functional profile.

The therapist's approach must be in accordance with the WHO's (World Health Organisation) proposed Bio-Psycho-Social model, according to which the subject's assessment must also thoroughly examine all the *Personal* and *Environmental Factors* that support the realisation of their activities and participation, in addition to factors related to *Body Functions and Structures.*

The rehabilitative intervention is composed through the activities of:

- *Functional assessment of the child*. It is implemented through standardised procedures and tools, to start a cross-sectional knowledge process that defines the child and his development within the context of his living environment. The purpose of the functioning assessment is to determine the child's overall functioning, which includes areas of strength and weakness, as well as personal and environmental traits that may promote or obstruct the child's growth.

- *Identification of the objectives*. Once the functional profile has been defined, objectives are identified in relation to the real needs of that individual child, in that personal developmental phase, and in that specific environmental context. The choice of the objectives must be functional to the realisation of a specific and generalisable rehabilitation project, aimed at favouring the child's growth as an individual which is known and shared by all the operators, who with different capacities and with different modalities and professionalism, intervene to realise it. This principle envisages multidisciplinary work aimed at overcoming the self-referentiality of individual operators;

- *Choice of the most suitable strategies for achieving the identified goals*. This phase also follows directly from the child's functional profile, which helps us to understand and suggest which contexts, approach modes, play proposals, and characteristics of activities are most congenial to the child and which, as such, guarantee his more immediate and complete involvement;

- *Checking the results against the objectives previously identified*. This is the phase in which the reliability of the assessment is carried out, the suitability of the objectives identified and the validity of the strategies adopted to achieve them are verified. It is important to constantly update the checking phase, due to the not-always-cyclical course of the developmental age. This makes it possible to reformulate the rehabilitative programme according to the child's needs at a given time.

The concept of an *interactive profile*, which results from the articulation between the observational-interactive function and the evaluative function (comparison of typical and atypical development) is particularly significant in choosing and identification of objectives (introduction of facilitators, which makes the observation of emerging competencies possible).

The definition of an interactive profile allows one to identify the child's expressive traits, situate them in the area of potential development, and specify the therapy goals, and intervention plan. Regarding the nosographic classification in which the subject is placed, the functional assessment of the subject assumes a predominating role. Therapeutic work is not centred on the disorder but rather on the functions and aims to develop effective strategies with the residual resources so that the subject can live in his life context more adaptively. After the functioning profile and therapeutic goals have been established, the course of treatment is outlined specifically for each.

Neuro and psychomotor therapy of developmental age (TNPEE, Ministerial Decree no. 56 of 17 January 1997) [17] consist of rehabilitative (but also habilitative and preventive) interventions in all kinds of neurological, neuropsychological, and psychopathological disorders of the developmental age. The TNPEE is in charge of a subject that is still being built, thus it is important to understand and acquire personal ways of reading and perceiving events, a matrix of manifest behaviour, self-regulation strategies, and individual reactive modes that point to hetero-regulatory abilities. The work always starts from the areas previously identified as zones of proximal development; this strengthens the relationship and the sense of self-efficacy within a therapeutic setting that is safe and predictable and where the child can experience himself in the motor, physical, cognitive, and emotional dimensions. The therapeutic relationship is always a privileged goal, implicit, and intrinsic in the treatment: it is in fact the engine of changes, as well as a solid base on which to live effective therapeutic experiences. The TNPEE is the child's emotional and physical container, the mirror in which the child's actions are reflected, the external regulator, and the source of security from which the child draws in the therapeutic context. The TNPEE has a plastic and flexible personality, which modulates his modes of interaction in relation to the subject in front of him so that he can embody this ideal of trust and can act as external support to build and generalise effective self and hetero-regulation skills. In the therapeutic relationship, moments of conflict and mismatching will also be necessary to be effective: these are moments in which the threshold of the child's window of tolerance is tested and an attempt is made to go beyond it and then to bring the subject back to a condition of homeostatic balance through strategies to built together and then generalise in significant living environments. The therapeutic intervention takes place, mainly, within a peculiar setting dimension, which due to its intrinsic characteristics, acts as a promoter in the organisation of the therapeutic experience of the patient and the dyad it forms with the TNPEE. The term setting etymologically derives from the verb "to set" translated as "to arrange, place, establish, stage". In the "-ing" form it is translated as the frame, the scenario, and the environment within which the action takes place. The first meaning encompasses the concept of the normative dimension of the setting, which refers to the definition of times and places in which the therapeutic session takes place, thus identifying not only emotional and representative boundaries for the patient but also organisational and managerial boundaries concerning the parental figures. The second meaning refers to the organisational aspects of the setting: a defined space and time acquire unique meanings from patient to patient in the way they are managed and organised. The setting of neuropsychomotor therapy can be analysed both in its temporal and spatial dimensions; from the temporal point of view, the therapy, which typically has a duration of 45–50 minutes appears to be marked by four main times: reception time, the time reserved for sensorimotor activities, time for structured activities, and time for the therapy concluding synthesis. The time scansion is not equal, but the longest times are, of course, those dedicated to the actual activities; as much as shorter, the time dedicated to the beginning and the end of the therapy has an important significance, as the subject experiences the therapy sessions with continuity and he can resume and reintroduce matured contents and at the end of the therapy will always come out newly reconstituted. The temporal scansion is then fully reflected in the spatial one; the first and the last therapy time tend to take place on a bench next to the room door. It is an intimate but foundational social moment. The time devoted to the sensorimotor space is spent in a dedicated space, which tends to be jointly organised between TNPEE and the child. It is the time when one fully experiences one's own bodily and tonic dimension, in a condition of fusion and physical investment. The child can see in the TNPEE his physical and emotional container and at the same time, the TNPEE fully supports all the expressive indexes, emotional elaborations, and cognitive and symbolic representations that the child elaborates, supporting, in particular, the harmonious development of social, communicative, motor, and cognitive skills. This is the space dedicated to pillows, balls and mats, which can be organised, structured, and deconstructed according to the patient's needs. Once this time is completed, the physical setting is rearranged, since clarity and legibility are necessary for the final purposes of it. In the structured space, which typically contains chairs, tables, and cabinets the child is reconstituted, focusing on the implementation of neuropsychological, cognitive, and communicative skills. The therapeutic relationship thus knows a new aspect. And also, the continuity of the dyad in different environments and activities allows the child to discover the other and himself in different dimensions. The final moment has an imposing regulatory potential in the global reading of the therapeutic session. The circle that closes is necessary to settle every interpretation, the lived experiences take on full meaning. Together with the rehabilitative intervention "aimed" at the child, it is not disregarded the *Active Involvement of the Parents* in treatment. Parents must be involved in both the planning and implementation phases of the intervention, to make them active partners and not consider them passive referents, bearing in mind the characteristics of the parental couple and the socio-cultural context.

The intervention for parents is also highly individualised and includes the following phases:

- Definition and individuation of needs and resources (*observational/assessment phase*);
- Identification and sharing of the intervention (*phase of the programme*);
- Evaluation of the change (*verification phase*);

Intervention with parents involves:

- Gathering and documenting information from various life contexts;
- Access to a common understanding of skills and difficulties;
- Focusing attention on resources rather than weaknesses.

The tools used to achieve these objectives are interviews, administration of questionnaires, viewing family films, viewing filmed therapy sequences and/or observation through a one-way mirror, and joint play sessions.

The importance of avoiding an attitude of "*educational palsy*" from the parents and the consequent tendency to observe the "*delegating*" problems solving to experts, is an attitude that must be discouraged from the outset, seeking to restore the parent's sense of competence and effectiveness.

It is necessary to progressively reorganise a system in which the parents' role is critical and decisive for the child's development. Often, experiences of inadequacy and incompetence in managing difficulties may emerge in parents, so it is appropriate to provide some general suggestions, namely:

- Place stimulation in the child's area of potential development and never on the deficient area, to avoid increasing the sense of ineffectiveness that is already naturally inherent in the condition;

- Maintain, while involving the family, the specificity of contexts, roles, and strategies, as the risks associated with "treated" family and/or educational environments are well known.

- Articulate the activation of stimulation areas in the family and/or the educational environment according to the child's actual developmental profile by providing:

    - opening play areas of intersubjectivity adapted to the child's specific interactive profile;

    - identification of educational strategies aimed at the harmonisation of the child's rhythms and the evolution of adaptive capacities and the related tonic, postural, and motor structure;

    - The organisation of sensory experiences adapted to the child's neuropsychological profile.

All this translates into an integrated system of collaboration and help, which is articulated in an enabling model that pays attention to the subjects, the contexts involved, and the strategies [18].

Author details

Francesco Cerroni[1*], Raffaella Salatiello[1], Paola Alessandra Albano[1] and Ludovica Cira Nocerino[2]

1 Clinic of Child and Adolescent Neuropsychiatry, Università degli Studi della Campania "Luigi Vanvitelli", Naples, Italy

2 Mestieri Campania, Job, Training, Corporate Welfare, Salerno, Italy

*Address all correspondence to: francesco.cerroni@unicampania.it

References

[1] Hill D. Teoria della Regolazione Affettiva. Un Modello Clinico. Milano: Raffaello Cortina Editore; 2017

[2] Siegel DJ. La Mente Relazionale. Raffaello Cortina Editore (Milano): Neurobiologia dell'esperienza interpersonale – III Edizione; 2021

[3] Freud S. Al di là del principio del piacere. Bollati Boringhieri (Torino). 1980

[4] Erikson EH. Gioventù e crisi d'identità – XII Edizione. Armando Editore (Roma). 1995

[5] Bowlby J. Attaccamento e Perdita. Bollati Boringhieri (Torino): L'Attaccamento alla Madre; 1999

[6] Sander LW. The regulation of exchange in the infant-caretaker system and some aspect of the context-content relationship. In: Lewis M, Rosenblum L, editors. Interaction, Conversation, and the Development of Language. New York: Wiley; 1977

[7] Beebe B, Lachmann FM. Infant Research e trattamento degli adulti. Raffaello Cortina Editore: Un modello sistemico-diadico delle interazioni; 2003

[8] Stern D. Il mondo interpersonale del bambino. Bollati Boringhieri (Torino). 1987

[9] Trevarthen C. Intrinsic motives for companionship in understanding: Their origin, development, and significance for infant mental health. Infant Mental Health Journal. 2001

[10] Trevarthen C. Infant intersubjectivity: Research, theory and clinical applications. Journal of Child Psychology and Psychiatry. 2001

[11] Singer T, Hein G. Human empathy through the lens of psychology and social neuroscience. In: DE WAAL FBM, Ferrar PF. editors. The Primate Mind. Cambridge, MA: Harvard University Press; 2012. pp. 158-174

[12] Premack D, Woodruff G. Does the chimpanzee have a theory of mind? Behavioral and Brain Sciences. 1978; **1**(4):515-526

[13] Manenti A. *Intersoggettività*, TreDimensioni, 2006

[14] Tronick E, Als H, Adamson LB, Wise S, Brazelton TB. The infant's response to entrapment between contradictory messages in face- to-face interaction. In Journal of the American Academy of Child Psychiatry, Milano. 1978;**17**:1-13

[15] Tronick E. Regolazione Emotiva, nello Sviluppo e nel Processo Terapeutico. Raffaello Cortina Editore; 2008

[16] Greenspan SI. *Infancy and early childhood: The practice of clinical assessment and intervention with emotional and developmental challenges*. Inc: International Universities Press; 1992

[17] Regolamento concernente la individuazione della figura e relativo profilo professionale del terapista della neuro e psicomotricita' dell'eta' evolutiva. (GU Serie Generale n.61 del 14-03-1997) [Internet]. Gazzetta Ufficiale. Ministero della sanita'; 1997 [cited 2023 Jan 31]. Available from: https://www.gazzettaufficiale.it/eli/id/1997/03/14/097G0084/sg

[18] Gison G, Bonifacio A, Minghelli E. Autismo e Psicomotrictà. Trento: Erickson, ristampa; 2016

Printed in the USA
CPSIA information can be obtained
at www.ICGtesting.com
LVHW072212261023
762119LV00015B/841

9 781837 683420